HUMAN INSTINCTS, EVERYDAY LIFE, AND THE BRAIN

HUMAN INSTINCTS, EVERYDAY LIFE, AND THE BRAIN

A paradigm for understanding behavior

Volume One

Numbered examples: #1 – #1155

A research series by Richard H. Wills

ISBN: 978-0-9920710-0-4

Printed in the United States

Distributed by

The Book Emporium
Charlottetown
Prince Edward Island
Canada

e-mail: bookspei@yahoo.ca

To everyone who participated in this research

CONTENTS

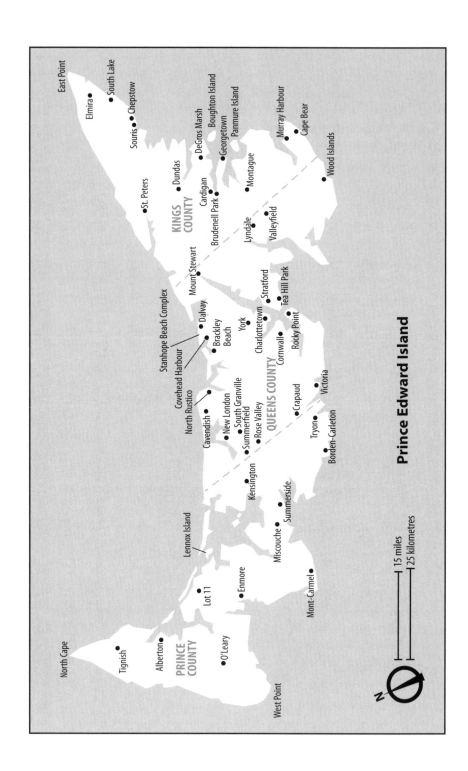

Prince Edward Island

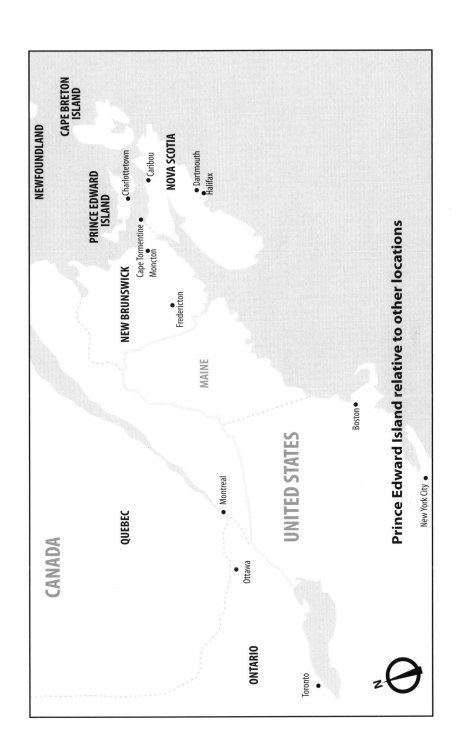

Prince Edward Island relative to other locations

PREFACE

One of the most significant impacts of science is demythologizing mankind. Over the centuries, science has markedly altered our view of ourselves and our place in nature. There have been key points in this process. In the sixteenth century Nicholas Copernicus demythologized our location in space, and we lost our place at the center of the universe. In the nineteenth century Charles Darwin demythologized our origin, and we lost our divine creation. As a result of this process, our view of ourselves as unique and separate from nature has been seriously eroded. This transition has met considerable opposition, however. At each stage science has had to struggle against entrenched religious and intellectual positions.

By no means has the demythologizing of mankind ended. We continue to glorify ourselves as a unique phenomenon. Althrough today educated people acknowledge our animal origins, we believe that these were shed as humans evolved to become something completely new and different. Regarding human behavior, we believe that we are free of the influences of nature and that human endeavors are limited only by our imagination. Such beliefs, or myths, determine our view of ourselves and other species. However, we are entering the period in which human behavior will be demythologized. We will have to face the extent to which nature structures and limits our behavior. This change in view will certainly be opposed by much of the intellectual community. Nevertheless, as we learn more about behavior, it will become increasingly difficult to preserve the myth of our godlike nature.

1. IMPLICATIONS OF THIS RESEARCH

Contents

continued on next page

Implications

Introduction

This is a partial list of ideas, or models, which have been produced by the research to date. These ideas result from the research reported in the published volumes and from the research which is currently in progress which has not yet been published. This is a working list which will certainly change as the research proceeds. There will be alterations, deletions, and additions to this list.

Feelings as instincts

1. Humans have biologically programmed feelings.

2. These feelings are present in all members of the species.

3. Feelings act as instincts.

4. Most instincts in humans and other animal species are experienced as feelings.

5. Responses to feelings in nonhuman animal species have been interpreted as instincts.

6. Feelings explain most of the behavior in humans and other animal species.

7. Feelings provide the motivational system of a species with voluntary movement.

8. Evidence that a species responds to any feeling, such as discomfort (hunger, thirst) or anxiety (running from threats, hiding from threats), indicates that the species responds to other feelings too.

9. Our behavior is directed by feelings, rather than by reason and learning. Reason and learning are used to help us satisfy our feelings. They serve as handmaidens of feelings.

10. Feelings encourage the individual to get and keep resources. Discomfort encourages us to find resources, such as food, water, and shelter, which will remove specific discomforts. Loneliness encourages us to establish relationships with friends and mates, who help us get resources, share their resources with us, and help protect us. Envy encourages us to get the same resources that others are getting. Anxiety helps us avoid threats to ourselves and our resources. Anger helps us defend ourselves and our resources. Guilt encourages us to take care of our human resources. The hurt produced by criticism, rejection, and embarrassment encourages us to avoid doing things which alienate other people, who provide us with most of our resources.

11. Feelings are activated at the first signs that resources are available or threatened.

12. Individuals act in response to feelings, or they act in advance of feelings to avoid or promote the feelings.

13. The three major types of feelings are the pleasures, the hurts, and the bothers.

14. The individual pursues pleasures while avoiding hurts and bothers.

15. Our lives are dedicated to trying to obtain pleasant feelings and avoid unpleasant feelings. Pleasant feelings are provided by the pleasures. Unpleasant feelings are provided by both the hurts and the bothers.

16. The pleasures are produced by sex, positive reactions, and positive stimulation. In addition, the removal of hurts and bothers releases tension and produces pleasure.

17. The hurts are produced by physical and mental effort; negative reactions from others (criticism, rejection); loneliness; envy; threats (anxiety); self-criticism, or guilt; pain; and physical discomforts, such as hunger and not breathing.

18. The bothers are produced by phenomena which are not categorized, inconsistency, phenomena which are not oriented, and differences between models and reality. The bothers hurt also, but usually to a lesser degree than the hurts.

19. Humans can experience and act on feelings without being consciously aware of them. For example, humans take each breath in response to the feeling of increasing discomfort that they experience when they do not take a breath. Humans are not normally consciously aware of this discomfort or of their decision to act and take a breath in order to get rid of it.

20. A considerable amount of excess behavior occurs in response to specific feelings which fails to obtain and conserve resources.

21. Individuals respond to current feelings and live in the present.

22. Human feelings and responses are constant in different cultures and in different historical periods.

23. There is a common set of feelings which is shared by different animal species. For example, in many species individuals associate together in order to obtain positive reactions from each other. Their desire for positive reactions is so strong that they engage in efforts to obtain positive reactions which attract the attention of predators.

24. Various animal species employ different behaviors in response to common feelings. For example, humans smile, cats purr, and dogs wag their tails to express pleasure.

25. Specific feelings are tied to specific muscle groups. For example, humans feel anxiety in their diaphragms, hurt in their lower eye sockets, and pleasure at the raised corners of their mouths.

26. Different feelings are experienced at different locations on the body.

27. Feelings which are experienced at separate locations on the body are separate feelings.

28. Feelings which are experienced at the same locations on the body are the same feeling.

29. The same feeling can be tied to different muscle groups in different animal species. For example, humans feel pleasure where they smile, cats feel pleasure where they purr, and dogs feel pleasure where they wag their tails.

Individuals

30. An individual is designed to a) get and keep resources, b) compete with other individuals for resources, c) cooperate with other individuals to get and keep resources, and d) exchange resources with other individuals.

31. Feelings encourage individuals to get and keep resources, compete for resources with others, and cooperate and exchange resources with others. An individual is encouraged to get resources by the feelings of discomfort, loneliness, and envy. Discomforts, such as

hunger, thirst, and feeling hot or cold, encourage one to obtain resources which will remove the discomforts. Loneliness encourages one to seek the company of others, who provide protection and other resources. Envy encourages one to obtain the same resources that others are getting. An individual is encouraged to keep resources by the feelings of anxiety and anger. Anxiety encourages one to take precautions. Anger enables one to aggressively protect oneself and one's resources. Also, the hurt produced by effort encourages one to avoid exertion and conserve time and energy. Because individuals experience their own feelings rather than the feelings of others, they try to satisfy their own feelings. As a result, they compete with others to obtain resources. Individuals are encouraged to cooperate with each other and exchange resources by the desire for positive reactions and the desire to avoid both negative reactions from others (criticism, rejection, and embarrassment) and guilt (self-criticism).

32. An individual experiences his own feelings. He learns about the feelings experienced by other individuals, but he does not experience them firsthand. Therefore an individual experiences his own feelings far more vividly than he experiences the feelings of other individuals. As a result, each individual spends most of his time acting for himself, thinking about himself, and trying to communicate about himself to others.

Communication of feelings

33. The members of an animal species share a well-developed means of communicating certain of their feelings to each other.

34. Such feelings are communicated to each other through the action of the specific muscle groups associated with each feeling.

35. Simulating the actions of these specific muscle groups will enable humans to better communicate with other animal species.

36. Indicating one's feelings to others is costly in terms of a) the biological systems required to be able to do so, and b) the time and energy expended when one does so. Nevertheless, individuals frequently make their feelings known to others by various means, including sounds, facial expressions, and the movement and position of body parts. Therefore, it must be advantageous to indicate what one is feeling to others.

37. Because feelings determine behavior, it is important to let others know what you are feeling in order that they can correctly predict how you will act and coordinate their behavior with your own. When others correctly recognize what you are feeling, they are more likely to act in an appropriate way at the appropriate time. When others correctly coordinate their behavior with your own, you have to exert less time and energy trying to get them to do so.

38. Because feelings determine behavior, it is important to know what others are feeling in order that you can predict how they will act and you can coordinate your behavior with their behavior. When you correctly coordinate your behavior with the behavior of others, you expend less time and energy dealing with them. Appropriate behavior expends less time and energy than does inappropriate behavior, and is more likely to be successful.

39. Signs of specific feelings carry specific messages which provide advantages. Signs of happiness (smiling, purring, tail wagging) provide others with positive reactions and enable one to obtain positive reactions and resources from them. Signs of discomfort and unhappiness, such as crying, enable one to obtain help and resources from others. Signs of anger warn others that one will aggressively protect oneself and one's resources. Signs of fear notify those one depends on for resources and protection that there are threats present. Signs of interest notify those one depends on about the presence of threats and opportunities.

40. Individuals experience their own feelings, but not the feelings of others. Therefore it is easy for individuals to fail to take into account the feelings of other individuals. When individuals show others what they are feeling, they notify others that they have feelings, they remind others that these feelings need to be taken into account, and they reveal precisely what these feelings are. Only when individuals reveal their feelings can others take them into consideration.

41. In many species a tail is a device for communicating both visually and physically what one is feeling to others. Cats use their tails to indicate alertness, interest, enthusiasm, irritation, affection, fear, discouragement, and relaxation. Humans and apes use facial expressions instead of tails for this purpose. Tails are particularly noticeable because they are a distinct appendage, move independently of the rest of the body, make pronounced movements, are frequently banded in contrasting colors, and hit against other individuals.

42. Both tails and faces indicate the nature and degree of the tension that the individual is experiencing.

Activators

43. Individuals have *activators*, or specialized behaviors which activate specific feelings in other individuals. Crying, smiling, and anger are three examples of activators in humans.

44. Different animal species use different activators to achieve a common purpose. For example, humans smile, cats purr, and dogs wag their tails as activators to obtain positive reactions from others.

45. Activators are the first social behaviors expressed by the infants of many animal species. Mewing and purring are two examples of activators in kittens.

46. Individuals cheat, or use an activator without experiencing the feeling which produces the activator, in order to get others to respond appropriately. Cheaters employ various activators, including crying, smiling, and anger.

47. The presence of activators can be used to trace the presence and evolution of certain feelings in various animal species.

Behavior

48. The regular use of a specific social behavior by members of a species indicates that the behavior frequently evokes a specific feeling and a specific response in other members of the species.

49. The Parallel Feelings Hypothesis: If two different species a) use the same social behavior, and b) produce the same response in others, then c) the feeling which is evoked in others by the social behavior is the same in both species. For example, because infant humans and infant birds a) both "cry," and b) in both cases their parents respond by feeding them, then c) the same feeling is evoked in both sets of parents, i.e., a desire to avoid self-criticism, or guilt.

50. In accordance with The Parallel Feelings Hypothesis, when we can identify the feeling that is evoked in one of the two species, we can assume the same feeling is evoked in the other species. Therefore, when we know what the feeling is in humans when humans are one of the two species, we can assume that the same feeling is present in the other species.

Association and extension

51. An individual recognizes what he thinks, does, says, and owns as extensions of himself.

52. An individual recognizes a positive reaction by others to anything he thinks, does, says, or owns as a positive reaction to himself.

53. An individual recognizes a negative reaction by others to anything he thinks, does, says, or owns as a negative reaction to himself.

54. An individual considers the other individuals he is associated with to be extensions of himself.

55. An individual treats negative reactions to those he is associated with as negative reactions toward himself.

56. An individual views the behavior of those he is associated with as though it is his own behavior. As a result, actions which would embarrass the individual if he did them himself, embarrass him when they are done by other people he is associated with.

57. When a person is familiar with another individual's experiences, he does not experience them as the other individual experiences them. Instead, the person experiences them as he would feel if the experiences had happened to himself.

58. People "adopt" others as an extension of themselves. Thus they adopt characters in novels and films, individuals in the news, and sporting teams and players. When something happens to someone or something that a person has "adopted," the person responds as though it is happening to himself. This is the case when those who are adopted (or their resources) are threatened, or when those who are adopted succeed and receive positive reactions. People have

difficulty adopting a character when the character does things which they would not do themselves, such as things which they consider bad, incompetent, immature, self-centered, selfish, foolish, stupid, rude, inconsiderate, narrow minded, or a result of bad judgment.

Tense and release

59. Feelings involve an increase of tension or a release of tension.

60. Tension is experienced as hurt.

61. An increase in tension produces a corresponding increase in hurt.

62. Difficulty releasing tension, or the inability to release tension, prolongs hurt.

63. We try to minimize physical and mental effort because they involve tension and hurt. When we conserve time and energy, we avoid effort, and we avoid tension and hurt.

64. The release of tension is experienced as pleasure.

65. When we complete a task or achieve a goal, we release the tension that was driving us, and we feel pleasure. Therefore we feel pleasure when we complete a paper we are writing, pay off a mortgage, complete our income tax return, win a sporting competition, or get the positive reactions we want.

66. Sources of stimulation, such as movies, novels, amusement park rides, and certain sports, produce entertainment by providing tension and releasing it. People seek out these sources of stimulation

in order to experience tension, its release, and the resulting pleasure. The more tension experienced and the greater its release, the more successful the entertainment.

67. The more tension released, and the more easily tension is released, the more pleasure experienced.

68. Humans and other animal species seek to a) avoid tension, b) release tension, and c) increase tension in order to release it and experience pleasure.

69. Warmth releases muscular tension, and this release of tension provides pleasure. Therefore humans like lying in the sun, hot showers and baths, hot tubs and whirlpools, saunas, hot drinks, hot food, smoking, heat lamps, hot-water bottles, and electric heating pads.

70. Many other species like lying and relaxing in the sun, which indicates that the release of tension also provides them with pleasure. This indicates that their bodies and minds operate on the same tense and release principles that human bodies and minds do.

71. Massage is pleasurable to humans and other species because it releases tension.

72. A living organism consists of an organized system of tense and release mechanisms. These tense and release mechanisms are able to perform respiration, circulation, movement, digestion, reproduction, nervous control, mental operations, and other activities, such as yawning and sneezing.

73. It may prove possible to explain all physiological phenomena and the origin of life with tense and release models.

74. The brain evolved to coordinate tense and release mechanisms.

Effort

75. People avoid physical and mental activity because activity requires tension. People experience tension as hurt. In order to minimize hurt, individuals a) tense as little as possible, and b) release tension as soon as possible. As a result they exert themselves as little as possible, and conserve as much energy as possible.

76. People engage in physical and mental activity in response to their other feelings. They act when a) the pleasure they obtain from the activity, or b) the hurt they feel from other sources when they do not engage in the activity, outweighs the hurt they feel from exerting themselves.

77. People avoid activities in which the hurt they feel from exerting themselves is greater than the pleasure they experience from the activity.

78. People avoid activities in which the hurt they feel from exerting themselves is greater than the hurt they feel from other sources when they do not engage in the activity.

79. Something is boring or tedious because one does not obtain enough stimulation from it to outweigh the hurt one feels from exerting oneself to do the activity. Thus one finds it boring to reread the same material, to continue to eat the same food, or to listen to someone say something one is already familiar with, because these things no longer provide stimulation.

Models and behavior

80. Behavior is structured by mental categories and models.

81. Without models, behavior is random.

82. Each individual uses categories and models in order to act in a non-random fashion.

83. When categories or models are changed, behavior changes.

84. Individuals develop and use their own categories and models.

85. Each individual employs models in order to deal with feelings.

86. Most behavior can be explained in terms of feelings and the models employed to satisfy them.

87. When models are inconsistent with reality, people experience tension.

88. People act in order to rid themselves of this tension. When they act they change reality to be consistent with their models. For example, there is a glass on the left side of the table, and you want the glass to be on the right side of the table. Therefore reality (the glass is on the left side) is inconsistent with your model (you want the glass on the right side). Because of this inconsistency, you experience tension. Therefore, you act to rid yourself of this tension. You change reality (by moving the glass from the left side of the table to the right side) to be consistent with your model (you want the glass on the right side). When reality (the glass is now on the right side) is consistent with your model (you want the glass on the right side), then the tension is released, you no longer experience tension, and you no longer feel pressure to act.

15

89. People act to remove their greatest sources of tension. The greater the tension, the higher the priority.

90. People select the model and action which produces the least inconsistency with their other models, i.e., the least tension.

91. Humans and other animal species develop models, select models, and act for the same reasons.

92. The mind evolved to a) recognize categories, b) recognize inconsistencies, c) deal with feelings, d) produce models, e) select between models, and f) execute models.

Language

93. A shared language based on sounds is a means by which individuals coordinate their use of the same sounds with similar categories and models.

94. In a shared language, specific sounds (or other phenomena) trigger the specific categories and models in the minds of other individuals that the sounds are associated with.

95. A shared language allows individuals to exchange and pool information about their individual categories and models.

96. In human language standardized sounds were associated with the individual categories and models that pre-humans were already employing as an animal species.

97. Human language enables humans to discuss their feelings, behaviors, and mental operations, which they and the other animal species have in common.

98. Humans are animals who can tell each other what it is like to be an animal. Humans are talking animals.

99. If we want to know what animals feel and think, all we have to do is listen to humans talk about themselves.

100. Humans speak because they feel tension to say something. Once they have said what they want to say, the tension, or pressure, is released and is no longer there. When person A finishes saying something, and person B asks person A to repeat or explain what he has just said, person A finds it annoying to do so, because the initial tension is no longer there and person A has to force himself to comply.

101. Certain animals make sounds to other animals or to humans a) when they want something, or b) when they are bothered by something (have something to say). They stop making the sounds when a) they get what they want, or b) they have said what they wanted to say. This indicates that animals feel the same tension to make sounds that humans feel and release it in the same way. This indicates that their minds operate in the same way that human minds operate.

102. Animal species have to form categories in order to recognize phenomena, and have to formulate models and apply them in order to act non-randomly.

103. Human categories and models are primarily sensory images. Consider buying a loaf of bread, eating an ice cream cone, or having sex with a specific person. You think about these things primarily in visual images, not in words. If I say, "A kangaroo buried a watermelon in my front yard," how do you experience this in your mind? You see your own visual images of a kangaroo, a watermelon, burying something, and a front yard, rather than collections of words in your mind which describe a kangaroo, a watermelon, burying something, and a front yard.

104. Members of a species use means such as sounds in an effort to communicate their feelings, categories, and models to each other. Thus cats use sounds for a variety of purposes, including calling, answering, indicating discomfort or pain, seeking positive reactions, trying to get others to comply with what they want (establishing consistency), criticizing, threatening, and expressing what is on their mind, such as telling about their experiences or complaining.

105. Many species use sounds in an effort to activate feelings, categories, and models in other individuals.

106. Human language enables humans to communicate in generalizations, or words, which individual humans relate to their own personal categories and models.

107. Species differ as to how specific their communications are, i.e., the degree of detail in which they can describe their categories and models. Words communicate categories and models in greater detail than basic sounds. However, human language is severely limited when it comes to communicating the full detail and complexity of categories and models. Consider how difficult it is to use words alone to describe a person's appearance to someone who has never seen the person before, and to do so well enough that he would have no difficulty recognizing the person within a crowd of people. Consider also how difficult it is to use words to describe to another person all of the details and feelings that you experienced when you watched a film, read a novel, listened to a piece of music, or took a trip. Although words enable us to easily distinguish between "a chair" and "a couch" when we talk, it is difficult to use words to accurately describe a specific chair or couch to another person. When we want to communicate something specific to others we have to provide them with a visual image by showing them the item, showing them a photograph or a drawing of it, or using gestures.

108. It is very possible that a species could evolve a language which enabled it to communicate categories and models in much greater

detail than human language. Such a species could communicate more accurately and rapidly, could achieve a much finer degree of cooperation among its members, and would be much more successful than a species that relied on human language. In fact, the gap in ability between such a species and humans might be at least as great as the present gap between humans and other animal species on earth.

109. Theoretically a shared language could be just as specific and descriptive as the personal categories and models held by individuals. Other things being equal, the closer the language of a species is to this ideal, the more successful the species.

110. One can view a potential progression taking place from sounds, to words, to increasingly specific words.

Culture

111. Because each individual uses his own categories and models, no two individuals have the identical understanding of a situation.

112. Inconsistency produces tension, and people seek to establish consistency to remove this tension.

113. In order to establish consistency, people try to get others to adopt and comply with their personal models.

114. When we see someone do something, we behave as though we are doing it ourselves. We consider others as an extension of ourselves. If they do, say, or think something we would not, we view it as a mistake on our part and act to correct it by trying to change their behavior.

115. People use a) resources, and b) negative reactions, such as criticism, to get others to adopt and comply with their personal models.

116. People adopt the personal models of those who control resources in order to get a share of their resources.

117. Culture is the net result of individual efforts to establish consistency within a specific group.

118. A society or culture is a collage of individual, group, and organizational models.

119. Many individual and group models produce more negative results than positive results.

120. The ability of humans to communicate in greater detail through words has enabled human individuals to communicate their specific likes and dislikes to each other and to establish a much more elaborate repertoire of correct and incorrect behaviors in their societies than have other species. Although other species are concerned with avoiding negative reactions, they do not communicate or understand criticism in as fine detail as do humans and therefore do not adjust their behavior to as fine a degree. Therefore other species do not a) wear clothes, b) hide their sexual activity and elimination from others, or c) stand up straight, cover their mouths when they yawn, and use napkins.

121. A species which uses a language which is more specific than human language will have rules for correct and incorrect behavior which are more detailed than the rules used in human cultures. Humans will be unable to understand these rules or act in accordance with them, just as animals do not understand or act in accordance with human rules. Therefore, human behavior will appear as crude and uncouth to such a species as the behavior of animals does to humans.

Categories and models

122. Categories are an efficient means of dealing with sensory phenomena.

123. Phenomena which are not categorized produce tension and attract notice.

124. Categories are formed by recognizing repetition. For example, when humans speak and write, they use synonyms in order to avoid repetition which will produce a second, competing, unwanted, distracting category in the mind of the listener or reader. In poetry and song, on the other hand, humans use repetition to produce additional rhythmic patterns in the mind of the listener. Music consists of repetitive sounds, sequences, and phrases which enable the listener to establish categories. It is significant that music relies heavily on numerous forms of repetition, and to a much lesser extent on symmetry, to produce categories.

125. The organization of phenomena into a category releases tension and produces pleasure.

126. The quest for stimulation is the search for unfamiliar phenomena to categorize.

127. People use the arts, learning, entertainment, and travel in order to organize unfamiliar phenomena into new categories and thereby experience pleasure. The arts include music, painting, sculpture, literature, poetry, photography, film, architecture, crafts, fashion, and decoration.

128. Successful art is designed a) to be different than existing categories so that it is not already categorized and therefore produces tension and is interesting, and b) to be easily categorized so that the tension is released with little effort and pleasure is easily produced. Orientations are employed by artists to enable phenomena to be easily categorized, and orientations are violated by artists to a limited extent to produce tension and interest.

129. The fewer categories that are needed to categorize phenomena, the less effort is required, and the more attractive the phenomena. For example, lakes and lawns can be categorized with few categories and are peaceful and pleasing, and because younger faces have fewer features than older faces (with spots, sags, and wrinkles), they can be categorized with fewer categories and are more attractive.

130. Once phenomena are categorized, they are no longer stimulating. No tension remains to be released. No matter how attractive a specific phenomenon is initially, once it has been fully categorized, it is no longer interesting. This is true of art, literature, music, clothing, jewelry, other possessions, and a person's appearance.

131. The play activity of the young provides parents and other adults with stimulation, i.e., pleasure. Members of a species value, maintain, and protect their sources of pleasure.

132. Models relate categories together, and are an efficient means of dealing with categories.

133. Models are also used to explain unknowns. It is important for our survival that we be able to recognize and explain unknowns, because unknowns may constitute threats or opportunities.

134. Learning consists of the placement of phenomena into categories and models.

Orientations

135. Phenomena which are not oriented produce tension.

136. The orientation of phenomena releases tension and produces pleasure.

137. The more oriented phenomena are, the less tension is produced, and the more attractive the phenomena.

138. The less oriented phenomena are, the more tension is produced, and the less attractive the phenomena.

139. Humans employ orientations in order to reduce the effort the brain has to make to organize phenomena into categories.

140. The use of orientations enables humans to easily organize phenomena into categories. Examples of human orientations include symmetry, repetition, rectangles, circles, lines, horizontal and vertical, parallel and perpendicular, consistency, centering, equidistant placement, simplicity, perfection, thoroughness, grouping on the basis of similarity, and the use of solid colors.

141. An orientation can be approximate; it does not have to be mathematically perfect. Thus the colored designs on the individual members of a species can be approximately symmetrical, centered, or repetitive. An orientation only has to be close enough to perfect for the members of the species to be able to recognize the orientation. Humans use tools to apply their orientations with mathematical precision.

142. The presence of an orientation in the appearance of members of a species indicates that members of that species respond to that orientation. For example, if the facial or bodily designs on

members of the species are symmetrical, centered, or repetitive, then members of that species respond to that orientation.

143. The symmetrical, centered, and repetitive designs on the faces and bodies of individuals are aesthetically pleasing to the members of that species.

144. Individual differences in designs on faces and bodies result in individuals appearing more or less attractive than other individuals to members of their species.

145. Specific orientations and violations of orientations are used to draw attention to specific areas of the body.

146. Many other animal species have the same orientations as humans.

147. The orientations that are used in the colored designs on nonhuman species are the same orientations that humans employ in their construction and decoration of clothes, vehicles, everyday objects, architecture, and the arts, and in their behavior.

148. The extensive use of repetition and symmetry in a) the designs on nonhuman species, and b) the designs that humans use for and on their clothes, vehicles, everyday objects, and architecture indicates that nonhumans and humans form categories in the same way and therefore their minds operate the same way.

149. Symmetry is a form of repetition. In symmetry, one half of the design repeats the other half, but from the opposite direction.

150. An individual's body maintains an approximate symmetrical appearance between the right and left halves as the individual develops and ages.

151. Humans apply orientations to their objects and behavior to produce the categories they want to perceive and want others to perceive.

152. Humans violate the orientations in order to produce tension and attract attention. In order to attract attention they use contrasting colors, off-center placement, diagonals, and inconsistency.

The mind

153. The fact that the mind and the body both a) resist effort, b) experience fatigue, and c) are better able to handle difficult tasks after a period of rest indicates that they operate in a similar manner.

154. The mind seeks to a) recognize inconsistency, and b) establish consistency.

155. The human brain gets humans to expend physical effort which enables the brain to reduce mental effort.

156. Humans can only focus on one category or model at a time.

157. When we focus on one category, we do not recognize other categories.

158. When we focus on a category, we have to give up our previous category. Therefore we often forget what our previous category was.

159. Other animal species also have single-focus minds.

160. Pack hunting is so successful because prey focus on one predator, or category, at a time.

161. Our progress in science is so slow because each individual has a single-focus mind. We can only focus on one category at a time. Therefore, when we consider one category, we can not consider others. As a result we only see what we focus on. Our single-focus mind can only perform one mental operation at a time. Thus we can only make one observation, develop one category (or model), or apply one category (or model) to data at a time. Also, we can not a) observe, decide, or act, and b) analyze at the same time. When we observe, decide, or act, we can not analyze; and when we analyze, we can not observe, decide, or act. Because we can not both do something and analyze what we are doing at the same time, we have little conscious awareness of what we are doing and why we are doing it. Because we have a single-focus mind, we have to do science through piecemeal accumulation, and add one bit of information or analysis at a time.

162. A species whose individuals have multiple-focus minds could deal with more than one category (or model) at a time, and could perform more than one mental operation, such as both observation and analysis, at the same time. Such a species could understand situations and behavior, respond appropriately, and develop science and technology at a much faster rate than a single-focus species. In comparison with a multiple-focus species, a single-focus species would be mentally retarded. A multiple-focus species could be produced through a) evolution in certain environments, or b) genetic engineering.

163. A group is a collection of individuals whose single-focus minds are focused in different directions. Therefore a group operates as a multiple-focus mind, which recognizes more opportunities and more threats than an individual would recognize alone.

164. The more individuals there are in a group, the larger the number of threats and opportunities that will be recognized.

Consciousness

165. Consciousness is a focusing mechanism. Consciousness enables us to focus on a specific subject and consider other factors relative to it. Consciousness can focus on broad subjects or highly specific subjects.

166. Consciousness and vision both focus on one subject at a time.

167. The mind forms one model, or image, at a time, and must dissolve the old model to form the new one. As a result a person often forgets what their previous model was.

168. Consciousness is a decision-making apparatus. Any species that makes decisions has consciousness.

169. The primary role of consciousness is to add, remove, and rearrange behaviors.

170. Any species that makes decisions to add, remove, or rearrange behaviors has consciousness.

171. Consciousness recognizes, selects, and applies models.

172. Physical and mental activities require conscious attention when they must be learned or changed. They must be changed when it becomes clear they are inappropriate and when obstacles are encountered.

173. Conscious attention is required to examine and select alternatives. Examining and selecting alternatives requires much more conscious attention than monitoring routines.

174. Physical and mental activities which are repeated without change become routines. They can be executed very quickly because they require little conscious attention except to monitor their execution and their relevance.

175. Because conscious attention and selection involves more mental operations than does the execution of routines, it is much slower.

176. The more tension produced by a phenomenon, the more likely one is made consciously aware of the phenomenon.

177. One must apply conscious attention when a) one recognizes things, b) one tries to find something, c) one tries to understand what is happening, d) one tries to understand why something is happening, e) one chooses between alternatives, f) one decides how to deal with a situation, g) one decides how to deal with changes, h) one decides what one ought to be doing, i) one sets objectives, j) one decides how and when to carry out objectives, k) one decides what one needs to have in order to carry out objectives, l) one establishes priorities, m) one decides whether to act, n) one decides what to do next, o) one decides what to do in the future, p) one thinks about what could happen, q) one decides why one should not do things, r) one takes precautions, s) one recognizes obstacles, t) one decides how to act when one encounters obstacles, u) one solves problems, v) one decides how to make improvements, w) one checks on one's progress, x) one recognizes that one needs to find an alternative, y) one realizes that the situation is different than one thought, z) one tries to change one's behavior, aa) one tries to change the behavior of others, bb) one imagines a possible outcome, cc) one imagines a desirable outcome, dd) one dreams, ee) one considers or decides what to do if something happens, ff) one recognizes when something significant happens, gg) one considers past events, hh) one thinks about what one should have done, or ii) one evaluates things and events.

178. Any species which does one or more of the activities mentioned just above has consciousness.

The study of brain and behavior

179. Rather than view each species as having a unique evolutionary past, unique mental operations, and unique behaviors, it is more useful to view different species as sharing a common set of mental operations and behaviors which have been modified for survival in particular niches.

180. We have assumed that the behavior of each species is unique.

181. However, the behavior that is unique to a species is a thin veneer over a common set of feelings, behaviors, and mental operations which are shared with other animal species.

182. By focusing on the differences between species and the differences between cultures we have overlooked the greater significance of the similarities between species. Differences between species and between cultures are inconsistent, produce tension, and attract our attention. Similarities between species and between cultures are consistent, do not produce tension, and do not attract our attention.

183. Feelings, categories, models, consciousness, and communication did not originate with humans. They originated with animals. Humans have them too because humans are animals.

184. Language and technology did not free humans from their animal programming, or feelings, but rather gave humans more power to implement their animal programming on each other and their environment.

185. Perhaps the biggest obstacle to understanding ourselves is our pretentiousness, or the belief humans are unique, special, and important, and more so than other species. This pretentiousness has interfered with and delayed our understanding of a) our location

in space, b) our evolution, c) our mind and behavior, and d) the similarity between human nature and animal nature, and our realizing that e) other species have as much right to the environment as we do.

186. The refusal of the scientific community to recognize the role of feelings and consciousness in animal behavior is the equivalent of the scientific community's refusal in the past to recognize evolution or the rotation of the planets around the sun. This refusal is a major impediment to our progress in understanding behavior.

187. If an alien attempted to understand human behavior, but ignored human feelings and consciousness, how accurate would the research findings be? Similarly, when humans attempt to understand the behavior of another species, but ignore feelings and consciousness, how accurate are the research findings?

188. Every behavior of humans and other animal species can be understood in a scientific manner.

189. Each and every thing an individual does reflects the structure and operation of the brain.

190. An understanding of human behavior and the human mind will likely precede and produce a greater understanding of the behavior and minds of other animal species.

191. Science seeks to accurately explain the maximum amount of phenomena in the simplest way. This should be the goal of behavioral studies also.

192. We will find simple ways to accurately describe and explain behavior, the mind, and the brain.

Humans and other species

193. Human exploitation of other species is based on superior power rather than natural right.

194. Humans act like the Nazis of the animal kingdom, and treat other species worse than Nazis treated Jews.

195. Just as the Nazis envisioned a Thousand-Year Reich for their race, humans envision a long and glorious destiny for their species on earth and in space.

196. Humans do not act any better or any worse than any other animal species would act if it had moved into the dominant position.

197. The argument that "it is acceptable for humans to harm animals provided humans are benefited" is no different than the arguments that "it is acceptable for Europeans to harm Africans provided Europeans are benefited," "it is acceptable for men to harm women provided men are benefited," and "it is acceptable for Nazis to harm Jews provided Nazis are benefited."

198. Other animal species are so similar to us, that when we do something to another species, we might as well be doing it to ourselves.

199. Humans live as though they are the only species on earth that matters. They do not consider the consequences of their actions for the members of other species.

200. Humans consider each individual human precious, but each individual member of other species insignificant.

201. The reluctance of humans to view members of other species as individuals makes it easier for humans to mistreat them.

202. Humans do not want to accept that members of other animal species have feelings and thoughts comparable to their own.

203. Humans show an almost complete lack of empathy and respect for members of other animal species, who are experiencing many of the same feelings and thoughts that humans would experience if humans were in their situations.

204. Human abuse of the members of other species far outweighs whatever good humans do.

205. The food chain is cannibalism on a large scale. Animal species are so similar to each other, that animal-eating species are effectively eating themselves.

Humans and the environment

206. Humans are in the process of converting the entire earth to human use at the expense of other species.

207. Humans find the appearance of nature chaotic and irritating. Therefore they apply human orientations to nature in order to reduce the effort of looking at it. Thus they produce lawns, gardens, and parks which conform with human orientations. Human orientations include the extensive use of rectangles, circles, lines, parallel and perpendicular, horizontal and vertical, repetition, symmetry, consistency, perfection, and grouping on the basis of similarity.

208. The better a species establishes and maintains an oriented environment which reduces the work of the brain, the more successful the species.

2. THEORETICAL INTRODUCTION

Contents

Human instincts

Human behavior is directed by biological programs within each member of the species. These programs are experienced by individuals as feelings. Feelings encourage humans to obtain and conserve resources. Individuals respond to these feelings by acting to increase or decrease their intensity and thereby act to obtain or conserve resources. Humans deal with these feelings on their own, and through social organizations and practices which are instituted in response to these feelings. The thesis of this series is that the behavior of human individuals and human society can be explained in terms of these feelings, or biological programs.

Resources

Resources are the means people use to satisfy their feelings and their needs. Resources include food and water, sex, positive reactions, stimulation, and the means to obtain them, such as time, energy, materials, jobs, money, information, and relationships. Resources are obtained from the environment and from other people. People provide resources for other people, and frequently exchange resources. Therefore people act as resources for each other.

Programmed feelings

Human social behavior is directed by programmed feelings, or feelings which are biologically based. Our species carries specific feelings which guide us in our interaction with our environment and other people. These feelings direct humans to obtain and conserve resources, and promote individual survival and the successful production of offspring.

Feelings guide humans to act in ways which improve their chances of getting resources and keeping them. Humans have feelings because they are more reliable than learning and conscious decision in directing human behavior in certain advantageous directions. As a result, human behavior is not left to the caprice of social and cultural practice or conscious decision. Therefore, human behavior is not left to chance. Without feelings individuals would act in a much more random fashion, respond slower, acquire and conserve fewer resources, and produce fewer successful offspring. As a consequence, individuals who lack the feelings would be at a marked disadvantage relative to those individuals who are directed by them.

In the human species these feelings function as instincts. Therefore people experience instincts as feelings. It is very likely that instincts are experienced as feelings in other species as well. From the perspective of the members of a species, feelings indicate which actions to pursue and which ones not to pursue.

Feelings have much to offer a species. They provide immediate re-inforcement. Therefore they offer quick direction as to which actions promoted survival in the past. The immediate impact of a feeling allows the members of a species to respond much faster than if they had to wait to see which outcomes developed, depended on their memory of past outcomes, or had to reason what the outcomes were likely to be. Out-comes, or functions, of a behavior usually become apparent some time later, and are by no means guaranteed. If a species depended on distant and uncertain outcomes rather than immediate feelings as a basis for action, messages would often be confused, misunderstood, and forgotten. By using feelings to guide behavior, a species requires no understanding of the consequences of its actions.

Feelings act as alarms. They dominate our attention. They tend to occur very soon following certain stimuli. Feelings are programmed to indicate the earliest signs of a possible change in our access to re-sources. Changes in our access to resources can have serious consequences for our survival and the survival of our offspring. The sooner we are aware that changes are occurring, the sooner we can attempt to strengthen our access to the resources or seek alternative resources. Feelings are keyed to occur in response to indications of possible changes in resources, rather than to final results. This gives people a maximum amount of time in which to act to strengthen their access to resources or to find alternative resources, and thereby maximize their gain or minimize their loss.

Feelings are highly flexible in terms of the stimuli which activate them. Thus a particular feeling can be activated by a great variety of different stimuli. As a result they are far more useful than programs which respond to a single stimulus. We live in a complex natural and social world, and there are many very different indications that one's resources may be affected. A feeling can notify people when any of these indications occur.

The term "feeling" refers to factors which encourage an individual to engage in a specific kind of behavior during his interaction with his environment and other people. The term is not meant to imply that the person must engage in the behavior, or that the behavior can only take one form. An individual can choose to respond in a variety of ways or not to act at all.

Certainly humans learn specific behaviors from each other. However, the primary purpose of learning is to help individuals acquire strategies which will enable them to effectively avoid or satisfy their feelings. This is also not to say that human beings lack rational control over their actions. Human beings certainly do have rational control, but the primary function of rational control is to enable human beings to select between alternative means of avoiding or satisfying the feelings they experience.

Although feelings and the behaviors they encourage improve the chance of survival, they do not ensure it. We live in a complex world where situations and outcomes are rarely identical. Feelings frequently miss their mark or are too strong or too weak to help the individual in a specific situation. Therefore they act as goads, but crude goads. It is useful to view feelings as rules of thumb, or rough guides for living, which have proven helpful in the past more often than they have not.

Specific feelings operate much the way that pain operates. People are biologically programmed to feel pain in situations in which immediate physical damage is occurring. Pain notifies people to stop causing, or to get away from, the stimulus which produces pain. This enables a person to avoid physical damage or to prevent additional physical damage. Pain also carries certain properties. One is varying intensity. Some stimuli feel more painful than others. A stimulus can be stronger or weaker and be encountered at different points on the body. Also, not all stimuli cause pain. Another property of pain is varying duration. Pain may continue for anywhere from a very short to a very long time. Pain of short duration can still be highly effective in changing our behavior. All people are born with the biological machinery to feel pain in response to certain stimuli. People carry this machinery with them and use it all of their lives.

At the same time, people employ learning, memory, culture, and conscious decisions to avoid pain. In regard to learning, people learn to avoid situations which produce pain. Thus people learn that a hot drink will burn their mouth and tongue. People also instruct each other how to avoid pain. Thus someone may suggest to another to sip his hot drink or wait until it cools, so it does not burn him. In regard to memory, people develop a great deal of respect for pain as a result of previous experience with it. People recall situations which produced pain in the past and how pain could be avoided. They have banged their fingers, feet, shins, and elbows; pinched their fingers in drawers and doors; burned their hands and mouths; twisted their ankles; broken bones; suffered electric shocks; had the wind knocked out of them; hit their heads on low ceilings, stairwells, and cabinet doors; been stung by insects; had their eyes poked; cut themselves with knives; stepped on nails and glass; stuck themselves with thorns and pins; experienced sunburns and freezing cold; dropped items on their feet; bitten their mouths and tongues; and had portions of their skin scraped off. As a result people spend all of their lives taking countless preventive measures and carefully navigating their environment to minimize further encounters with pain. In regard to culture and society, means are developed and provided to avoid and counteract pain. Thus we have anesthetics, medications, massage, hard hats, shoes, goggles, protective clothing, seat belts, and air bags. In regard to conscious decisions, people avoid unfamiliar situations which could cause pain. They may decide not to stick their hand inside a machine, eat an unfamiliar substance, or pick up a strange insect. In addition, people make conscious decisions to do things which they expect will cause them pain. They may decide to play a contact sport which produces injuries, wear pointe shoes in ballet, or have dental work or surgery performed.

The fact that people use learning, memory, culture, and conscious decisions in dealing with pain in no way negates the fact that pain has a biological basis. Without a biological program such as pain, people's behavior would be very different. If they did not experience pain, then in order to avoid destruction, infection, and disease which result from damaging physical stimuli, people would have to carry with them accurate knowledge of the correlation between a) kinds and intensities of physical stimuli, b) the locations on the body where the stimuli occur, c) types of destruction, infection, and disease, and d) the impact of specific kinds of destruction, infection, and disease on their viability. Moreover people would have to recall and apply this knowledge instantly whenever they experienced stimuli which could cause physical damage. As it is, because people have a biological program of pain, they are able to respond to damaging stimuli very quickly and do not need to understand destruction, infection, disease, and recovery. The biological program of pain has been and still is extremely important for the survival of our species, and for other species as well.

Specific feelings operate much the way that pain operates. People are biologically programmed to experience feelings in situations in which resources become available or are threatened. These feelings notify people to alter their behavior to obtain or conserve resources. Pleasant feelings tell people to welcome certain kinds of situations. Unpleasant feelings tell people to avoid other kinds of situations. As a result a person obtains additional resources and prevents further loss of resources. Feelings also carry certain properties. One is varying intensity. Some situations feel more pleasant or unpleasant than others, and not all stimuli activate feelings. Another property is varying duration. A feeling may last anywhere from a very short to a very long time. A feeling of short duration can still be highly effective in changing our behavior. All humans are born with the biological machinery to experience pleasant or unpleasant feelings in certain situations, and they carry this machinery with them and use it all of their lives.

At the same time, people employ learning, memory, culture, and conscious decisions in connection with their feelings. In regard to learning, people learn to avoid situations which produce punishing feelings, and to seek out those situations which produce pleasant feelings. People also instruct each other how to avoid the punishing feelings and promote the positive feelings. In regard to memory, people develop a great deal of respect for punishing feelings as a result of previous experience with them. People recall situations which produced punishing feelings in the past and remember how they could be avoided. As a result people spend all of their lives taking countless preventive measures and carefully navigating their physical and social environments to minimize further encounters with punishing feelings. Similarly, people develop considerable desire for pleasurable feelings as a result of previous experience with them. People recall which situations produced pleasurable feelings in the past and remember how the feelings could be encouraged. As a result they spend all of their lives trying to maximize further encounters with pleasurable feelings. Even the occasional experience of pleasure is enough to get people to continue to engage in an activity. In regard to culture and society, means are developed and provided to avoid and promote the feelings and people learn to use them. As for conscious decisions, people avoid situations which are likely to cause punishing feelings and accept situations which are likely to cause pleasant feelings. In addition, people make conscious decisions to act contrary to their feelings. They do things which they expect will cause them punishing feelings, such as leaving their family in order to find work. They also avoid things which will cause them pleasant feelings, such as taking addictive drugs or a second dessert.

The fact that people use learning, memory, culture, and conscious decisions in dealing with feelings in no way negates the fact that the feelings have a biological basis. Without the feelings, people's behavior would be very different. People live in a complex, multivariate world. If they did not experience feelings, then in order to best obtain resources and avoid loss of resources, people would have to carry with them accurate statistical knowledge of the likely outcomes of their actions. Moreover people would have to recall and apply this knowledge instantly whenever they experience opportunities or threats in regard to resources. As it is, because people have feelings, they are able to respond to opportunities and threatening situations very quickly and do not need to understand distant, uncertain outcomes. Feelings have been and still are extremely important for the survival of our species, and for other species as well.

This is what happens with hunger. Hunger is a programmed feeling. Hunger encourages us to eat and thereby helps us consume sufficient calories. However, despite the biological nature of hunger, the individual has the freedom to decide when, where, what, and how to eat, and whether to ignore the feeling altogether and not to eat at all. Certainly our social groups and personal decisions heavily influence our eating practices. Nevertheless the feeling of hunger continues to encourage us to eat and often overrides social rules and conscious decisions which tell us that certain food is not good for us, or is unappetizing or taboo. The fact that people use learning, memory, culture, and conscious decisions in dealing with hunger in no way negates the fact that hunger has a biological basis.

The natural state

It is helpful to view the natural state of humans and other animal species as remaining at rest, both unmoving and unthinking. This state minimizes the expenditure of energy and therefore, other things being equal, is more advantageous than other states which expend a larger amount of physical and mental energy. However, this state by itself does not promote survival of the individual or result in the production of successful offspring. Therefore, species supplement this state of inaction with certain behaviors. These behaviors include such things as avoiding pressure sores, obtaining food, escaping predators, attending to personal cleanliness, and procreating. As has been stated, the human being is not left on his own to decide which behaviors to engage in. Instead he is programmed with a set of feelings to ensure that he acts in the interest of his own survival and acts to produce successful offspring. These feelings take the form of discomfort, pain, hunger, loneliness, anxiety, interest in stimulation, pleasure, envy, and so on. Were it not for these feelings, the individual would remain inactive.

Association and extension

Individuals do not view themselves and they are not viewed by others as independent entities. Instead, individuals are viewed in association with their possessions, clothes, food, statements, beliefs, ideas, fantasies, relatives, friends, organizations, experiences, goals, and the groups and individuals they identify with. As a consequence, everything associated with an individual is considered an extension of the individual. Thus when others act in a positive way toward the things associated with the individual, this is viewed by the individual as acting and feeling positively toward the individual himself. Similarly, when others act in a negative way toward the things associated with the individual, this is viewed by the individual as acting and feeling negatively toward the individual himself. An individual also considers the people he is associated with as extensions of himself. When others criticize or attack the people an individual is associated with, the individual experiences this as criticism of or an attack on himself. Likewise, an individual considers the behavior of those he is associated with as though it is his own behavior. If an individual would be embarrassed to do something, he is also embarrassed if those he is associated with do it. But he is not embarrassed when people do it that he is not associated with. Also, when an individual is familiar with the experiences of another person, he experiences them as though they are his own experiences, and feels the way he himself would feel in that same situation.

Excess behavior

Humans engage in a great deal of excess behavior in response to their feelings which does not achieve the purposes the feelings were designed for. Although feelings have evolved to encourage people to act in ways which promote their survival, they also encourage people to act when their survival is not promoted. The resulting waste of time, energy, and other resources can be counterproductive and decrease the chance that the individual will survive. For example, a feeling has evolved which gets people to seek stimulation and this enables people to identify new resources. However, this same feeling encourages people to investigate novelties even when a novelty does not produce new resources. As a result people waste enormous amounts of time and energy when they continue to investigate unproductive novelties, such as music, video games, and most television programs. Similarly, sexual pleasure encourages people to engage in sex, which produces offspring. However, sexual pleasure causes many people to engage in a larger quantity of a) sexual behavior which is unlikely to produce offspring, than b) sexual behavior which is likely to produce offspring. As a result, people waste an enormous amount of time and energy engaging in sexual behavior which is unlikely to produce offspring. In regard to excess behavior, one is reminded of an insect whose attraction to light causes it to be burned by a light bulb or trapped by an entomologist. Feelings serve as shortcuts that encourage certain patterns of behavior which have proven useful more often than not. On the whole, the benefit of having feelings is greater than the cost of responding to them in excess.

An alternative paradigm

This research does not use the traditional paradigm which presently dominates studies of human behavior. The traditional paradigm assumes that practically all human behavior is based on reasoning and learning, and practically all animal behavior occurs as a result of biological programming. The traditional paradigm conceptualizes a) the human individual as infinitely malleable putty, capable of all things and moldable into any shape by those around him, and b) other animal species as marionettes moving in response to highly specific biological programs. Differences between the traditional paradigm and the paradigm presented in this series are outlined in Model 1 on pages 44 and 45.

The traditional paradigm of *Human reasoning and learning versus Animal programming* places man on a pedestal and supports the idea of human uniqueness and superiority. In contrast, the alternative paradigm of *Programmed feelings* presented here treats human behavior as a natural phenomenon rather than a supranatural one, and examines the behavior of humans and other species within a single evolutionary framework. In addition, the *Programmed feelings* paradigm explains why species have feelings. Feelings are constantly present in association with behavior. They are quite expensive in terms of the time and energy they consume. It is highly unlikely a species would carry this much apparatus if it were useless ornamentation. Also, the paradigm of *Programmed feelings* permits us to explain behavior on both the individual and the group levels. Traditional explanations that focus on the group level often encounter difficulties when an individual's behavior is not identical with that of the group or statistical norm, and are inclined to consider this behavior deviant or maladaptive.

Astronomers have been able to make considerable progress by adopting a new model which exchanged the positions of the earth and the sun. The earth was moved from a major, independent position at the center of the universe to a minor, dependent position circling the sun; and the sun was moved from a minor, dependent position circling the earth to a major, independent position at the center of the solar system. As a result of this exchange, the earth lost its extraordinary significance and became one of many planets. The paradigm presented here exchanges the positions of reason and feelings. Reason is moved from a major, independent position in charge of human behavior to a minor, dependent one; and feelings are moved from a minor, dependent position to a major, independent one directing human behavior. As a result of this exchange, humans lose their extraordinary significance and become one of many species.

Program of this research series

This research is presented in a series of volumes. The series examines the behaviors which humans initiate in response to their feelings. Several volumes deal with specific behaviors motivated by feelings. Each behavior is considered in terms of when it occurs, the feeling which motivates it, the functions it serves, its excess forms, and the way it structures human society. Two volumes deal with a) the use of consciousness to select models and behaviors to satisfy our feelings, and b) efforts to get our environment, other people, and ourselves to act in accordance with what we want. Two other volumes illustrate how feelings direct everyday life in a specific society, that of Prince Edward Island, Canada. During discussions in the individual chapters, the reader is referred to other chapters in this series. These chapters appear in this volume and subsequent volumes, or they are planned for future volumes.

In some of the chapters of this series there are a few simple exercises for the reader to do. Please do the exercises. They will help you understand why certain conclusions were reached. There are no exercises in this volume, but there are in later volumes of this series.

Model 1: Contrasting paradigms

BEHAVIOR:

Traditional paradigm: *Human reasoning and learning*
versus
Animal programming

Humans:

Practically all human behavior is based on reasoning and learning. People acquire their behavior by reasoning, watching and listening to others, and through reinforcement. Human minds act as blank slates, capable of selecting and learning almost any kind of behavior. A few instincts occur in infants, such as a tendency to smile at faces or grasp with hands.

Animals:

Practically all animal behavior is determined by programs. Programs are biological instructions which produce unconscious obedience and highly specific behaviors. Many of these programs are unique for each species. The more advanced animal species have brains which are sophisticated enough to supplement these programs with some learning and reasoning.

Alternative paradigm
of this research: *Programmed feelings*

Humans and animals:

Both people and animals find and use behaviors in an attempt to satisfy or avoid a specific set of feelings, which are either pleasant or unpleasant. The behaviors used are learned from others or invented. These behaviors increase the chance that the individual will obtain and keep resources.

FEELINGS:

Traditional paradigm: *Human reasoning and learning*
versus
Animal programming

Humans:
Feelings are a unique and important part of the human experience. Literature, music, art, and relationships between people are founded on feelings. Certain feelings, such as joy, happiness, and love, are healthy and should be encouraged. Other feelings, such as anger, anxiety, envy, frustration, and guilt are unhealthy and should be avoided. Feelings are the product of a higher consciousness and greater intelligence and serve no purpose other than personifying the human experience.

Animals:
Animals do not have feelings. It is anthropomorphic and unscientific to suggest they do.

Alternative paradigm
of this research: *Programmed feelings*

Humans and animals:
Feelings are the primary motivator of behavior in humans and other animals. They are an innate feature of a species and are biologically inherited. A species has a specific set of pleasant and unpleasant feelings which motivates the species to find and use behaviors which satisfy or avoid the feelings. These feelings are programmed to occur in certain situations, and have encouraged behavior in the past which increased the likelihood of obtaining and conserving resources. Many feelings are experienced as soon as there are signs that a change in access to resources may take place. This provides the individual with a maximum amount of time to obtain, conserve, and replace resources. There are many similarities in the feelings experienced by different species.

45

The information in this series was collected between 1973 and the present time by the writer of this series, research assistants, and students. Numerous quotes are given in the series. These quotes were gathered from people on Prince Edward Island. A small percentage of the material deals with experiences that people on Prince Edward Island have had in other provinces and in other countries. The person quoted is not identified by age and occupation because in most cases the person would not want this information known. Given the small size of the province, the amount of information that people know about each other, and the effort they put into learning more about others, facts such as age and occupation would confirm the identity of many of those quoted. Unimportant details in the quotes and case studies are sometimes changed to protect the identities of the subjects.

3. SPECIFIC BEHAVIORS IN RESPONSE TO FEELINGS

Contents

SEEKING POSITIVE REACTIONS

Brief contents

Detailed contents

Detailed contents

continued on next page

Introduction

People crave signs that other people have positive feelings toward them. They want others to provide them with recognition, appreciation, admiration, respect, praise, understanding, agreement, concern, sympathy, affection, and love. Moreover, they want to receive these positive reactions from the people who are meaningful to them, and they want to receive them when they want them. They go to considerable trouble to get these positive reactions, and when they receive them, they bask in them. People also want positive reactions when they expend energy on other people. They look for positive reactions when they speak to others and when they give them resources. People employ a great many tactics to get positive reactions. They provide others with positive reactions in order to get positive reactions from them. They give others the kinds of positive reactions they would like to receive themselves, expend resources on them, seek to cultivate and maintain relationships with them, and try to gain recognition as the kind of people others would like to receive positive reactions from.

When people do not receive positive reactions, they feel lonely. Therefore, people seek positive reactions in order to avoid loneliness. Loneliness helps people obtain resources. Resources include food and water, sex, positive reactions, protection, and stimulation, and the means to obtain them, such as time, energy, materials, money, jobs, information, and relationships. Loneliness encourages people to search for those who will provide them with positive reactions. People who provide a person with positive reactions are often willing to provide the person with additional resources. People who do not provide the person with positive reactions seldom provide the person with additional resources. Therefore, positive reactions from people serve as an initial indicator that other resources are likely to follow. The quest for positive reactions sends people to the primary source of resources, i.e., other people, and sends them to the individuals who are most likely to provide them with resources, i.e., those who provide them with positive reactions.

When people receive the positive reactions they want, they feel pleasure. A second reason people seek positive reactions is in order to feel pleasure. A person who experiences pleasure expresses it through facial expressions, such as by smiling, which provide the onlooker with a positive reaction. Feeling pleasure and expressing pleasure help the individual obtain resources. People seek the company of individuals who will provide them with positive reactions, and they frequently include gifts of resources in their attempts to get positive reactions. Therefore, individuals who are better able to express pleasure and provide positive reactions are more likely to obtain these resources.

Positive reactions provide people with release from loneliness and with pleasure. However, the feelings that are produced by positive reactions are experienced only temporarily. Therefore people associate together and form lasting relationships in order to obtain a continuous supply of positive reactions. The need for positive reactions is like hunger. All individuals need to be regularly fed with positive reactions, probably several times a day, and when fed they are satiated only temporarily.

Smiling and humor are activators which enable people to obtain positive reactions from others. Smiling and humor often provide other people with pleasure, and others normally express their pleasure through smiling and laughing. The person who causes others to smile or laugh interprets their response as pleasure in response to his presence, feels he is receiving a positive reaction, and experiences pleasure in return.

The feelings of pleasure and loneliness occur as soon as sources of positive reactions become available or disappear. One feels pleasure immediately upon receiving positive reactions. Similarly, one feels loneliness as soon as one loses an important source of positive reactions. Therefore, pleasure and loneliness serve as sensitive indicators that resources are available or threatened, and allow one a maximum amount of time to exploit or rectify the situation.

People interpret the efforts of others to get positive reactions from them as genuine liking of them. Thus when person B gives person A positive reactions and/or other resources in order to get positive reactions for himself, person A considers person B to be showing signs of genuinely liking person A. Conversely, when person B is unwilling to give person A positive reactions, person A considers person B to be showing signs of genuinely disliking person A.

Although positive reactions are a resource, it is helpful in the following discussion to distinguish between positive reactions and other resources. Therefore in this chapter the term resources will often be used to refer to resources other than positive reactions.

Obtaining positive reactions

Types of reactions

It is useful to distinguish between positive and negative reactions. Positive reactions occur in forms such as praise, sympathy, and affection, and show that the other person is valued. In contrast, negative reactions involve an unfavorable response, such as disagreeing with, criticizing, or rejecting the other person. One can think of positive reactions as signs that one likes the other person, and negative reactions as signs that one dislikes the other person.

People frequently give others positive reactions in order to get positive reactions from them. In addition, people give others positive reactions when they are not trying to get positive reactions for themselves. They do so to get resources from others, to do the best thing, to avoid criticism or rejection, because they think others have done something meaningful, and because it is their job and they are paid to do so.

People employ a great many tactics to try to get positive reactions from others. Most of these efforts involve providing other people with positive reactions and with resources. Many efforts are successful and do succeed in getting people the positive responses they want. However, many efforts are unsuccessful. Often others fail to provide people with the positive reactions they want, because others are preoccupied with something else, are not interested enough in the people to make the effort, do not find the subject matter being dealt with meaningful, or are busy trying to get positive reactions for themselves. At the same time, people receive many positive reactions that they are not looking for from other people. Some of these positive reactions they are pleased to get; others they do not want. These come from other people who are trying to get positive reactions for themselves and are employing positive reactions and other resources to get them. Often people are not consciously aware that they are trying to get positive reactions from others.

People do not want just any kind of positive reaction from others. They want appropriate positive reactions. These are positive reactions to their current activity or concern. Thus they want positive reactions in the form of pleasure on seeing them, interest in what they say, concern over what bothers them, sympathy for their bad experiences, agreement with their opinions and decisions, treatment of what they consider meaningful as meaningful, understanding and support for their behavior, praise for their achievements, enthusiasm about their successes, criticism of those who cause them problems, laughter at their jokes, pleasure at their efforts to be playful or entertain, concern for their comfort, appreciation of their efforts on the other person's and on other people's behalf, compliments on their efforts to look nice, agreement with their purchases, admiration for the possessions and experiences they bring to the other person's attention, and affection when they want it. People are disappointed when the other person fails to respond appropriately.

There are certain types of reactions which people would rather not receive. They do not want positive reactions from others who are not meaningful to them who are attempting to get positive reactions and resources for themselves. People's time and energy are limited, and they need them for their own purposes. They do not want negative reactions, such as arguments, criticism, and rejection. In addition, people do not want to have others react to their mistakes and failures, or to stupid things they do.

When you play on a sports team, it's no fun to be teased by the members of the other team for losing or playing badly. It makes you feel worse. [#1]

I remember watching a guy make a presentation in class one day who accidentally drooled on himself. That is something you definitely do not want others to see or hear about. [#2]

I have a forty-five-year-old friend who wanted to do something with her hair, and decided to cut it herself. She removed more and more hair as she kept trying to get it the way she wanted. In the end she had a crew cut, which was too short to do anything else with. She looked like a teenager. When I went out with her two days later, she was very self-conscious. Every time someone glanced at her, her posture stiffened or she commented that she didn't care what others thought. Later she told me how uncomfortable she was. "It was the first time I did anything so outrageous. I felt like people were staring at me, and snickering because they thought I was trying to look younger than I am. I realize now that after the first glance most people probably didn't think twice about my hair." [#3]

People often do not appreciate having others snoop, or direct attention, into their private affairs, because of the danger others will discover something which they will criticize them for.

> At every school dance, whenever I was out of my brother's sight, he wanted to know where I'd been. I felt like telling him it was none of his business. [#4]

In order to avoid negative reactions, many people do not make overtures to someone they are attracted to, give speeches, or play a musical instrument, sing, or dance in front of others.

> I took piano lessons for several years when I was a boy. It was a total waste, because I never learned to read music and seldom practiced. One time I was with friends and they started asking me to play something on the piano. I knew I would do a shitty job, so I refused. One of the girls present said, "He just wants us to beg him to play." I felt like killing her. [#5]

People try to avoid putting themselves in these situations because they think they may provide others with grounds to criticize them. Often people have learned to fear such situations because their efforts were criticized on previous occasions, or they have seen others in the same situation criticized.

When people fail to get positive reactions through acceptable behavior, they occasionally turn to unacceptable behavior. Often any reaction is better than no reaction at all.

> When children don't succeed in getting attention by being charming, witty, or coy, they'll sometimes switch to whining, screaming, kicking, biting, or causing damage. I was visiting a friend who was ironing, and her three-year-old boy, James, wanted her to pay more attention to him. "Mom, I want you to stop ironing now!" he demanded. "I have two more shirts to iron, and then I'll be done," she replied. James left without further comment, and five minutes later his mother went to find him. James had stuffed toilet paper in the toilet and squirted toothpaste on the walls. James was spanked, but didn't seem very upset by it. [#6]

I've noticed that kids who come from single-parent homes usually cause more trouble. The parent is so absorbed with financial and personal problems, that she or he has no energy left at the end of the day. The parent gives the kids nothing more than a roof over their heads, a full stomach, and clothes on their backs, and simply isn't able to provide them with the attention they need. #7

One suspects that people who employ unacceptable behavior to try to get positive reactions often lack better means to get positive reactions. Also, in many cases unacceptable behavior takes less effort than acceptable behavior to get positive reactions. It takes less effort to break a musical instrument than to learn to play it, and less effort to disturb a class than to earn good grades. Unacceptable behavior does sometimes evoke concern and other forms of positive reactions. In addition, there is behavior which receives negative reactions from some, but positive reactions from others. Thus the use of cigarettes, alcohol, or drugs may be viewed negatively by one's parents, but evoke positive reactions from one's peers.

When people want positive reactions

People want positive reactions a number of times a day from other people who are meaningful to them. They attempt to get these reactions from their spouse, children, other relatives, friends, colleagues, subordinates, and others.

My wife and I get our attention primarily from each other. We talk together and are sometimes affectionate while we're getting ready for work, in the kitchen before dinner, over dinner, and in the bedroom before bed. Every afternoon I call her at work to see how she is, and when I finish work I go see her at her business until she's ready to go home. We frequently go out to lunch together, take walks together, or watch TV or a rented film together. We usually talk about what we've been doing during the day, our children, decisions we are making, things that are happening to other people we know, and TV programs and films we see.

At work I talk to one colleague about how our work is going, to another colleague about new computer equipment we need, and to two others about investments. I also talk to all four about office politics when problems arise. I talk to these four, and rarely talk to my other colleagues. One of these four plays basketball with the same people at noon each day, and plays fantasy games once a week with fellow enthusiasts at his home. Another spends an hour each day gossiping with other personnel over lunch, and also plays poker with people from work. In addition to talking to these four colleagues, I frequently drop in to see my stockbroker and we regularly call each other. My wife also gets attention from her customers, her employees, and the woman who owns a business next door.

Our daughter, who is fifteen, gets her attention primarily from my wife and me. She frequently wants to know what we think of what she's wearing and whether we appreciate a chore she's done. She also talks about TV programs and movies she's seen, and we ask her about school and outside activities. When she comes home she likes to tell us what has happened to her during the day. She often joins my wife and me when we go out to eat or to a movie, and she frequently sits and watches TV or a rented film with us. Occasionally she wants a hug before bed. She does very well in school and at swimming and music, and gets attention from her teachers. In addition she talks to her friends at school.

My son, who is eighteen, rarely talks to my wife and me, but he does talk to his sister. When he's grounded, he comes to talk to us more often. He spends most of his time with his friends during and after school and gets his stroking from them. [#8]

In addition, people want positive reactions when they expend energy on other people. They look for positive reactions when they speak to others and when they give them resources.

People do not want someone to give them a specific type of positive reaction when they are not ready for it. Instead, they want to receive the positive reaction when they feel like getting it and seek it out. They do not appreciate having someone interrupt their thoughts and activities to give them a positive reaction they are not prepared for.

My son is just like my cat. If you try to pet my cat and he doesn't want you to, he struggles to get away. If you try to pet him when he's sitting in the back doorway thinking about going outside, he'll snarl at you. But other times he'll come to you and cry for you to pick him up. For a couple of minutes, he's happy for you to hold him and pet him, and he purrs loudly. My son's no different. If you speak to him when he's watching TV or playing a video game, he barely grunts at you. He hates to have you ask him what's happening in school or about his friends. Sometimes he reacts angrily and tells you to stop bugging him. But other times, such as when he's learning a new juggling trick, he wants you to watch and praise him for a half hour or more. Every time you try to leave and do something else, he follows and wants you to watch him some more. [#9]

People do not want to be interrupted when they are busy with something else, even when the positive reactions are provided by those they have a relationship with or regularly interact with. They may be concentrating on another activity, interacting with another person, or have somewhere else to go or something else to do in order to execute a model. When this happens people are unlikely to react positively to the other person.

Mom, I'm trying to do my homework. Can we talk later? [#10]

This TV program will be finished in about ten minutes. Could you tell me about it then? [#11]

People also do not appreciate the other person's efforts to get positive reactions when they are tired.

It was eleven o'clock at night, and I was exhausted and really glad to finally be in bed. Then my wife crawled under the covers and began to tickle me. The physical sensation was so irritating that I reacted, "Could you please stop? I'm just too tired." My reaction upset her. [#12]

At certain times people are more likely to seek positive reactions. These include times when they have accomplished something or had something really nice happen to them, when they have an insight or experience they want to talk about, when they feel upset or discouraged, or when they lose a source of positive reactions, perhaps as a result of someone dying or moving away.

When I get a good mark on a test or paper, I want to show it to my parents and get their praise. [#13]

After my roommate wrote his midterm exam, he said, "Let's go shoot a game of pool and have a beer, and I'll tell you how I did on my exam." [#14]

> My son needs attention most when he's tired or upset. He usually wants me to scratch his back or rub his head. Actually, it almost doesn't matter what I do as long as I give him enough attention. [15]

People are also more likely to seek positive reactions when they are in the presence of someone they regularly get positive reactions from, and when they are not concentrating on something else.

There are certain times when people are more likely to give others positive reactions. These include times when the other person devotes considerable effort to an undertaking, has something happen that is important to him, has a bad experience, suffers a loss or setback, or uses tactics to get positive reactions. One also gives a person positive reactions when one wants to restore good relations with the person.

> One of my closest friends was up for reelection in her political party. Her party work and position are really important to her. When I heard she lost the election I went to see her that very day to console her. [16]

> When the woman I'm living with has a bad dream, I ask her about it and listen carefully. It helps me understand her better and I want to show concern and support. [17]

> Every time I have a test, my girlfriend wishes me luck. One day she made a special trip to my home before I left for university, just to wish me well on my exam. [18]

> When my boyfriend's grandmother died, he was very sad. I bought him a charm for his gold chain to show him I cared about his loss. [19]

> As a piano teacher I know when a student has worked really hard on a piece. If it still doesn't sound very good, I can't just tell them so. I have to lie a little in order to encourage them. Otherwise they'll conclude they can't do it and will stop working hard. [20]

> When one of our players hits a home run, we all go out to congratulate him as he crosses the home plate and pat him on the head, back, or ass. [21]

Sources of positive reactions

A critical factor in seeking positive reactions is who provides them. There are people one wants positive reactions from, and others one does not want them from. When one receives positive reactions from the person one wants them from, events are consistent with one's model of what one wants, and tension is released and one feels pleased. When one receives positive reactions from people one does not want them from, events are inconsistent with one's model of what one wants, and one experiences tension and feels displeased.

> When you play for certain sports teams, you get lots of attention. The one thing you don't want is the ugly girls who chase after you. [#22]

Positive reactions from people one does not want them from are a nuisance, because they absorb time and energy one would rather direct elsewhere.

There are a variety of factors related to choosing sources of positive reactions. For example, one prefers to obtain one's positive reactions from as few people as possible. This is more efficient than depending on many people and having to move back and forth between them to get positive reactions. Therefore, when one acquires a mate who supplies most of one's positive reactions, one no longer needs a number of friends to do so. One also prefers to obtain one's positive reactions from people one considers meaningful. These may be family members or those one considers more attractive, industrious, wealthy, knowledgeable, skillful, moral, or something else than other people. One values positive reactions from people one respects and admires, and does not value positive reactions from those one does not think well of. Frequently one wants positive reactions from those who are highly successful at the same endeavors one is engaged in, i.e., the activities one considers meaningful. One also appreciates positive reactions from the people one would like to obtain other resources from. Also, one likes to receive positive reactions from people one feels guilty about having hurt, because the positive reactions imply that one has been forgiven. Finally, one prefers to obtain positive reactions from individuals who give fewer negative reactions and make fewer demands on one's time, energy, and other resources. This includes those who do not criticize as much, require less help, and are less violent than others. When one does not have access to better sources of positive reactions, one uses poorer sources. However, when better sources become available, one frequently exploits them and discards the poorer sources.

> My closest girlfriend began making demands on me when I started to spend lots of time with my boyfriend. She wanted to get together at inconvenient times, and tried to test whether I still valued our friendship. It's true I was spending less time with her, but she should understand that I was more interested in being with my boyfriend. Eventually, I decided she was creating too many problems, and stopped seeing her. [#23]

People normally give positive reactions to those they want to continue getting positive reactions from, those they would like to get positive reactions from, those who give them resources, those who have resources they would like to have, and those they would feel guilty about not giving positive reactions to. These usually include relatives, mates, friends, colleagues, those in authority positions, pets, and others they consider attractive or successful.

> When I have a good-looking waitress, I often ask her questions about herself, and I tip her more than usual. I do so because I want her to be attracted to me too. [#24]

One also gives positive reactions to individuals who are associated with the people one wants to receive positive reactions from.

> I spent this last Christmas with a close friend and her daughter. The daughter's boyfriend stays at their place much of the time, and I was friendly toward him and bought him a Christmas present too. I knew this would please both the mother and the daughter. [#25]

People usually do not give positive reactions to others they do not want positive reactions and other resources from, except when they have a job which pays them to do so.

A woman I know asked me to come see a play she was directing. I planned to go, but the night of the performance I felt tired and didn't bother. I would have gone if the woman were a close friend, or if I were interested in getting to know her better. But my relationship with her doesn't really matter to me, so I didn't go. [26]

When people do give positive reactions to those they do not want positive reactions from, they often do so in order not to appear rude or uncaring, and to avoid guilt. People give few positive reactions to others who do not give them positive reactions, or have ceased to do so. Therefore they are likely to cut back on the positive reactions and other resources they give to people who do not show signs of appreciating them.

I became friends with a beautiful woman in Bermuda last year. After I got home I sent her some books she was interested in and wrote her repeatedly. When I didn't hear from her, I quit writing. [27]

When I hold a door open for someone and they don't acknowledge the fact, I get upset. I say to myself, "Well, screw you. I'll not do this for you again." [28]

Although people seek positive reactions from others, the individual who provides most of a person's positive reactions is the person himself. People frequently monitor their own appearance and behavior and comment to themselves on how well they are doing. People often do things for others in order to be able to praise themselves and feel good about themselves. They usually provide themselves with recognition when others fail to do so. In addition, people speculate and fantasize about the positive reactions their endeavors will bring them. Sometimes they fantasize that the shoe will be on the other foot, and the people they seek positive reactions from will seek positive reactions from them. It is very important for people to feel good about themselves and what they are doing in order that they can give themselves positive reactions. This is just as important to a person as it is for him to be able to avoid negative reactions from himself in the form of self-criticism, or guilt. Nevertheless, it is clear that the positive reactions people accord themselves do not suffice. People still require positive reactions from other people.

Pets

People and certain pets provide each other with positive reactions. In fact, each can be the major provider of the positive reactions received by the other. Frequently pets hang around and follow the individual humans who provide them with positive reactions.

> When we are sitting or lying on the bed, our cats like to get up on the bed with us. Occasionally they start to purr when they jump up on the bed, even if we don't pet them. They often lie down near us or on top of papers or magazines we are reading. They seem to know exactly where our attention is focused. During the night they frequently go from one bedroom to another to sleep next to different members of the family. [#29]

The popularity of the members of a species as pets depends on their ability to provide humans with positive reactions. Because people and certain pets provide each other with positive reactions, they can develop as strong a feeling of love for each other as they do for members of their own species.

> Although I retired this year, and plan to go back to Australia to live, I can't do so until my dog dies. If I take her back to Australia, they'll put her in quarantine for a year. It'd be an awful experience for her. [#30]

Depending on the kind of pet, when people feed and take care of a pet, they are acting to maintain a source of their positive reactions. Even when a pet uses a different activator than humans do to obtain positive reactions, such as purring by cats and tail wagging by dogs, humans can correctly interpret these as activators and respond appropriately.

> A few times each day our cat yowls for us to hold him. If he wants to be fed or go outside, he yowls some distance from you, and as soon as he has your attention he heads for the kitchen or the back door. If you try to pick him up, he struggles to get down. But when he wants to be held he stays close to you. If you pick him up, he presses against you, and when you rub and scratch him, he purrs loudly. He makes it clear he really appreciates it. Then when he's had enough, he stops purring and acts like he wants to jump down. [#31]

Interaction and positive reactions

A person constantly seeks signs that others feel positively toward him, and frequently approaches others with the desire for positive reactions. One receives a positive reaction when others act pleased to see one, are interested in what one says, agree with one, laugh at one's jokes, smile, provide praise or compliments, show concern, sympathize, express support, or express affection. One fails to get a positive reaction if others do not respond, give a minimal response, talk about something else, look elsewhere, work at something else, try to make a funny comment when one wants to be serious, voice their own opinions, or disagree, criticize, or argue. A major reason why people interact with others is in order to get positive reactions from them. In order to receive positive reactions, however, they frequently have to provide positive reactions in exchange. Each person has to want positive reactions from the other badly enough to be willing to expend time and energy giving the other positive reactions. However, people are rarely aware that they are seeking positive reactions. People also interact with other people for reasons other than to get positive reactions. For example, they seek stimulation, try to get others to perform tasks, or seek information.

A person's reaction is viewed as an extension of that person and a reflection of how he feels toward the person he is interacting with. If person A says something and person B reacts positively to it, person A thinks that person B feels positively toward him. If B reacts negatively to what A says, then A thinks that B feels negatively toward him. When B expresses pleasure in a positive reaction, A acts as though B's pleasure is in response to A, rather than in response to something A said or gave to B. During interaction each person looks repeatedly for signs of positive reactions to what he says. When a person does not receive a favorable response, the person often feels disappointed, rejected, or annoyed, and may continue to use the same means to get a positive reaction, try to get a positive reaction by another means, or withdraw. When B does not agree with what A says, A frequently tries to argue his case until he obtains a positive reaction. This is seldom successful. Continued opposition by B is stressful for A.

Conversation provides both parties with opportunities to receive positive reactions. People make attempts to get positive reactions, often by asking the other person about himself, presenting the person with novel information, talking about themselves, or by discussing a topic of mutual interest. Normally in conversations one tries to find topics of mutual interest, so that one will have something to say and feel motivated to talk, and can expect positive reactions from the other person to what one says. One avoids topics that the other person has no interest in, because the other person will not feel motivated to react. One also avoids topics one is not interested in oneself, because one finds them meaningless and tedious and usually has little to say. If one fails to get a positive reaction, one may introduce a new topic or type of interaction. When people meet for the first time, they often try to identify topics of mutual interest. In many conversations, the primary purpose of talk is to obtain positive reactions. When this is the case, the topic being discussed is unimportant, except as a vehicle for seeking and providing positive reactions. As a result, conversation in a crowded room is similar to the noise made by a large number of crows or fruit bats in a tree. Talk is also used for purposes other than obtaining positive reactions. Such purposes include establishing consistency and obtaining stimulation.

In conversations, statements are frequently made in an enthusiastic and animated fashion in order to hold the other person's attention. This willingness to be active and animated in order to get positive reactions reveals just how important positive reactions are for people. Normally people seek to conserve time and energy (see the chapter on Conserving Time and Energy in Volume Two of this series). We see considerable "wastage," or expenditure, of time and energy when people seek positive reactions, try to avoid negative reactions, seek stimulation, seek sex, or employ orientations.

When a person talks, he frequently looks at the other person and pauses in order to see and hear the listener's reactions. Special efforts are made to identify the listener's reactions when it is difficult for the speaker to see or hear them.

> I was riding in the back of a taxi, and the driver told me her mother had invited her over for Thanksgiving dinner. Then she mentioned a clever reply she made to her mother. As she said this she turned around and looked at me to see if I was amused. [32]

> My son made a comment as I left the room. So I turned to show him I was smiling at what he said. [33]

The listener feels obligated to respond, and provides signs of his interest with head nods and shakes and very short expressions while looking at the speaker, such as "Uh-huh," "OK," "Yes," "Yeah," "Alright," "Good," "True," "Sure," "That's great!" "Wow!" "Really?" "Go way!" "I know," "I see," "That's right," "That's crazy," "Course not," "Oh, well," and "I know what you mean." These expressions do not interfere with what the speaker is saying. Occasionally the listener asks a question or makes a short comment about what the speaker is saying, which encourages the speaker to talk more. The speaker appreciates comments and questions which help him talk more about his topic. He does not appreciate comments which interfere with what he wants to say. If the speaker finds the listener is not looking at him, not responding, or responding without enthusiasm, he realizes the listener is not interested in what he is saying. Often the listener is waiting for an opportunity to deliver what he wants to say. Once the speaker has finished saying what he wants, the listener has an opportunity to become the speaker. The problem for the speaker is to interest the listener enough with his topic and presentation that the listener provides positive reactions. Otherwise the listener may fail to provide positive reactions, introduce a topic of his own to get positive reactions for himself, or be bored with the conversation and leave. The problem for the listener is to think of something he can present to get positive reactions for himself, and then find an opportunity to present it. What a speaker says helps the listener recall material he can use to get positive reactions for himself. Otherwise, the listener may make a humorous comment about something the speaker says or introduce a new topic. The listener may wait for the speaker to finish what he wants to say, or the listener may interrupt. The longer the listener waits, the more likely he is to forget what he wants to say, and the more likely the topic will shift, so that what he is waiting to say will no longer be relevant. Often people become annoyed if the speaker dominates the conversation and does not give them opportunities to get positive reactions. However, if they interrupt the speaker, the speaker does not finish what he is trying to say, does not finish releasing the tension which encouraged him to talk, and feels annoyed. Because the speaker wants to finish what he was saying, he frequently tries to do so at the first opportunity. Therefore, he is unlikely to listen to what the person who interrupts him is saying, and does not provide much of a positive reaction. During conversations, the listener often pretends to be interested in what the speaker says. If he does not, the speaker is likely to lose interest in the conversation and will be less likely to listen to what the listener wants to say. Most conversations provide both parties with a series of positive reactions. In groups, people direct what they say toward the individual, or individuals, they most want positive reactions from. Conversations between two people frequently end because one person has to leave to do something else.

When person A talks, the better the positive reaction that person B gives person A, the more pleased person A is. The more pleased A is, the more likely A is to give B's positive reaction a positive reaction. Thus if A tells a joke and B laughs (a positive reaction), A is likely to look pleased and laugh too, thereby providing B with a positive reaction.

> My wife told me about all the difficulties she was having with an employee, and I agreed with her as she talked. Then she gave me a kiss and thanked me for my support. #34

The more animated the reaction of the listener, the more satisfied the speaker, and the more attention the listener gets from the speaker. Frequently listeners react with various facial expressions, such as smiles, and with laughter. Often when a speaker feels he is losing his train of thought, he looks away from the listener, because the listener's reaction may make him forget what he was going to say.

Many conversations are pleasant experiences for participants, because the conversations provide positive reactions, including laughter. People intentionally get together with others in order to converse with them. People drop in to visit each other in homes and offices, get together for coffee breaks and meals, attend various forms of entertainment and sporting events together, talk on the telephone, and take walks and trips together. Conversation is the primary activity in most of these situations.

Relationships are reciprocal arrangements for getting positive reactions. People in relationships take turns getting and giving positive reactions. Successful relationships depend on allowing both parties to obtain positive reactions. People in relationships also give each other positive reactions and other resources at times when they are not seeking positive reactions for themselves. They know the other person appreciates this, that it helps maintain the relationship, and that they will be likely to get positive reactions in the future.

When my best friend wants to get together "for a coffee," I know there's something important she wants to talk about. I make it a high priority to see her as soon as possible. When we meet I listen carefully to what's happening and give her lots of support if she wants it. I know sooner or later I'll be the one calling her and needing her emotional support. [35]

Nevertheless, there are often times when one person's efforts to get positive reactions interfere with the other person's efforts to get positive reactions.

There's a computer specialist in town who has helped me a lot. When I saw him today, I tried to tell him about my new computer system. He wasn't the least bit interested and would only talk about his own. [36]

When I learned that a good friend of mine had returned from his year in Spain, I went to see him. I was really glad he was back because I wanted to get his advice on what was happening in my social life. But when I arrived, his primary concern was showing me how proficient he was at squirting a stream of wine from a wine flask into his mouth. I must not have seemed very interested, because he said, "It's not easy to impress you." [37]

I guess I'm not a very good listener. While my family and friends tell me things, I'm usually trying to think up a clever or funny response. What they really want is a sympathetic ear, not a stand-up comedian. [38]

Lots of times I've had a wearing day, and want some tender loving care. But when I get home I realize I'm not going to get it, because my wife has had a hard day too and is in no better shape than I am. Neither of us has enough energy to do much for the other. [39]

People are seldom aware that their own attempts to get positive reactions prevent them from successfully providing positive reactions to others.

Both parties in an interaction or relationship do not necessarily receive the same quantity of positive reactions. Often there is an imbalance. However, arrangements in which one party gets all the positive reactions and the other gets none are usually very short-lived. People expect to receive some positive reactions in return for the positive reactions and additional resources they provide, and often become unhappy when this does not occur. If they realize that they are getting few or no positive reactions, they often cut back on the positive reactions they give the other person and may terminate the relationship.

There's a guy at work who frequently wants to join me over coffee or lunch. He loves to tell me what he thinks, and I comment on what he says. But when I tell him what I think, he never listens to me. Although he lets me talk, he doesn't respond to anything I say. Instead, he launches immediately into another one of his position statements. I don't like talking to him and I avoid him whenever possible. [#40]

There's this boy I'm interested in in my tenth-grade class. I figured out when he leaves school and twice I walked home with him. I asked him for his phone number and he asked for mine. He hasn't called me, but this weekend I phoned to see if he wanted to go to the movie with me and some friends. His mom answered, and he wasn't at home. The problem is he's really shy, and I have to work very hard to get any kind of response from him. I keep asking him questions, but he barely says anything. He has a tiny smile, and it's very nice. The other day in class, without saying anything he handed me a piece of chewing gum. It made me feel really happy. But I'm wondering what to do. I make all the effort, and he does nothing. Should I keep trying to get to know him? Should I ask him to go steady? Or should I just forget about him? I haven't found anyone else in my classes I really like. [#41]

My girlfriend has a nine-year-old daughter. I pay lots of attention to her, but she's not very responsive. When I say something to her or ask her a question, she frequently stares right at me, then turns away without replying. I decided I would give her a taste of her own medicine, and the next time she asked me a question I ignored her. She repeated her question several times and I never responded. When I glanced at her she looked like she was about to cry. [#42]

My wife and I are separated and she and my son live in another country. I regularly send my son presents for his birthday and Christmas. This past summer I went to lots of garage sales and flea markets, and I decided I would send him any neat toys I found. During the next six months I sent him eight or nine boxes full. However, I never received the least word of thanks or appreciation, so I quit doing it. [#43]

Who you give a Christmas card to is quite interesting. Normally I give one to people who give me one, so I won't appear rude. Usually these are colleagues where I work. I also send them to past friends that I still care about, and to people who were particularly nice to me during the year. I keep a list of people I received one from the previous Christmas, so I won't forget anyone. However, when people stop sending me a card, I frequently stop sending them one. [#44]

When my best friend became seriously involved with a man, she quit making any effort to get together with me. Then she didn't give me a birthday present. So the next month, when it was her birthday, I purposely didn't give her one. When Christmas came I took her a neat gift. She rushed upstairs and wrapped up a tacky little trinket that she must have had lying around. I just feel I'm not very important to her anymore, and I rarely call her now. [#45]

When a person is upset or angry with another, she reduces the positive reactions she provides.

When my daughter feels offended by something we say, she quits talking to us for the rest of the day. If I ask her something, she won't look at me and gives a one-word reply. [#46]

There are some real jerks where I work. I used to be friendly and have good conversations with them. Then when our offices were renovated and we had to share offices, one of them refused to share the last remaining double office with me. Another asked me to nominate a friend of his to an administrative position, and I did so. He neglected to tell me that if I didn't make the nomination, a friend of mine was assured the post. Afterwards he boasted he set me up. I wrote letters for the third one to help him get a better job. Later on he publicly blasted a woman I'd started dating because she was seeing me, and then gave her the worst evaluation she ever had. I'm civil to these jerks, but that's all. When we pass I say their name and give them a nod. But I do so with a deadpan expression. [#47]

Relationships break down when person A no longer wants positive reactions from person B enough to expend the energy giving person B positive reactions.

72

When people refuse to look at a person or talk to him, the person can not get positive reactions.

> The people I dislike most are the unfriendly ones. They know you, but they never smile or say hello, and if you speak they ignore you or give you the barest reply. [#48]

An unfriendly person can be defined as someone who does not want your positive reactions, and therefore does not give you positive reactions to get them. People with unpleasant facial expressions are often avoided and disliked because they appear unwilling to give positive reactions. People with pleasant facial expressions, on the other hand, are very approachable because they look quite willing to give positive reactions. Often a person believes that people he knows who do not bother to give him positive reactions must dislike him or think they are better than him.

Strategies to get positive reactions

Much of life is spent seeking positive reactions and learning the best ways to obtain them. People observe what others do to get positive reactions, discuss strategies with other people, put plans to obtain positive reactions into play, and learn through trial and error what works for them and what does not.

> My teenage daughter tries out various methods to get attention. Sometimes she acts like she's really put out about something, but everyone knows she's just acting. Other times she'll answer everyone with a one-word answer, such as "Hi!" "Yep," "Nope," and "Bye!" [#49]

How one goes about gaining positive reactions varies with the age and sex of the person seeking positive reactions, the settings in which one seeks positive reactions, and the individuals and groups one deals with. Such differences cause people to adopt very different tactics for winning positive reactions. For example, ballet students learn that positive reactions are given to an appropriate body, good posture, proper technique, strength, flexibility, ballon, performing multiple turns, and the ability to learn combinations quickly. In contrast, university teachers learn that positive reactions are given for high rates of publication, publication in prestigious journals, national and international awards, clear writing, entertaining lectures, offices in professional societies, obtaining grants, and offices in university administration.

I baby-sit for two families and there is an extraordinary difference in the behavior of their children. In the Thomas family the parents spend a lot of time with their two kids. The parents work with them and teach them the difference between right and wrong. They are very patient, and never yell at or strike them. Their children are very quiet and well-behaved. They watch TV or read. They are never loud, and do not talk back or show off in front of others. They enjoy having a story read to them before they go to bed. The parents are well organized and always leave a note telling me what the children can have for snacks, what time they should go to bed, and what they should do beforehand, such as brush their teeth. Often the children are already in pajamas when I arrive. The kids frequently say, "It's 8:30. Can we go to bed now?"

In contrast, the parents of the Edwards family seldom speak to their children, the house is always in an uproar, and there are usually dirty dishes in the sink. The parents are always in a rush and seem to have little time for the children or for me. They frequently ignore their children or scold them. Their two children are roughly the same age as the children in the Thomas family. However, their children repeatedly run around the house screaming and yelling, jump off the furniture, and constantly try to show off in front of me. They repeatedly turn the stereo and TV on and off. They always want me to watch them. Sometimes they tell me to "Shut up!" and "Get lost!" When bedtime comes they try to stay up later than they are supposed to. Sometimes they sneak into each other's room to talk or they come downstairs and tell me they can't sleep. If I were to try to read a bedtime story to them, they would talk and giggle.

I think these differences between the two families exist because the parents in the Thomas family spend a lot of time with their children and give them lots of instruction, praise, and affection, while the parents in the Edwards family have little time for their children, and their children have to act out to get attention. #50

There are differences in the approaches that various groups of university students use to get attention. For example, the "Jocks," or male athletes, wear varsity jackets and strut around campus like they are the king of the hill. A few have wild haircuts, such as shaved heads, which make them stand out in public. When Jocks go out to clubs they tend to dress in the latest fashions, such as Ralph Lauren polo shirts and casual dress pants, and wear a conspicuous gold chain around their necks. At bars they act as they want with little consideration for others. They are also very flamboyant dancers who like to steal the show. Many would like to become professional athletes, but the chances of success are very small.

In contrast, the "Bios," or male biology majors, act in a much more conservative fashion. They are rather inconspicuous in everyday dress and behavior. They seek attention through running campus activities and by organizing local charity drives. One such drive raised over $2000, which was used to help support a soup kitchen for the needy, organize a "Save a Stream" project, adopt a foster child in India, and set up a scholarship fund for a graduating student. Often it is a biology student who wins the Governor General's award for the graduating senior with the top grade-point average. After graduation many Bios enter professional training programs to become doctors, veterinarians, dentists, pharmacists, and researchers. [51]

Because a person's social environment frequently changes, a person has to remain attuned to changes as to where and how he can obtain positive reactions. At different points in his life he must alter his approach toward his parents, friends, mate, children, pets, school, community, career, and hobbies in order to receive positive reactions.

As people learn how others obtain positive reactions, they attempt to get positive reactions in the same way.

I have two daughters. Sarah is eleven and Jane is nine. When Sarah does something which gets attention, Jane often does the same thing in an attempt to get attention too. The other night at the dinner table Sarah told a joke she had heard at school and everyone laughed. Immediately afterwards Jane told the identical joke, but there wasn't much response because we'd just heard it. On another occasion, Sarah sprained her thumb and had to go to the emergency department for X-rays. She came home sporting a bandage and received lots of attention and sympathy from our family and later from teachers and friends at school. Three days after Sarah's little accident she had a bad day in school, fell out with her best friend, and then had a fight with Jane. Sarah was extremely upset and she and I talked about her problems for an hour. Meanwhile, Jane accidentally hurt her foot while making her bed, and although I comforted her at the time, she continued to complain that her foot hurt and needed an X-ray. She found an old bandage and wrapped it around her foot. She limped and hopped around the apartment all evening and said she needed crutches. I wasn't very sympathetic, because I'd examined Jane's foot and didn't think there was anything wrong with it. Also, I was busy trying to make Sarah feel better. By bedtime Jane's bandage had fallen off and she was fussing about putting it back on. I told her rather impatiently that there was nothing wrong with her foot and it would be fine by morning. Jane burst into tears and said I didn't care about her; all I cared about was Sarah's sore thumb. [52]

People often copy others they see who are successful at getting positive reactions, in the hope they will get positive reactions too. They sometimes dress and act like the individuals who are most successful in obtaining positive reactions.

When Madonna became such a popular rock star, I don't know how many girls in my junior high school started to dress like her. It worked too, because the boys fell for it. [53]

People tend to direct their efforts in directions which net them the greatest number of positive reactions. They often continue to use patterns of behavior which were successful in the past in getting them positive reactions.

I got my daughter a dinosaur kit to assemble. When she put it together really quickly, I praised her. Then she asked for another dinosaur kit. When I didn't get it for her, she tried all kinds of ways to get it, including not speaking to me. I realized she probably wanted the kit so she could get more praise, and I promised to get her one. [54]

I have a photograph of my daughter at five. She has a half-dozen ribbons which she won in a sports competition pinned on her shirt, and the happiest smile on her face. Thereafter, throughout her school years, her primary interest was sports. This year is her last year in high school and she plays on several teams. She is working hard to win the award of top female athlete of the year. She constantly watches the sports channel on TV, and all her boyfriends are athletes. [55]

In addition, people adopt activities which obtain a greater number of positive reactions and drop those which receive fewer positive reactions.

I've noticed that young kids are often involved in a variety of activities. Then as they get older they tend to slough off most of them so by the end of high school they are focused on just one or two. One girl I knew was in Girl Guides, competed in figure skating, and studied piano and viola. By the end of high school she was playing the viola in the local orchestra and everything else had fallen by the wayside. I think she concluded she had the best chance of excelling with the viola, and it took so much of her time and energy to do so, she didn't have time for other things. [56]

My father spends all his leisure time involved with amateur athletics, and my two brothers have tried to live up to his standards and become all-star players. My older brother, Dean, never quite made the grade. Dean didn't make the best hockey teams and Dad wouldn't go to watch the games he played in. Dean eventually quit hockey. Although Dean was on an all-star baseball team, he spent most of the time on the bench and eventually gave up baseball too. In contrast, my younger brother, Gordie, was a better player, was on the best teams, and got much more attention from my father. Dean used to talk about never being able to please Dad and say how much he hated Dad. In junior high Dean rebelled against authority and became "a punk." He dyed and spiked his hair, cut the knees out of his jeans, and wore shirts and pins with far-out sayings on them. This drew negative comments from the teachers, but Dean seemed to thrive on the attention he received. Then in high school Dean joined the local militia, where he has been very successful. He has risen through the ranks and plans to enter the armed forces. [57]

Most of the university students I know take their studies very seriously. Getting praise is important to them. If they don't get praise or good grades, some of them become depressed, slack off on their studies and class attendance, and pay more attention to their social life. [58]

People pursue activities which they estimate will deliver a larger number of positive reactions in the future, and quit those which they believe will produce fewer positive reactions.

Now that I'm twenty-one I realize I need to find a career. I want a career that gives me lots of acknowledgment for what I do. When I'm acknowledged it's very satisfying. I worked in a restaurant and did artistic designs on desserts and many people told me how much they liked them. In my martial arts classes, I feel really good when my teachers praise me. But in several jobs I've held, I haven't had fun. It bothers me when what I do isn't noticed, and I feel frustrated. I don't want a career in which I won't have much contact with other people, because there's little opportunity for acknowledgment. #59

I've been trying to decide what kind of research to do my Ph.D. dissertation on. I have considerable experience with human smell, but there's a lot to be said for brain research. If you make a breakthrough on how the brain works, you'll get a lot more recognition than if you make a breakthrough in smell research. #60

When I worked for the local government and later for the shelter for battered women, people always said things like "Well done!" and "That's a good report you wrote." Then I moved and took my present job teaching English to foreign students. The people who run the English school are really cold and don't care at all for their staff. They never say anything positive. I'm leaving the school and taking a different job. #61

From time to time I take up a new activity such as chess, or bridge, or fencing. Eventually I reach a point where I realize if I am going to get good at the activity, I'm going to have to put a great deal of time into it. Then I decide that it's not worth it to me. If I do devote myself to the activity, I know I'll never get as good at it as I am at my profession. I know I'll gain a lot more recognition and satisfaction if I just put the same time and effort into my career. So I let the activity slide. #62

People increase their contact with those who give them a larger number of positive reactions and decrease their contact with those who give them fewer positive reactions.

My current girlfriend and I got together because she kept acting interested in me. I wasn't really interested at first, but she kept contacting me. Then we had a couple of lunches together, and as I got to know her better I realized that she had an awful lot on the ball. As a result, I really wanted to get involved with her. [#63]

When I buy new clothes, I like to put them on and go see my friend Michelle. Michelle always notices what I'm wearing and frequently gives me compliments. [#64]

People also prefer locations where they receive a larger number of positive reactions over those where they get fewer positive reactions.

I grew up in England, but Canada is my home now. I'm treated as special in Canada because of my music and academic accomplishments. But my family in England just treat me the same as they always did. That's why I never want to live in England again. [#65]

Activities, relationships, and locations which are good sources of positive reactions are usually considered meaningful by people.

People try to make sure that their efforts are producing the positive reactions they want to receive. Thus people regularly check their mail, e-mail, and telephone answering machines and services. Those who publish look to see if their publications are in bookstores and libraries, read the reviews of their books, and examine other publications to see if their work is being cited.

Despite their desire for positive reactions, adults do not want to be thought to be striving for them. People who are seen as deliberately seeking attention and calculating how to get more are viewed negatively by others. Seeking attention is considered childish, and often criticized. In order to avoid such criticism, adults often try to disguise their efforts so that they appear motivated by a desire for achievement in sports, politics, business, science, the arts, or other fields. Adults also frequently try to act properly humble when they receive positive reactions. In some cases, people are uncomfortable when they receive compliments and praise from others because they do not know how they should respond. In a sense people walk a tightrope. People want positive reactions, but if their efforts to win positive reactions are too blatant, they are likely to be criticized by others for being boastful, obnoxious, unprofessional, or for simply seeking attention. People fear criticism because it hurts. Consequently people learn to avoid ways of seeking positive reactions which result in their being criticized.

Competition for positive reactions

People frequently compete with each other in their attempts to get positive reactions. There are numerous forms of such competition, including keeping up with the Joneses, trying to top another person's story, dominating or monopolizing the conversation, interrupting others, seeking greater credit for an achievement, and hiding information which others could use to get attention.

In my neighborhood people constantly compete with each other through their possessions. When one neighbor, David, bought a new car, he showed it to another neighbor, Kent, and boasted about its features and how much he paid for it. The next day Kent went out and bought a car which was bigger, better, and more expensive than David's. Even small children do this. When Vicki's mother bought her a new doll, Vicki began to brag to her friend, Jennifer, that she had the best doll. Jennifer then pestered her mother until she bought her a better doll. [#66]

I live in an apartment house, and Kim, an elderly woman down the hall, invited me in to have a glass of wine with her and her two friends. After I arrived and sat down, Kim tried to completely dominate the conversation with me. When her friend, Donna, attempted to tell me that her son-in-law is in the same profession I'm in, Kim told Donna she shouldn't interrupt and that I wouldn't be interested in what she was saying. Kim kept talking loudly to keep my attention and was extraordinarily rude to Donna. When her other friend, Helen, tried to talk to me, Kim interrupted her too. In the end everyone was forced to listen to Kim. [#67]

If I'm talking to someone or explaining something to them, and someone else tries to talk too or to explain the same thing to them, it's annoying, and I don't like it. [#68]

Gail and I did a research paper together which we planned to present at a conference of chemistry students. We talked about who would have lead authorship on the paper, and Gail said we would flip a coin. But when Gail typed it up, she put her name first. This must have been by design, because if she had listed the names alphabetically, my name would have gone first. I was so tired of arguing with her about the correct wording of each sentence, I didn't want to get in another argument about this too. But I do feel Gail acted behind my back. It wasn't fair. If anything my name should have been first, because the experiment was my idea. #69

Several history majors at the local university planned to apply for an Ontario scholarship for graduate school. One of them, Sherry, filled out her application and sent it in by the deadline, which was in October. The others had no idea that the application was due this early, and Sherry continued to tell them that she didn't know when it was due. As a result all of the others missed the deadline. #70

Probably the most notorious form of competition for positive reactions is sibling rivalry.

I have two daughters, and when we listen to one tell us about something, often the other tries to tell us about the very same thing. The one who introduced the topic usually tells her sister, "Shut up! I'm telling this." #71

After the birth of my second child, my eight year old tried to get more attention by setting the living room curtains on fire, putting a pillow on the baby's face when she was sleeping in her crib, and running away from home. #72

My sixteen-year-old brother, Patrick, hates for our family to give attention to anyone other than him. If my sister is sitting next to Mom and getting attention, Patrick will come over, pull his sister off the couch, and sit in her seat. Sometimes he'll say, "How come she gets all the attention?" He also hates to see his sister pay attention to her boyfriend. He teases her and tells her that her boyfriend is a fruit, wimp, or no good. She gets angry and fights with Patrick, so he succeeds in getting her attention again. Patrick's efforts are quite obvious to the other family members. They comment, "Did you get enough attention yet?" "Trying to get more attention are you, baby?" and "You wouldn't want your sister to get any attention now, would you?" #73

People adopt a variety of strategies in their competition for positive reactions. These include upstaging competitors, undercutting competitors, attacking competitors, advertising themselves, and seeking recognition in areas where they encounter less competition.

People sometimes try to upstage others by doing more work and better work than their competition so that their own efforts will receive positive reactions.

> My sister and I do chores for Mom. We each try to do the most in order to get her attention. [#74]

> All of my students are required to type their papers for my course. One of my students uses a computer to print her paper so it looks typeset. Her paper is much more professional looking than the others. It's impressive and I've commented on it to other teachers. [#75]

People frequently try to outdo others in making a clever comment, relating an interesting experience, telling a joke, and reporting gossip. Often they are so busy getting ready to upstage others that they pay little attention to what others are saying.

Undercutting others consists of efforts to make competitors look undeserving of positive reactions, or to get other people to give competitors negative reactions.

> My sister and I were both in the same high school. When I did shitty on a test, Caroline would announce this as soon as we got home to humiliate me in front of Mom. Then Mom would be cool to me and praise Caroline for getting good grades. [#76]

> "Mom, Eddie is standing in the living room eating a sandwich!"
> "Well tell him to go to the kitchen. He knows better than to eat in the living room." [#77]

> When it was my bedtime, my older brother used to try to put me to bed before my parents did. If I didn't want to go, he would make a big deal of it, and make me look like a brat. Then Mom and Dad would thank him for his help and yell at me for being bad. [#78]

> I have two younger brothers, eighteen and twenty years old, who gang up on me in front of Mom. They say I go to bars all the time, never have to shovel snow like they do, keep my room messy, and stuff like that. They make Mom think I'm lazy. She acts really friendly to them afterwards, because she thinks they are good kids and are concerned about her. [#79]

People also undercut their competition by claiming their competitors have an unfair advantage or are just trying to get attention.

> Ross, a five year old, follows you everywhere and wants to sit on your lap. He has a younger brother, Terry. When Terry tries to be noticed, Ross states, "Don't pay any attention. Terry is just showing off." #80

Attacking competitors consists of verbal or physical attacks to damage them or drive them away.

> My two brothers are each jealous of the attention the other receives and they argue constantly. The other night they were going at each other again and one said, "Do you know the difference between you and a bucket of shit? The bucket!" The other replied, "Do you know the difference between you and an outhouse? The outhouse smells better!" #81

> Sally, a four year old, comes to stay with my mother while her parents are at work. Sally wants to be the center of attention, and asks my mother at least five times a day if she loves her. When another child is present, Sally tries to get the child in trouble. When my mother paid attention to Joan, Sally broke Joan's crayons, ruined her painting, spilled her milk, and hit her. When my mother praises Joan, she has to be sure that she also praises Sally. If she doesn't, Sally will become very upset and begin to cry. I have seen Sally purposely break one of my mother's ornaments because my mother was talking and playing with Joan. If Sally can't get attention by being polite, she will talk back, fight with other children, and get into as much trouble as possible. #82

> There were ten men and three women attending the three-day conference on management training. Barbara and Diane introduced themselves to each other at the conference and exchanged a few facts about their backgrounds. During one of the morning sessions Barbara made several contributions to the group discussion, but Diane didn't say anything. That noon everyone went to have lunch together. In the restaurant Barbara and Diane sat next to each other across from Glenn, a seminar leader, and they talked about how the seminar

had gone that morning. Then Diane suddenly asked Glenn if he approved of divorced women, and whether he thought they should date widowers. When Glenn didn't answer, Diane stated she felt men should be wary of dating divorced women because all they could think about was their ex-husbands. Widows, on the other hand, were more likely to be true to a new relationship because their husbands were no longer around to interfere. (It so happens that Diane is a widow, and Barbara is divorced.) At this point, Barbara told Diane firmly that her personal life was none of Diane's business and such comments had no place in a professional environment. Glenn looked relieved, and Diane didn't say another word during the rest of the meal. Barbara felt Diane was trying to make her look less appealing to Glenn by taking a stab at her personal life. [83]

My husband never abused me physically until I became pregnant. Then he began to beat me. He felt threatened that the unborn baby was taking my attention away from him. Men who physically abuse their wives often start when they get pregnant. [84]

Advertising refers to bringing one's claim for positive reactions to the notice of others. If one does a better job of advertising than others do, one is more likely to receive the available positive reactions.

I met my current boyfriend at a lounge. In the first few minutes of conversation he mentioned he is a doctor. Not many guys in the lounge could say that. [85]

When I ran an ad in the personal column of the newspaper, I decided I wouldn't do what everyone else does and say I like listening to music and walking on the beach. Instead I listed all of my positive traits I could think of, like good listener, giving, intelligent, sense of humor, and so on. When I'd finished, my ad was four times as long as other people's. I got more replies than I knew what to do with. [86]

If there is too much competition, or others have a clear competitive advantage, then one may direct one's efforts into alternative activities where one is more likely to achieve success and recognition. For example, a male of medium height with a stocky build may decide to forget about basketball and pursue soccer.

I've trained and competed in gymnastics for years. But early this year I injured my arm badly when I landed off the mat. The doctor said it would never be fully straight again, which meant I didn't have a future in gymnastics. So this fall I started ballet classes. #87

Competition for positive reactions occurs because positive reactions are a limited resource. One has to expend time and energy to provide positive reactions, and one has to expend time and energy to obtain them. People normally direct their attention at one person at a time. When people provide positive reactions to one person, their positive reactions are not available to other people. Therefore, the more positive reactions a specific individual captures, the less there are available for everyone else. Most people would like to obtain a larger number of positive reactions from certain people, but in order to do this they usually have to take them away from others who already receive them from those same people. People can become annoyed and angry at the efforts of others to obtain the positive reactions they want too. In addition, people experience feelings of envy when they see others actually obtain resources they would like to have. This is certainly true of positive reactions. Feelings of envy encourage people to try to obtain the positive reactions others are getting and this generates additional competition. There is another reason why the amount of positive reactions people can give to others is limited. People expend so much effort trying to obtain positive reactions for themselves, that they do not have much time and energy left over to give positive reactions to others.

Resources and positive reactions

A primary reason why people want resources is to use them in their efforts to obtain positive reactions. Often resources help people obtain other resources which attract positive reactions. Thus money, information, and savings in time and energy enable people to acquire possessions, sources of stimulation, experiences, education, and careers which help them get positive reactions. People often use resources to help them get positive reactions, and they often receive resources from those who give them positive reactions. When people first approach a person, they are usually more concerned with obtaining positive reactions than with obtaining resources. As a relationship develops, however, people expect that resources will accompany the positive reactions they receive. When they do not, people frequently reduce the positive reactions and resources they give the other person. In order to continue getting positive reactions from a person, one must continue giving resources to the person or to those meaningful to him. Moreover, these must be resources that others are currently interested in receiving. The more appropriate the resources are, the more likely one is to receive positive reactions.

Nevertheless, there are numerous instances in which people approach others in order to obtain resources, instead of positive reactions, and they provide positive reactions as a means to that goal. This is often the case when people are looking for jobs, money, sex, or help.

> One of the employees where I work is a classic troublemaker and does everything he can to attack and embarrass our division. But to protect himself he gets outsiders to carry out the attacks for him. He wins their support by praising their brilliance. He also tells them, "If you weren't here, I would have left this job long ago." This is heady stuff and none of us could ever hear enough of this. This wins him staunch supporters who will do whatever he asks. He also gets these supporters to help protect his job by telling them that the rest of us have got our knives out to get him. Naturally his supporters want to protect the one person who is perceptive enough to recognize and praise their brilliance. [88]

When people seek resources and do not use positive reactions, they are less likely to be successful.

> The first time I met my new colleague, he asked me to make him a list of the training videos we have and those we can get from the government. I mean who does the guy think he is? If one of my friends asked me, or let me volunteer, I'd be happy to do it for him. Does this guy think I have nothing better to do with my time? [89]

> I get really mad at my kids at times, because they can be so unfriendly and rude. They frequently ignore me or respond minimally when I greet them or try to talk to them. Every time it happens I want to quit giving them money for the things they want. [90]

My teenage son can make me so angry. This morning I tried to tell him not to use the expensive shampoo and conditioner because it's the only kind my daughter can use for her hair. I tried to tell him twice, but each time he interrupted me and wouldn't let me finish my sentence. He said he'd heard it all before and that he never uses them. He shows no respect. I told him if he's not willing to listen to me for half a minute, he'll have to listen to a ten-minute lecture on how rude he is. Then he claimed he isn't rude. So afterwards when he wanted lunch money for school, I told him I wasn't giving him any this week. He can come home to eat, or he can use his own money. He can't treat me like a nobody and expect me to keep giving him things. [#91]

Often the fewer positive reactions one provides, the fewer resources one receives.

Individuals are viewed in association with their resources. An individual with more resources is viewed as a more desirable source of positive reactions than is an individual who has fewer resources. The more positive reactions and other resources that a person acquires, the more he has available to exchange for positive reactions and other resources from other people. The more he has to exchange, the better the positive reactions and resources that he can obtain. Thus those who become famous are able to attract others who are famous and establish relationships with them. People are more willing to give positive reactions to those with more resources. Therefore those with more resources receive a larger number of positive reactions and have to expend less effort to get positive reactions.

People frequently use positive reactions to express appreciation for the resources they receive. They often express their thanks verbally or with affection, send a thank-you note, or give a gift to the person who has done something for them.

My daughter is not very affectionate. But when I give her a fair amount of money for something she wants, she comes over and hugs me. Last night I spent twenty minutes helping her with her homework. When I finished she thanked me and gave me a hug. [#92]

I had a problem getting my key to work in the back door of my apartment building. When I told this to the security guard, he said to turn the key slightly in the wrong direction before turning it in the right one. I tried this and it worked fine. The next time I saw him, I told him his suggestion had worked. I appreciated his help, and knew he'd feel good knowing he had been helpful. Also, I do need his help from time to time and I want to maintain good relations with him. [93]

When your father is a politician, people sometimes come up to you and say things like "You're Frank's son? He's a great man. It was wonderful what he did for us." [94]

A colleague asked me to read a paper he had written. I did so, and went over all my suggestions for improving the paper with him. When I finished he stated, "You've earned a dinner from me. When can you come over?" [95]

People also frequently inform others when they have followed their suggestions and advice and the outcome is positive.

I read that book on creativity you recommended. It's great. I showed it to several other artists, and they really liked it too. [96]

If people do not use positive reactions or other means to express appreciation, others are likely to stop doing things for them.

Activators

People use two activators to obtain positive reactions from each other. These are smiling and humor. Both are based on giving the other person pleasure. When person A smiles at person B or says something funny to person B, person B experiences pleasure and feels happy, and this shows on his face in the form of a smile or laugh. This response by B provides A with a positive reaction. When a person feels pleasure or happiness and smiles or laughs, others interpret this as pleasure or happiness in response to their presence and as liking for them.

People also cheat. They provide fake smiles or laughs when they do not experience pleasure or feel happy, but want to provide the other person with a positive reaction. They also cheat when they provide smiles and laughter, but have no intention of backing these up with other resources.

Smiling

When people feel pleasure and happy, it shows on their faces. They smile. Smiling is a visible sign of pleasure.

> My daughter had the main role in a short dance number at the annual concert. After her performance I told her repeatedly how well she had done and how good she looked. She just glowed. [#97]

In fact, it is often difficult for people to avoid smiling.

> It's kind of embarrassing when you walk down the street by yourself and you can't stop smiling, because of something really nice that happened. I keep thinking how foolish I must look to everyone who sees me. But it's really hard to stop. [#98]

Such smiles are often infectious.

> Have you ever been at a party or convention where everyone is in a party mood? Everyone smiles and laughs and is very pleasant to everyone else, and no one seems worried or upset about anything. It's impossible not to get caught up in it. It's a real high. [#99]

When people show signs of pleasure, such as by smiling, this provides those they are facing with a positive reaction.
Smiling is used as an activator to obtain positive reactions.

> I don't know how many times I've stood by and watched my aunts, cousins, and grandparents huddled around my baby sister as she performed the simple act of smiling. [#100]

Smiles often cause the other person to smile in return. A smile from the right person causes the recipient to feel pleasure, and this is indicated by a smile on the face of the recipient. Smiles are valued positive reactions. People are more likely to feel pleasure when the person who smiles at them is someone they want to receive positive reactions from. People frequently smile when they interact with someone that they receive or want to receive positive reactions or other resources from.

A smile is considered an attractive feature, and individuals are recognized for having a particularly nice smile. In order to improve their appearance and their smiles, people have their teeth cleaned, whitened, straightened, veneered, capped, and replaced. In addition, clothing, stuffed animals for children, and other objects are sometimes decorated with smiles, and smiles are frequently painted on the faces of clowns and carved into pumpkins at Halloween.

It is advantageous not to smile all the time. A person is willing to provide positive reactions to those he wants positive reactions and other resources from. However, he is not willing to provide positive reactions to those he does not want positive reactions and other resources from. A person does not want to attract and have to fend off others that he is not interested in. Each person's time, energy, and materials are limited, and if a person distributes these indiscriminately, he will not have them available to give to those few he wants to give them to. By having a smile he can turn on and off, a person is able to indicate who he does and does not want to provide positive reactions and other resources to and receive them from. (See the chapter on Avoiding Those Who Reject You in this volume.)

Humor

Humor is also used as an activator to get positive reactions from others. When a person finds something funny he feels pleasure and this shows on his face in the form of laughter. Laughter is a visible sign of pleasure. Laughter is an exaggerated smile, and a highly desired positive reaction. When a person says or does something funny and gets another to laugh, he generates a positive reaction toward himself from the other person. When the other person laughs and smiles widely, makes sounds of appreciation, and looks at the person who made him laugh, the person who caused him to laugh experiences this as a strong positive reaction directed at himself. The person who caused the other to laugh has exchanged a resource, the effort to produce pleasure, for a positive reaction, laughter. Also, getting the other person to laugh provides one with concrete evidence that one has given the other person pleasure. Knowing that one has succeeded in giving another pleasure causes one to feel happy about oneself.

I'm happy when I can make people laugh and smile. When I know I can make someone else happy, it makes me happy. [#101]

When a person can get others to laugh, seeing them laugh encourages him to laugh and feel pleasure too. A person who causes another to laugh, normally smiles, laughs, and experiences pleasure in response to the other person's laughter. People get others to laugh in order to be able to laugh and feel pleasure themselves. Laughter is often infectious and provides a pleasurable experience for the participants. People who overhear others laugh often feel a desire to join them.

I heard my wife and children laughing downstairs in the kitchen. I felt I was missing out, and went downstairs to find out what they were laughing at and to join in. [#102]

Humor and laughter are very important parts of many conversations. Often people try to make funny or clever comments when they greet others, talk to them, react to their statements, or depart a conversation. People frequently interrupt others in order to get laughs. Many conversations are largely laughter parties with participants vying with each other to make others laugh in order to obtain positive reactions for themselves.

My husband and I were at a dinner party the other night, and I couldn't believe how inane the conversation was. All the others there were singles and they spent the whole evening sitting around the table joking and laughing. They were having a good time, but the things they talked about were just so trivial. The two of us went home before eleven, but the party continued until four in the morning. [#103]

People frequently use puns, exaggerations, ridicule, misinterpretations, mimicry, and childish expressions to try to get others to laugh. They also recount humorous things they have heard, read, and observed.

My co-workers and I are middle-aged men. When we want to get a laugh from each other we use expressions we hear our children use, such as "It's all your fault," "You made me do it," and "Tell Charlie to stop picking on me." [#104]

Often people repeat their humorous remark, if others seem to miss the point or do not seem to hear it. Others frequently respond with laughter even when not amused in order to be polite. If they fail to be polite and laugh, they are likely to appear unresponsive and unfriendly, and may be seen as rejecting those who are trying to be funny. Also, if they fail to laugh, others will be less likely to laugh at their own attempts to be funny. People are much more likely to laugh at humorous efforts made by people they want to maintain contact with. They are less likely to laugh at comments from people they have little interest in. People are normally much more interested in getting others to laugh at what they say, than they are at laughing at what others say. In other words, they are more interested in getting positive reactions for themselves than they are in giving positive reactions to others. As a result there is considerable competition to get to speak and crack jokes.

People adopt various tactics to get others to laugh. One tactic is to constantly make funny or clever remarks in response to what others say, or in response to shared experiences, such as a television program or observations of someone's behavior. The speaker attempts to get the listener to laugh as often as possible. When the speaker says something he wants others to laugh at, he usually laughs himself. The sight of the speaker laughing, encourages the listener to laugh.

> My wife and I frequently get together with a couple of middle-aged men who are single and who try to make one funny crack after another the whole time you are with them. It's nonstop. To be polite, I feel compelled to laugh with them. But after an hour or so of this I notice it's tiring me out. #105

Another tactic which is used to get others to laugh is to present one's normal statements in a laughing manner. There is no attempt to be funny. Instead the speaker appears to be very pleasant, and the listener is more likely to respond in a laughing and pleasant way.

> My taxi driver talked most of the way home, and each time he said something he would chuckle or laugh in the middle of it or at the end. Nothing he said was funny. What he said during the drive was "So how was work today?" "I'm a driver and a dispatcher, and I don't do either of them good," "I work for a truck company too. When you don't see

me around, I could be anywhere between here and New Brunswick," "At least my phone's working now," "This is the best-paved street in town," and "Home, sweet home." Nothing he said was the least bit humorous. But that didn't stop him from laughing each time he said something. [#106]

A third tactic is to laugh with considerable enthusiasm. An enthusiastic laugh encourages others to laugh harder in response, which provides a stronger positive reaction. Some individuals are recognized to have particularly enthusiastic laughs. When any one of these tactics is used, the speaker shows a great deal of interest in the reaction of the listener, and expects the listener to laugh. Although people employ tactics such as these, they are often unaware that they are doing so.

When an individual solves a problem or understands a situation, he releases mental tension and feels pleasure. The release of tension is experienced as pleasure. With the development of a shared language it became possible for a speaker to provide listeners with verbal problems and puzzles and to help them solve them, which produced tension and released it, and thereby provided others with pleasure. When listeners experienced pleasure, their facial expressions provided the speaker with a positive reaction. Humor enabled humans to capitalize on an existing mechanism, the pleasure experienced by individuals when they release mental tension, and provided humans with a new means to obtain positive reactions. Humor offers certain advantages over other means of getting strong positive reactions. Attempts to make humorous comments do not require much time and energy. Other means of obtaining strong positive reactions, such as giving the other person money or other resources, are usually much more costly in terms of the effort required to obtain them.

Cheating

People commonly pretend to feel pleasure or to feel happy in response to another person, and provide the other person with a fake smile or laugh. In the case of smiling, people frequently smile in response to someone who smiles at them, and do so when the other person's smile does not give them pleasure. A smile is often part of a greeting. People know they are expected to smile in response to those who smile at them and do not want to appear rude. People are so accomplished at faking smiles that they can smile when requested to do so by someone taking their photograph.

People also laugh when they do not find something funny. They recognize when another person is attempting to be funny, often because the other person laughs to encourage them to laugh. People know they are expected to laugh and do not want to disappoint the other person. Therefore people become quite adept at faking laughter.

Nevertheless, sometimes it is not easy to fake the facial expressions associated with feeling happy.

> When you go out to clubs, you know if you smile and look confident, it's easier to meet people. Well, it's easy to joke and laugh if you're with friends. But if you're by yourself, you feel pretty self-conscious, and it's hard to look pleasant. Not only are you lonely, but you know you're going to have to deal with rejection. [107]

It is usually difficult to smile when one is unhappy to see someone or when one feels hurt.

Another form of cheating occurs on the part of individuals who provide strong smiles and laughter, but are unwilling to back this up with other resources. Because their smiles and laughter are much more pronounced than those of the average person, others notice and remark how friendly they are. However, this is the limit of their expenditure of time and energy on others. Other people are frequently duped into thinking that the cheats genuinely like them and are willing to commit resources to them. As a result, other people commit resources to the cheats, but discover belatedly that this will not be reciprocated. Through their use of strong smiles and laughter, the cheats are able to obtain a considerable amount of positive reactions and other resources for themselves for no additional expenditure of time and energy.

> Betty is the friendliest person you'll meet. Whenever she sees you, even if she's a hundred feet away, she breaks out in a huge smile and calls you by name. The impression she creates is "Wow! Is she happy to see me." When she's with other people, she frequently throws back her head and lets loose the most exuberant laughter. But if you ever need to borrow anything or need her cooperation, forget it. Superfriendly is all you get. [108]

Whenever you see a gathering of people, you are likely to see Grant. Grant is a middle-aged man, who is always pleasant and friendly, and constantly smiles and cracks jokes. Grant seems to know everyone, and people who meet him comment on how friendly he is. Grant spends most of his time drinking and eating out with people who are willing to pick up the tab. You can count on seeing Grant at every party. When he is invited to a party, he calls at the last minute to ask if he can bring others with him. Grant asks, "How many people can I bring along? I have so many people I have promised a party to." If there is a potluck dinner, Grant shows up with a number of his friends, and Grant and his friends rarely bring anything with them except the liquor they plan to drink themselves. Grant keeps asking the people he knows if they know of any parties being held. When a party is being held that he hasn't been invited to, Grant frequently asks people who are invited to find out if he can come too. When Grant isn't invited to a party, afterwards he mentions the party to the people who held it. I think he wants to make them feel guilty or uncomfortable about not inviting him. Year after year Grant continues to say he'll have to hold a party himself someday. But he'll never go to the trouble to straighten up his place, and will never spend any money on others. Grant's a classic taker, and uses the fact he is so friendly to get things from others. [#109]

Nelson is the friendliest and most enthusiastic person you'll ever meet. He is always smiling and happy and joking, and talks very openly about himself. Once you respond to Nelson, he starts to ask you to do favors for him. He continues to get you to do favors, and criticizes you when you do not do them exactly the way he wants. But he never does anything in return. People who get to know Nelson say he's the most self-centered person you'll ever meet. I have never met anyone who lies as easily or as much in order to present himself in the best possible light. He has few scruples and little sense of responsibility. He won't hesitate to exploit or destroy anything or anyone to make things more convenient for himself. [#110]

Praise is another type of positive reaction which is frequently used by some cheats. They will praise others to gain resources from them. Most people receive so little praise that they are very susceptible to praise from cheats. Praise does not require much expenditure of time and energy on the part of cheats. Cheats seldom back up their praise with other resources, regardless of the amount of resources they receive from others.

Tactics used in seeking positive reactions

People use a great variety of tactics to obtain positive reactions from others. These include the following:

1. Making it possible to get positive reactions
2. Making noise
3. Taking center stage
4. Initiating contact
5. Bringing something to a person's attention
6. Expressing interest
7. Treating others well
8. Spending time with others
9. Attempting to be acceptable
10. Establishing and maintaining relationships
11. Having children
12. Joining in a group effort
13. Talking
14. Teasing
15. Asking for help
16. Doing things for others
17. Doing things others approve of
18. Entertaining others
19. Giving others pleasure
20. Praising others
21. Acknowledging the accomplishments of others
22. Giving affection
23. Developing and displaying physical attractiveness
24. Developing and displaying personality traits
25. Developing abilities
26. Producing achievements
27. Displaying achievements
28. Displaying achievements of one's family members
29. Acquiring and displaying possessions
30. Displaying experiences
31. Associating with people who attract positive reactions

32. Being influential
33. Controlling desirable resources
34. Acting upset
35. Revealing misfortune
36. Acting differently than others
37. Failing to do what one is supposed to do
38. Doing something not approved of
39. Being a nuisance
40. Asking for attention
41. Accusing a person of not paying attention

These tactics are not logically distinct from each other, and overlap in some cases. Also people often use two or more tactics at the same time. In addition, people employ many of the same tactics for reasons other than getting positive reactions from others. Such reasons include obtaining stimulation, sex, and help, and avoiding guilt, criticism, and rejection.

1. Making it possible to get positive reactions

One of the most important ways in which people seek positive reactions is by deliberately putting themselves in a position where they are more likely to get positive reactions from others. By getting out of the house or apartment and going to public places one may encounter someone one already knows or talk to someone new. This involves being present at places and events where other people are found, such as a park, store, café, bar, party, public library, church service, flea market, sporting event, concert, or movie.

> I find the time goes by so slowly when I'm alone. It's not that I'm lonely, it just seems longer. When this happens, I usually go somewhere where there are people, such as a movie, or just to the park to watch the children play. You wouldn't believe the things you see people do when you are paying a little attention to your surroundings. [111]

> When I'm at a performance, I always go out to the lobby during the intermission. I see people I know and others I'd like to know. Sometimes the only reason I go to a performance is to meet people. [112]

Lots of times I go downtown just to leave the house and get out around people. I usually hope to see someone I know so we can have a coffee and talk together. Normally I go to the downtown mall. I'll go up to the fast-food section on the second floor and see who is sitting there. If I know someone, I'll often join them. But usually I don't know anyone, so I sit by the rail, where I can see everyone who comes up to the fast-food section and I can look down and see everyone who is walking around the shops on the first floor. I have a coffee just to be doing something.

Sometimes I'll walk around the mall and look into the shops to see if anyone I know is there. I usually take the long way around the shops to give me a greater chance of seeing someone. Then I'll leave the mall and go over to the public library to see if I know anyone there. I walk through the library to the most distant seating area, and sometimes through the stacks if people seem to be there. Usually I don't see anyone I know that I'd like to talk to, so I leave immediately. Occasionally I'll stop and look at a magazine in the library so it won't look so obvious that I'm not interested in using the facility. I'd feel embarrassed if everyone knew I'm just walking around looking for someone to talk to. There are also some benches outside near the library, and sometimes I choose a route which will take me past them in case someone I know is sitting there. While I'm walking from one place to another, I sometimes bump into someone I know.

Then there are several downtown restaurants where I may run into people I know. One of them is outdoors and I carefully check out the clientele when I pass by. Another is a cookie shop and snack bar with its entrance on the street, and I look in their glass door when I go by to try to see who's there. I usually leave the mall through the shop on the other side of the cookie shop so I can walk past the cookie shop door. If I used the regular mall exit, I would have to make a special trip to get to the cookie shop and then have to turn around again to go back to the mall door, and what I was doing would be obvious to others, particularly if I did it a couple of times a day. Sometimes I go in the cookie shop and get a snack so I'll have a reason to see who's there. There are a couple of other restaurants where I may run into people I know. One has a telephone, and I go in and make a call while I have a look around to see who's there. I call my own home number because there's no one at home and I get my coins back. To anyone watching, it looks like I failed to reach my party. The other restaurant has a series of booths with high backs. It doesn't have a phone, so I usually order a coffee there. I'll often walk all the way to the back of the restaurant so I can see who is in the booths before I choose a seat for myself. Sometimes I'll go ahead and sit down in a booth and then get up and go to the bathroom in the back of the restaurant which also allows me to see who's sitting in back. I would feel silly if I walked in the restaurant door and all the way to the rear, and then back out to the street again. I do so occasionally, but if I did it on a regular basis, what I am doing would be very obvious to others.

Some days I spend an hour or two sitting and walking around downtown trying to run into someone I'd like to talk to. There are periods when I've done this practically every day. Sometimes I succeed in finding someone, but usually I don't. [113]

One can also participate in an activity with other people. Thus one may work in an organization, take a class, or play a game or sport. Because one does these things with other people, one interacts with them and is more likely to receive positive reactions from them.

I cut grass for the elderly widow next door. She always gives me a popsicle, provided I eat it there so she can talk to me. She was telling me that senior citizens develop places to go to so they are around people. Some sit on a bench regularly in the shopping mall with their buddies. Others go to church, attend the horse races or bingo games, or shop for groceries, but only buy enough so they'll have to return in a couple of days. [114]

In most settings, people frequently look up at others who enter their vicinity. They hope to see someone they get positive reactions from or someone they would like to receive them from. When they are not successful, they look elsewhere or return to what they were doing. People also make it easier for others to get in contact with them. Thus they get a telephone and give their phone number and address to others.

I have a long extension cord for my telephone so that I can carry it into other rooms when I'm home. If I want to take a shower or operate a noisy appliance such as a hair blower, I place the phone nearby so I'm sure to hear it if someone calls. When I leave home, I turn on my answering device to make sure I don't miss any calls. [115]

2. Making noise

Another means of attracting attention to oneself is by making more noise than others in the vicinity. People talk or laugh loudly, yell, or shriek or scream.

I was in the student union and heard a loud, piercing scream from a girl wrestling with a male. The male tried to lift her while her girlfriends laughed at her struggles. Apparently the girl didn't mind the glares from other students, because she continued to talk and laugh loudly. [#116]

My husband and I like to sleep late on Saturdays. The kids know this so I usually wake to the sound of their whispers which become progressively louder. Then the kids turn the TV on in the living room and slam the door "so the TV won't wake Mommy and Daddy." By now I'm wide awake and go downstairs and start breakfast. Later my husband comes downstairs and bangs around the kitchen making coffee without saying anything. However, all hell breaks out when one of the kids enters the kitchen. "When are you goddamned kids gonna learn to shut up and let me sleep on Saturdays? It's the only goddamned day I don't hafta go to work!" His yelling gets the attention of all the kids, as well as the cats on the porch and the dogs in the basement. Now that they know he's up, the cats scratch to get in, the dogs whine to get out, and the kids hide out in the living room. My husband looks at me and grins. He's got everyone's attention and he loves it. My husband's favorite methods for getting attention are raising his voice, and ranting, raving, and roaring. He says, "If one approach doesn't get results, I try another. Being calm sure doesn't work at all." [#117]

People also use objects to make noise to try to get positive reactions from others. They squeal the tires on their cars, use loud mufflers, and turn up the volume on their radios, stereos, and tape players. Most objects can be used to make noise which attracts the attention of others.

I try to get my three kids to do their homework when they get back from school. This works for a while, but eventually they start to sigh and fidget and squirm. The oldest one will start to rearrange her books as noisily as possible and the middle one will tell her to shut up. About this time the youngest one will decide to read a page out loud from his reader. The middle one responds by glaring at him as hard as she can, slamming her book shut, and exclaiming, "I can't do anything around here!" #118

At my fitness center the bodybuilders sometimes grunt loudly or let their weights fall to the floor. They want to draw attention to the fact they are working with a really heavy set of weights. #119

3. Taking center stage

Another method people use to obtain positive reactions is to place themselves in a location or act in such a way so that they are the center of attention, i.e., "take center stage." For example, people may sit in front of others at a public gathering, make an announcement, speak out at a meeting, read to others, or dominate a conversation and interrupt others. They may even take a leadership or other position which gives them the opportunity to take center stage.

Sally, who is four, spends weekdays in our house because both her parents have jobs. She is always looking for attention. Once when a neighbor came to visit, Sally talked nonstop about her hair, her dolly, and her parents. The neighbor thought she was delightful and Sally refused to be quiet. #120

In the early grades in school, children race to get their hand up first so they can be called on when a question is asked. They want to show how much they know on a topic. One little girl loved the attention so much, she didn't even wait to be called on and would blurt out the answer. The teacher finally had to have a talk with her. #121

My boyfriend has a best friend, Gary, who thrives on attention. The more people Gary can get to listen to him, the better he likes it. Whenever our friends play cards or watch films together, Gary's voice is the first one you hear when you enter the room. As long as everyone listens to him, Gary's happy. #122

I went to hear a talk, and the speaker was one of the most gorgeous men I've seen. I had to ask a question so he'd notice me, and by the end of his talk I'd thought of a good one. In his reply he developed a humorous scenario in which the two of us were hypothetically involved with each other. It was clear he knew why I asked my question and he was interested in me too. #123

People also take center stage by preventing others from continuing what they are doing. For example, a person who wants attention may put his hand over the page someone is reading, stand between someone and the television program he is watching, or even turn off the television.

4. Initiating contact

People often attempt to initiate contact with specific others in order to obtain attention from them. People initiate contact in a number of ways, such as by producing a physical stimulus, establishing physical proximity, making eye contact, making inviting facial expressions, initiating physical contact, and initiating verbal contact. Examples of physical stimuli include knocking at a door or ringing a doorbell, whistling, clapping, raising or waving one's hand(s), flashing one's car lights or honking one's horn, slowing down or stopping one's car, and throwing an object at a person. Instances in which one establishes physical proximity include standing, sitting, or walking nearby in order to initiate interaction.

When you baby-sit you can't help but be impressed by the methods children use to get your attention. Sometimes they stand right in front of you when they speak. You can't ignore a child who is a foot in front of your face. #124

Often I choose a place to sit where I am sure to be seen by others. When I have a snack in the shopping mall I take a table at the entrance of the food section, where I'll be certain to see and be seen by anyone I know. The other day I went to study in the library. There were two girls that I hoped to meet who were reading at a large table. I sat down right across the table from them so they'd be sure to notice me and it would be easier to start a conversation with them. #125

I skipped half of my early morning biology classes this semester. I wanted to hang around a particular guy who eats breakfast in the cafeteria at that time. #126

When I see a friend approaching who hasn't noticed me, I sometimes pretend that I haven't seen her either and act like I am going to walk right into her. This gives her quite a start, and is good for a mutual laugh. #127

People frequently seek to establish eye contact by trying to look directly into another person's eyes.

When I see someone I know, I look at them until they look over at me so I can say hello. But if they don't look at me, I don't say hello because they wouldn't notice. #128

Probably the most common technique used to make contact in clubs consists of staring or glancing repeatedly at the person you're interested in. If they are interested too, they look back. I was out with two friends recently and one spotted a male she wanted to meet. She stared at him for several minutes and then she and my other friend went over and started dancing right in front of him. While she danced she faced the guy directly and stared right at him. When the guy finally realized what she was doing, he stared back. This might have worked, except that some other girl went up to talk to him. We think it must have been a girlfriend. So my friend decided to direct her attentions elsewhere. #129

Making inviting facial expressions includes smiling and flirting.

If I see a guy I like across a crowded room, perhaps in a bar, I first make eye contact. It's not staring; it's the kind of eye contact where he knows you want him, or what's called "bedroom eyes." If that doesn't get his attention, I give my hair a twirl and bat my eyelashes. If he still doesn't clue in, I walk by with a big sexy smile and say, "Hi! Have I seen you somewhere before?" If this doesn't get his interest, I say, "Fuck him!" and turn my attention elsewhere. #130

People initiate physical contact when they touch or poke the person they want attention from.

When I want my dad to listen to me, I tap him and say, "Dad." If this doesn't work, I tap him again and repeat, "Dad," but this time I say it louder. [#131]

Examples in which people initiate verbal contact include saying or calling a person's name; speaking a person's title; using a greeting, such as "Hi!" or "Hello!"; introducing themselves; saying something to a person; and making a telephone call.

I was in the college cafeteria, and a male student seated at a table called to a professor at the checkout counter, "You're wearing those glasses that make you look intrepid." The professor looked back with a funny expression on his face. It was clear he didn't know how to respond. Two minutes later the same student started to call the name of a female student seated on the other side of the room. He called her repeatedly, but she never looked over at him. Finally he got up and walked to her table and began talking to her. [#132]

5. Bringing something to a person's attention

A common tactic people use to try to get positive reactions is to bring something to another person's attention.

I was standing at the counter of a bookstore. Three male high school students entered and began to look around the store. One called the other two over. "Hey guys! Did you see this?" He showed them a calendar he had picked up. [#133]

Mom, do you notice anything new about me? I trimmed my bangs. [#134]

When I have people over at my apartment, I like to put on music they haven't heard before and show them craft items I've picked up on my travels. I think it is neat to expose people to classy things they aren't aware of. [#135]

Often the more meaningful and unfamiliar an item is to the person it is shown to, the more likely he is to give positive reactions to the item. The person who shows another person an item interprets positive reactions to the item as directed toward himself.

6. Expressing interest

People frequently express an interest in others they want to get positive reactions from. They express this interest in a number of ways, including looking at a person; acting pleased to see him; taking time to talk to him; asking him how he is; asking about his activities; encouraging him to talk about himself; listening to him; responding to what he says; expressing concern, sympathy, or encouragement; laughing at his jokes; and wishing him well.

How was school today? #136

What's that you're eating? #137

There's a woman I keep running into downtown who's really interested in me. She keeps coming up, putting her arm around me, and asking me about my love life. I feel embarrassed when she does this in front of my friends. #138

Saturday was such a busy day at the restaurant, I was run off my feet. I had ten tables to wait on and it was all I could do not to scream. One man told me to slow down before I had a stroke. I just laughed. It was so nice of him to notice. When he left he told me the service was great, thanked me, and gave me a ten dollar tip. I smiled and thanked him too. #139

People encourage those they are interested in to talk by looking directly at them when they speak and by making comments, asking questions, and using short expressions which indicate they are listening. They may indicate interest through the warmth of their voice or through inflection. Sometimes people ask others the questions that they hope they will be asked in turn. Thus someone who did well on an exam may ask another how he did, and a person who has returned from an interesting trip may ask another how he spent his summer. People wish another well in a variety of ways, such as saying, "Good luck," "Have fun," "Take care," "Happy Birthday," "Merry Christmas," "Happy New Year," "Have a nice weekend," and "Have a nice day." People express interest face to face, and through phone calls, letters, and greeting cards. In addition, people express interest by talking to a third party about the person they would like to get positive reactions from. Normally, the more time a person spends at each of these activities, the greater his interest in getting positive reactions from the other person.

7. Treating others well

A person attempts to treat others well in order to obtain positive reactions from them. Thus one uses respect; employs good manners; recognizes other people's needs, interests, and wishes; acknowledges their presence, efforts, and accomplishments; deals with them reliably and responsibly; and avoids upsetting them. This may include greeting them; saying goodbye to them; acknowledging the people they are with; inviting them to join oneself; introducing them to other people; offering them food and drink; opening doors for them; letting them enter a door first; helping them with their coat; not interrupting them; not keeping them waiting; doing what one says one will do for them; not attacking their beliefs; not ignoring, criticizing, or belittling them; not criticizing their friends or relatives; remembering their birthdays and anniversaries; going to see them when they are sick or have suffered a loss; recognizing their contributions; and apologizing to them when one fails to do the above.

> I've started dating a girl I'd like to have a lasting relationship with, and I try to treat her right so she'll want to stay with me. I do all kinds of things, like get her to tell me about her day, rub her back, read her stories, and walk her to her car when she has to go home. Because she likes fruit, I always get interesting fruit for her to eat, such as mangoes and custard apples. [#140]

> After my father died, I was feeling down and depressed and had a lot of things on my mind. My teenage son is at the age where it's not cool to show affection to your mom. However, one day he walked in with the prettiest bouquet of flowers I have ever seen. The card on them said simply, "I love you Mom." Well that did it. I cried, and hugged him, and cried some more. The poor guy; it's a wonder I didn't drown him. There's just no words to express how much that gesture meant to me. [#141]

8. Spending time with others

One of the most effective means of obtaining positive reactions from others is to spend time with them. One approach is to stay physically close.

> We have a young girl, Sally, staying at our house while her parents work. She is starved for attention. My mother says that Sally follows her around the house the whole day, and she frequently bumps into Sally when she turns around. #142

> When I was in grade school we had a favorite teacher. If she was on duty at recess time, we would race to get outside and walk with her. #143

People like to be with those they normally receive positive reactions from.

> I think you like to hang around the people you feel close to. It doesn't matter whether you say anything or not, what counts is you're with them. When I get home from work I like to sit in the kitchen while my wife prepares dinner. Sometimes we talk, and sometimes I read. After dinner when my wife and I are upstairs on our bed, our daughter likes to come in and watch TV with us or just lie on the bed to be with us. It's nice to be around the people who care about you and pay attention to you. #144

Another means of spending time with other people is to do activities together. People frequently do things with one or more other people. Thus a person may go shopping, attend a movie, play a game, go for a walk, get a coffee, or take a trip with others.

> When I'm lonely or bored, I feel like I'm suffocating. I just want to get out and do something with someone else. I feel better when I get away from myself. #145

> Isn't anyone else going to watch TV? I don't want to watch it all alone. #146

When I was younger, I wouldn't go to an event unless a friend was going to be there too. I chose specific sports and courses so I could be with my closest friends. I would do things I didn't really like in order to be with them. I didn't do things I was really interested in, because I would have had to do them alone or with strangers.

My six-year-old neighbor is the same way. Last year he joined soccer with another boy. He went only when his friend went, and didn't have a good time when his friend wasn't there. But this year he's taking karate even though none of his friends go. He loves it, and I'm amazed he can do something on his own this young.

I notice other people caught up in the same thing. On Fridays people run around finding out which club everyone is going to. Later that night there will be a long line of people waiting for hours to get inside, while down the street another club will have almost no one there. Occasionally a group of people won't feel like going out and the feeling will spread. Then the clubs can be quite empty. #147

My teenage son and I have a great relationship, and it's because of the time we spend together. Several times a week we play ball or take in a sporting event. I really enjoy his company, and we have a lot of fun. Besides, when you're living in a house full of females, you have to band together. #148

9. Attempting to be acceptable

Many people make a considerable effort to be acceptable to others they would like to get positive reactions from. They often imitate them by dressing like them, wearing their hair the same way, pursuing the same interests, and behaving in the same fashion.

I act the way I do because everyone else does too. I don't want to do something which they'll think is sissy-like. If I want to go to all my classes in school and they want to skip, then I have to skip too or they will call me down and say that I'm chicken or a goody. Then when they skip and I go to class, they come to me for homework, assignments, or to write notes for them when they're caught. I would like to say no, but I can't. I need my friends. I'd like to be my own person, but I guess I can't until I get out of here and away from them. You have to do the things they do and try the things they offer you. Like smoking. I didn't want to, but I did it because everyone else was and I wanted to fit in. Now I'm hooked. #149

I was a tomboy when I was growing up. I took the attitude that "girls can do anything boys can do" and "I'll show them my stuff their way." I played soccer, football, and hockey, and my slap shot was quite impressive. I always wanted to be recognized as being better than the guys at their own game. At the time it seemed like the best way to get their attention. A girl in boy's clothing could tag along, but a girl in girl's clothing was just a girl. I tread on my brother's heels for three years so I could get attention from his friend Mark. But I was always treated as one of the guys. The more bruises I got, the more unladylike they thought I was. One girl, a good friend of mine, was a tomboy like me, and was she tough. She had a reputation for beating up the boys and they feared her. She got attention too, but never a guy. The boys didn't see us as girls, just as teammates. Little did they know how we killed ourselves to have them notice us. [150]

When we moved here I had to make friends at my new high school. I hate sports and I'm not really into school spirit. But in order to have my new friends approve of me, I had to try out for the cheerleader squad. I don't enjoy the games or the way I have to fake my enthusiasm, but I'm accepted by the people I want to be accepted by. Their approval has made the difference between my liking or disliking my new home. [151]

After high school I went to hairdressing school in another province. When I came home to visit a few months later, my friends told me I looked, acted, and spoke completely different. It's true. I left a brunette, and now I'm a blond. Before this my hair was red, and before that, pink. It's been so many colors lately that I'm not sure what color it is until I look in the mirror. I had to show the other girls in school that I was as interested in hairdressing as they were, and that I wasn't afraid to experiment with my own hair. It was almost like an initiation. I've made friends quickly and I like it there. [152]

In an attempt to be acceptable, people also seek to be pleasant, avoid disagreements, and express opinions similar to those held by the people they want to be accepted by.

10. Establishing and maintaining relationships

In order to obtain positive reactions on a regular basis, people establish relationships with other people. Relationships enable one to spend less time and energy hunting for positive reactions. People form relationships with individuals who are willing to provide them with many more positive reactions than they receive from other individuals. Relationships involve spending a great deal of time together, interacting in many different ways, and providing each other with a large percentage of the positive reactions each receives. In a relationship, people are in frequent contact and accord a high priority to spending time together and giving positive reactions to each other. Often they live together; make a formal commitment to stay together, such as through a marriage ceremony; and maintain close contact for large portions of their lives.

> I always wanted to be with my boyfriend. We would meet between all our classes in high school and we ate lunch together. If I knew he wasn't going to school, if he was sick or something, I wouldn't go either. If I couldn't be with him, I was happy to talk to him on the phone. We would talk for hours. My parents thought I was nuts. They even threatened to have the phone disconnected. [#153]

> My wife and I do practically everything together. We have the same interests and friends. We skate together, go to movies together, and even spend evenings reading together. [#154]

The success of a relationship normally depends on the types, quantities, and timing of the positive reactions each gives the other.

People often go to considerable effort to maintain relationships.

> A close friend of mine has started to organize dinner parties several times a year for her friends. I find most of her friends quite uninspiring, but I always try to attend these parties. I know they are important to her, and my friendship with her is important to me. [#155]

> Last Saturday a friend of mine organized a yard sale, and I knew she would have trouble carrying tables and all her odds and ends outside. So I volunteered to help her set everything up and then carry things back inside at the end of the day. She was really glad to have my help.

It would have been pretty chintzy if I hadn't helped; she always does so much for me. #156

Often people do not want to alienate a person who is an important source of their positive reactions, and they can become quite anxious that they may do something which will cause them to lose a relationship. They frequently try to avoid disagreements with the other person, and if they do upset him or her, they want to set things right.

11. Having children

People also have children in order to obtain a source of positive reactions. Children depend on their parents for positive reactions and other resources, and frequently provide positive reactions in return.

When I was a child I always worked to be the center of attention. But once I had kids, I no longer needed to try. The kids just naturally made me the center of attention. #157

Those who have contact with children frequently decide they want to have children of their own. After children grow up and leave home, their parents often visit them and the grandchildren. Sometimes their parents move to be near them in order to obtain positive reactions on a regular basis.

My mom used to live in Toronto, but she moved to Halifax so she could be near me and my children. She lives right next door to us now. #158

People sometimes warn others that if they do not have children they will be lonely when they become old.

12. Joining in a group effort

People also cooperate together to obtain positive reactions for themselves. Many people join organizations because they will receive positive reactions from outsiders. Thus one may join a community service organization which others think well of, work together on a sporting team to beat other teams, join a band and perform in public, or seek to obtain visibility and public support as a member of a political party.

> I joined the student social committees at the university to get known. I mean what better way? You come to the university, which has thousands of students, and no one knows your name. A couple of months later your name and picture are in the campus newspaper, and since everyone reads it, you're known. #159

13. Talking

Talking is a very common means of trying to get positive reactions from others. There are many different ways of talking which are used to obtain positive reactions. These include talking about oneself, providing information, exaggerating, breaking verbal taboos, repeating oneself, and increasing the amount one talks.

People very frequently talk about themselves. They tell others about their current activities, plans, and opinions. (Also see Tactic 30, Displaying Experiences.)

> "Hey, Jeannie!"
> "What, David?"
> "You know what happened to me?"
> "What?"
> "I overslept. I'm half an hour late for class." #160

> I can't believe this. I got up at five o'clock this morning to study for all my exams. Then at eight o'clock when I got my coat on and called a taxi to take me to school, the taxi company told me school is cancelled because of the weather. Because there isn't much snow outside, I never thought to listen to the radio for an announcement. What a waste. I could have stayed in bed. In fact, I'm going back to bed right now. And look at my hair. All full of spray. It's a good-hair day, completely wasted. #161

> Mom, it's so weird. I was in the bathroom and burped. It was just a little burp, and fireworks exploded in my ears. It was like a cannon being fired. Maybe it's because I have a cold. #162

I've bought a new house which has four bedrooms. Now each kid will have a bedroom of their own. It's right across the street from the school, and I won't have to spend my time driving them back and forth. #163

People also provide others with information in an effort to get positive reactions. The information may deal with something they have heard, read about, or observed. Information is interesting to others when it is not already known and deals with something they consider meaningful.

Most of my friends like to go to movies and eat out. When one of us tries a new restaurant or sees a new film, the rest of us are very interested in learning how good it is. #164

I like to have coffee with my stockbroker because we both get excited by young high-technology companies. I locate new companies for us to follow and he gets up-to-date information on their earnings and stock prices. He's just about the only person I know who shares this interest with me. #165

People usually want to be familiar with subjects that others are interested in, because they are assured of attention when they discuss the subjects with them. Many men are interested in sports and many women are interested in talk shows and soap operas on television. As a result males watch sporting events in order to have something to say that other males will be interested in hearing. Similarly, females need to be familiar with the latest developments in popular talk shows and soap operas. If one can not discuss topics that others are interested in, one runs the risk of being ignored and having others get all the positive reactions.

One also has something interesting to say if one has information that others do not know about a mutual acquaintance. This is known as gossip. People are extremely interested in information about others they know, because other people are their primary source of resources. Changes in people's lives alter their potential to provide and act as resources. The greater the impact of information on one's own resources, the greater one's interest in that information. One has only to consider the impact of news that someone very close to oneself has either died or won the lottery. Information about "bad" things that people do is particularly

113

interesting, because these people a) will be viewed negatively and criticized by others, and b) may repeat the same "bad" behavior with oneself and those one is associated with. Consequently one can no longer associate with them, unless a) one wants to be viewed and criticized the same way that they are, and b) one is willing to risk having "bad" things happen to oneself and those one is associated with. Therefore when people do something wrong, their potential as resources is considerably changed.

Another method of getting positive reactions when talking is exaggerating. The more extreme one's information, the more attention one gets.

> My husband frequently exaggerates, but I've learned how to correct for it. "That stupid bitch" means that a woman disagreed with something he said. "That guy has arms like tree trunks" means the man must be pretty strong. "The damn thing is smashed all to hell" usually means there's a crack in it. And "these damn cats shit all over the place" means it's time to change the kitty litter. [#166]

> My friend Richard must be the most gullible person on earth. I've been telling him lies all my life, but he's so naïve and trusting that he always takes for granted I'm telling the truth. The lies aren't outrageous, but they are things I would not normally do, such as get in a fight, get drunk for an entire week, or buy a car. When we talk together I'll tell him a couple of lies and he automatically accepts them as truth. Then when he mentions what I've said to someone else, they set him straight and he feels embarrassed. He'll ask me about it later and I'll laugh and tell him I was only bullshitting. He gets angry and says, "I don't know why I always believe your bullshit! You're always lying to me!" [#167]

One can also obtain attention by punctuating what one says with strong language, such as swearwords.

When one says something that is ignored, a tactic which is used to get positive reactions is to repeat what one has already said.

> When another person is talking to me I like to slip in a humorous comment. If the person doesn't seem to notice, I'll often repeat it so my joke isn't wasted. I want the other person to recognize I've said something quite clever. Sometimes I'll repeat it a third time when I don't get any recognition. [#168]

People can also try to increase the number of positive reactions they receive by prolonging a conversation, or by talking more than others do.

> He's all right at times. It's just when someone new comes around he never shuts his goddamn mouth. He should have a fuckin' cork shoved in it. [169]

> Our daughter frequently talks a mile a minute. I tell her to slow down, but she's scared our attention will shift elsewhere and we'll stop paying attention to her. [170]

14. Teasing

Another form of seeking attention from others is to tease them. Teasing is usually directed at a trait of the other person or at something associated with him or meaningful to him. If one can say or do something that gets a rise from another person, one obtains a reaction, and sometimes the reaction is a positive one. Often the person being teased tries to respond in a positive way in order to appear to be a good sport. However, a great deal of teasing is not directed at obtaining positive reactions from the person one is teasing. Instead, it is an attempt to create one's own stimulation by producing a reaction in the other person that one enjoys causing and watching. Or else it is an attempt to provide third parties, or spectators, with something they enjoy watching, and therefore is a way to obtain positive reactions from third parties for oneself.

> Some people tease me about my bald head. One woman claims there is no need to turn on the lights when I'm around because my head reflects so much light. [171]

> One day my sixteen-year-old son brought his schoolbooks home, hid them, and then claimed he'd left them at school. He knew I'd get angry at him, because without his books he can't do his homework. Later that night he told me he had hidden them just to get me going. [172]

> My closest friend is very concerned about discrimination against women. I tease her that women should be paid less than men because

they are smaller and need less food, space, and cloth for their bodies. I point out that we will not have true equality between the sexes until we adjust the pay scales and working conditions of women to the degree that their life spans are equal to those of men. I also tell my friend that we have to get rid of sexism in chocolate bars by introducing a His-he to compete with Her-shey. [#173]

A friend of mine has a house cat whose color is a mixture of blacks and oranges. The cat looks like she's been rolling in mud. I tease my friend about the cat's appearance and call it Motley Mew, in reference to the rock group, Motley Crue. The cat hates to go outside and I point out it's because the other cats laugh at it. I also accuse my friend of abusing a poor mole by treating it as a common house cat. This always gets a reaction from my friend. [#174]

15. Asking for help

People sometimes seek help from others as a means of having contact with them and getting attention from them. People may ask for information; advice; physical effort, such as help carrying an object; or the loan of something, such as a tool or an ingredient for a meal. Those who respond by helping them, frequently spend time with them and ask them questions about themselves.

One child in my class at school deliberately mispronounces words. He knows how to pronounce them correctly; he just wants me to spend extra time helping him. [#175]

I've watched Marie, a four year old, try to get attention from her mom. Marie says, "Mommy, Mommy, I have to pee and can't get my pants down." "Yes, you can. You're a big girl now and big girls can do things like that." Tugging on her zipper, Marie makes a few half-hearted attempts to pull her pants down. Placing her bottom lip over her top one, she looks sad and disheartened. "All right, sweetie. Come here and Mommy will help you. But only this once." [#176]

When you see an attractive girl, one of the best ways to get to talk to her is to ask her for directions or advice. Lots of times I've asked how to get to places I know full well how to get to. Other times I'll ask what stores or restaurants she recommends. [#177]

Positive reactions with a pet

1-2. Exchange of positive reactions between a human and a purring cat. H.H.

Smiling

3. Smiling children in Katmandu, Nepal. H.S.

4. Smiling children and an adult seated at a table on the beach at La Union, Philippines. H.S.

5. Two travelers at a youth hostel operated by nuns. Venice, Italy. E.T.

6. Smiling university students. Charlottetown, Prince Edward Island.

Smiling as an activator

Smiling continued

Scenes from Ongaia Village,
Kilenge - Lolo District,
West New Britain,
Papua New Guinea. M.Z.

7. *(opposite)*
Children on a canoe.

8. *(above)*
Man making a fishing
spear.

9. *(right)*
Two boys.

10. Female friends and relatives. Ho Chi Minh City, Vietnam. H.H.

11. Wedding reception. Thốt Nốt (pronunciation: Tote Note), Vietnam. N.N.

Smiles in photographs
12. Photographs on the wall of a photography studio. Studio 51, Charlottetown, Prince Edward Island.

13. *(left)*
Picture of Queen Elizabeth. Queen Elizabeth Hospital, Charlottetown, Prince Edward Island.

Smiles on objects

14. *(right)*
Human smiles drawn on animal faces. Door of veterinarian clinic. Charlottetown, Prince Edward Island.

Smiles on objects
continued

15-16.
Clown in Old Home Week parade. Charlottetown, Prince Edward Island.

17. *(left)*
Plastic clown on a bench in a shopping mall. Charlottetown, Prince Edward Island.

18. *(right)*
Scarecrow in a store window for Halloween. Charlottetown, Prince Edward Island.

19. Ông Địa, or Mr. Earth. He accompanies and fans the dragon which performs in front of houses during the Vietnamese New Year to bring good luck and prosperity to the household. Thốt Nốt, Vietnam. H.H.

20. Smile on a backpack. Charlottetown airport, Prince Edward Island.

21. Smiling faces sewn on a backpack by a student. Charlottetown, Prince Edward Island.

Smiles on objects
continued

22. *(right)*
Smiles on men's
underwear in a
store window.
Charlottetown,
Prince Edward Island.

23. *(below)*
Smiles on gift wrapping
paper and a greeting
card used for a birthday
present.
Charlottetown,
Prince Edward Island.

24. *(above)*
Smiles on a row of
plastic snowmen for
sale for outdoor
Christmas decorations.
K-Mart, Charlottetown,
Prince Edward Island.

25. *(right)*
Smile painted on
a traffic light.
Panmure Island,
Prince Edward Island.

Laughing
26. *(above)* Married couple enjoying a joke. Charlottetown. E.T.

28-29. *(lower left and right)* Student laughing at remarks during a university
reception. Charlottetown.

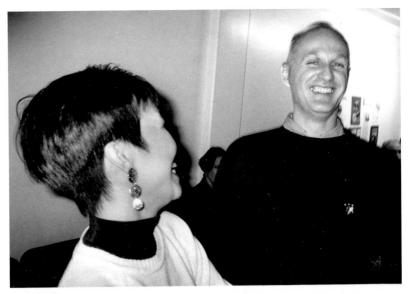

27. *(above)* Friends laughing during the intermission at a public entertainment. Charlottetown.

30. Children playing on the beach with an adult during a river festival. Pattaya, Thailand. H.S.

31. Children pretending to perform a ceremony. Ongaia Village, Papua New Guinea. M.Z.

Laughing
continued

32-34. *(right)*
Two students
talking during
a party in a
student lounge.
Charlottetown.

35-37. *(left)* Two people talking at a Philippine-Canadian Christmas party. Charlottetown.

38-43. Students laughing in a student lounge. Charlottetown.

39.

40.

41.

continued on next page

42.

43.

Laughter on objects

44. *(above left)* Laughing snail in a park. Ontario, Canada. U.T.
45. *(above right)* Figure in a Christmas parade. Charlottetown.

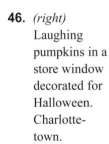

46. *(right)*
Laughing
pumpkins in a
store window
decorated for
Halloween.
Charlotte-
town.

Entertaining others in order to get positive reactions

Entertaining others

47. *(opposite)* Female entertaining villagers. She is caricaturing a dancing drunken white male. She has powdered her face with lime to have a white complexion, and is wearing a powder-blue polyester leisure suit. Earlier she was carrying a liquor bottle filled with water. A number of villagers are laughing, but this is difficult to see because their teeth are stained from chewing betel nut. This entertainment is part of a small ceremony, the Narikanga, which is held for firstborns who return to the village after a long voyage. The females take on male roles by dressing and dancing like males and by playing drums, and the firstborn's parents are dunked in the sea. Ongaia Village, Kilenge-Lolo District, West New Britain, Papua New Guinea. M.Z.

48. *(above)* Adults at a Halloween costume party. From left to right: man dressed as a woman, a witch, and a pregnant nun. Charlottetown. H.H.

Positive reactions through affection

49. Couple on a bench outside the Kremlin wall. Moscow, Russia. R.E.

50. Family members from Prince Edward Island in Florida. H.S.

51. Sitting in a person's lap in a pub. Torremolinas, Spain. H.S.

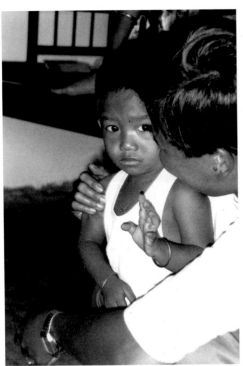

52. *(left)*
Child and parent.
Thốt Nốt, Vietnam.
H.H.

53. *(below)*
Draping one's arm
around another
person at the airport.
Ho Chi Minh City,
Vietnam. H.H.

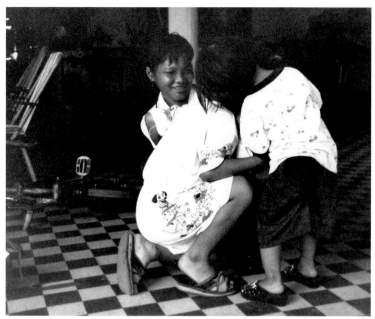

54-55. Two children kiss a baby and then separate. The kiss is made by touching one's nose against the other person and sucking air audibly into it. Cần Thơ Province, Vietnam. H.H.

56. Signs of affection between students at a school. Kwangtung Province, China. H.S.

57-59. *(above and below)* Hugs at a Latin American/Canadian party. Charlottetown.

Laughing at the reaction of a person in an embarrassing situation

60-63. Pouring soda pop on the head of the man in the white shirt. Panmure Island, Prince Edward Island.

61.

62.

63.

Laughing at people who are made to appear foolish

64. Blindfolded child guided into position to strike a piñata. Panmure Island, Prince Edward Island.

66. Adults laughing at the failure of a child to strike the piñata.

65. Child attempts to strike the piñata.

67. Children and an adult laughing at the failure of the child to strike the piñata.

68.

69.

70.

71.

72.

Laughing at people who are made to appear foolish
continued

The scenes in photographs **60** through **75** are from a summer picnic for Canadians of Philippine, Indonesian, Vietnamese, and European ancestry held on Panmure Island, Prince Edward Island.

68-72. Adults laughing at the failure of a child to strike the pinãta.

Embarrassment and entertainment

73-74. *(opposite page, above and below)* Onlookers watching and laughing at children competing in a game of musical chairs.

75. *(below)* The last two contestants in a game of musical chairs.

Scenes from a Christmas party for Canadians of Philippine and European ancestry, Charlottetown.

76-77. *(above left and right)* Adults watching and laughing at pairs of children who are competing to be the first to finish eating an apple without using their hands.

78-79. *(below left and right)* Competition to see which adult can finish eating a cupcake first without using his or her hands. Other adults watching and laughing.

80. Postnatal class. Surrey, British Columbia, Canada. V.H.

Children crying

81-83.
Girl crying in a
daycare center.
Charlottetown,
A.M.

Children crying continued

84-86.
Boy smiling and crying.
Ho Chi Minh City,
Vietnam. H.H.

Crying

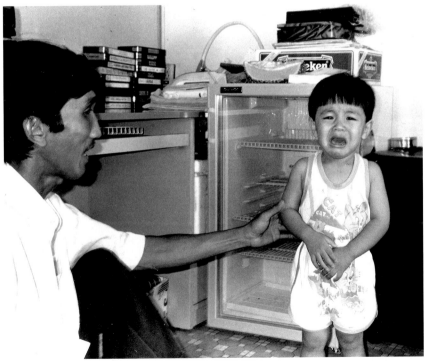

Crying because of hurt caused by inconsistency between a model and reality

87-88. *(above and below)*
Boy crying because he wanted a cookie and was given a section of an orange to eat instead. Daycare center, Charlottetown. A.M.

Crying because of hurt caused by inconsistency

89-90. *(above and below)*

91.

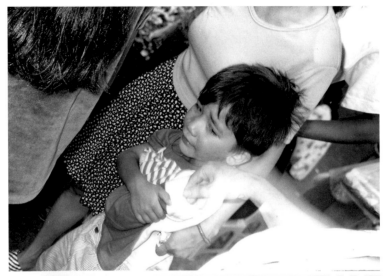

92.

Crying because of hurt caused by inconsistency between a model and reality continued

91-93. Boy throwing a temper tantrum because his parents refuse to buy him a toy. Bến Thành Market, Ho Chi Minh City, Vietnam. H.H.

93.

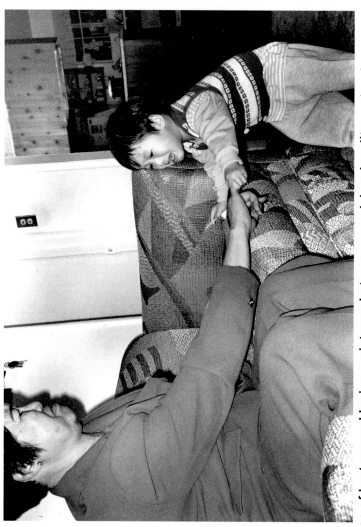

Crying because of hurt caused by inconsistency between a model and reality continued

94. A crying child tries to get his grandmother to give him additional vitamin supplement. The supplement tastes like candy. Vietnamese-American household. Los Angeles, California, USA. H.H.

Crying children being comforted

95. *(above)* The girl who is standing on the right is the sister of the boy who is squatting at the far left. Cần Thơ Province, Vietnam. H.H.

96. *(below)* The same girl is being comforted by her brother. H.H.

Crying children being comforted continued

97-99. A crying child is given a positive reaction by her mother. Thốt Nốt, Vietnam. H.H.

Crying children being comforted

Crying children being comforted continued

100-102. The boy who is crying on the floor is picked up and held by a staff member. Daycare center, Charlottetown.

Crying as an activator

Crying and looking sad when relationships separate

103-105. Departure area for international flights in Ho Chi Minh City, Vietnam. H.H.

Crying and looking sad when relationships separate continued

106-108. Departure area for flights in Ho Chi Minh City, Vietnam. H.H.

Crying and looking sad when relationships separate

109. Departure area for international flights in Ho Chi Minh City, Vietnam. H.H.

Crying and looking sad when relationships separate continued

110. Female relative grieving at the side of the grave during a funeral. Portne Village, Kilenge - Lolo District, West New Britain, Papua New Guinea. M.Z.

16. Doing things for others

Another method which is used to get positive reactions from others is to do things for them. This includes being helpful, giving gifts, sharing with others, and loaning them things. Being helpful is a common means people use to get positive reactions from others. For example, people may pick up things others have dropped, do household chores for others, drive them somewhere, provide advice or instructions, or otherwise do them favors.

When I come home from work, Lisa, my two year old, finds my slippers and brings them to me. I tell her what a good girl she is and she's happy. She does this every day. [178]

My daughter, Robin, shows her love all the time. Her favorite way is helping me with my housework. Robin likes to dry dishes and sweep. There are so many ways children show their affection. It's important that their gestures not be ignored, or they'll stop making them. [179]

My little brother cuts the grass without being asked, just so Mom and Dad will give him more attention than the rest of us. [180]

My wife was quite tired and was decked out on the bed. I could see her glass was empty, and I asked if she'd like me to go get a glass of warm water for her. She agreed. So I went to the kitchen, fixed it, and brought it to her. [181]

I often volunteer to do things for people I'm interested in getting closer to. I may help them with a job application or loan them books. Sometimes this takes a lot of time and trouble on my part. But I often get to know the person a lot better in the process. [182]

Last night I made Ted his favorite dish for supper. He loves it and I only make it on special occasions because I hate it so much. It's a dish his mother made for him, and like a fool I got the recipe from her. Once in a blue moon I make it. But shit, does he love it. It's all worthwhile when he says, "It's orgasmic." When my boy is happy, he gets in a mood no words can describe. I should make it more often. [183]

People frequently give others gifts in hope of getting positive reactions from them. Gifts are often used to facilitate, maintain, and strengthen ties with the recipient. Such gifts take many forms, and include presents, meals or snacks, drinks, tickets to movies and performances, trips, and money. People give gifts both spontaneously, and at designated times such as Christmas, Easter, birthdays, anniversaries, graduations, weddings, Mother's Day, Father's Day, and Valentine's Day. People frequently go to special trouble to give others something they think they will really like, and to present it in a particularly nice way, such as wrapped with decorative paper and ribbon.

We were at a party Saturday night and the boys went into town to get takeout Chinese food. John is interested in Amanda and asked her if she'd like an order. She told him she'd had dinner with her family and wasn't hungry. John returned with a double order of food, and Amanda was touched that he bought some for her too. He wanted to show her she is special to him. [184]

I was so surprised when my husband came home from work last week with a giant bundle of flowers in his arms. He knows I just love getting flowers. Then he hurried me outside and we went to a nice restaurant for a candlelight dinner. It was so romantic! [185]

Dad gives me money for school, helps me pay for my boat, and lends me the truck. He does this so he can say how much he does for me and get my appreciation. [186]

People also loan and share items, including food, clothes, money, and tools.

My roommate had a very important interview and started to get all dressed up, but couldn't find her black pumps. I never even thought twice when I told her to use mine. When your friends are in need, you have to come through for them. [187]

One month I had so many bills to pay that I ran short and didn't have my rent money. I didn't know what to do. Well, as soon as a friend of mine found out I was broke, she offered me the money for my rent, all one hundred and fifty dollars of it. I was so grateful, and was able to pay her back within two weeks. I thought that was a very nice gesture, because it wasn't like I only wanted twenty dollars. It's not often we find true friends like that. [188]

When my daughter was four, her aunt and uncle gave her a bag of candies. She sat on the living room floor playing with them, occasionally eating one. Then she came over to me with several in her hand. "Mommy," she said, "I want you to have some because I really, really love you." Well, I thought it was so nice, I hugged her to death. [189]

When I worked at a day camp for children, one girl brought bags of makeup with her every day. She had collected the makeup from her mother and aunts, and bought some of it herself. Then she and the other girls spent at least an hour every day putting it on. They pretended to be their favorite singers, actresses, teachers, and even their mothers. Then they acted like them and put on skits for all the children. Other kids loved the skits and the girls loved the attention. [190]

I started dating a girl I really like, and arranged a trip with her because I thought it would bring us closer together. We went to a nearby city for the weekend. The first day, when we were walking around, I found ninety dollars lying on the sidewalk. I could have kept it all for myself, but I decided it would be much nicer to use it to help pay for our hotel bill. Normally, whenever we do things together, each of us pays our own way. But I felt that the more we share, the more likely we are to become a couple. [191]

People frequently try to make sure others know how much effort they have put into helping them or in getting a gift for them, in order that they will be fully appreciative.

I went all over town trying to get a white scarf for your birthday. The owner of the best store in town said if he were getting it for himself, he would get a polyester one, not a silk one, because it will hold up better when you clean it. He searched all through his storage area to find one for me. [192]

I spent the afternoon moving the junk out of the garage so everyone can get to the stuff they need. When I finished, I told my wife how much easier it is to get at things. Then I took her out to the garage and showed her. [193]

Sometimes in order to get more recognition people continue to remind others of things they have done.

> My brother painted the house in June, and we weren't allowed to forget it all summer. He wanted Mom and Dad to tell him over and over again how much they appreciated it. [#194]

17. Doing things others approve of

People also seek to obtain positive reactions by doing things others approve of. This includes acting in desirable ways, living up to expectations, and avoiding the things which are disapproved of by others. Many adults seek to be a proper spouse, parent, and neighbor; perform their work in a reliable and industrious way; take part in community affairs; attend church and participate in church organizations; donate to and collect for charities; and dress suitably on various occasions. In the case of children, many try to perform household chores; do well in school; pursue programs and careers preferred by parents; participate in activities favored by parents and friends, such as playing a specific sport or musical instrument; and date individuals that their parents and friends approve of.

> I try to get good grades, not only to please myself, but mainly for my family. I want them to be proud of me. [#195]

> My sisters and I compete for attention from our parents. Both of my sisters are much prettier than me and have accomplished more, but they aren't interested in school. So one way I please my parents is by doing well in my courses. Also, both my sisters are lazy as hell. I am the one my parents can depend on when they need help. Both Mom and Dad work, so I clean up around the house and sometimes start supper before they get home. I can tell they really appreciate this. [#196]

> My parents are very much concerned about my choice of university courses, and want me to select ones which will benefit me in the future. When I choose suitable courses, they pat me on the back for a job well done. I just hope I live up to their expectations and do well in them. Now that I am away from home, my parents still expect me to go

to church. I do go and they are happy about it. Every time I go, I know my parents are going to be pleased with me. I'll attend church for the rest of my life. During the summer and on weekends when I am home, I often go out with my friends. I usually get home at a time my parents approve of and that makes them happy. They commend me for being considerate of their feelings. I have also been working at a part-time job for the last two years. My parents praise me for being responsible enough to hold the job and for earning my own spending money. I enjoy getting their approval. [197]

In order to receive recognition for acting in desirable ways, people try to avoid the activities that others disapprove of. Thus many people drink in moderation, avoid recreational drugs, do not break laws, and remain faithful to their mate. When people engage in activities which are disapproved of by others, they commonly try to hide the fact from them.

18. Entertaining others

People try to get positive reactions from others by entertaining them. They make clever and witty comments; tell jokes and stories; mimic others; act, sing, and dance; and put on costumes.

People frequently attempt to say things in a clever or witty way.

It is remarkable how many people don't say hello, or ask how you are, or answer a simple question in a straightforward way. Instead, they always try to use a witty remark and impress you with how clever they are. They want you to smile or laugh at what they say. [198]

We all have pet expressions that we use with people we know. When things take more time and effort than one would like, I comment, "In for a penny, in for a pounding." When someone complains about something someone has said about them, I point out, "It's only the truth that hurts." When a person does something particularly foolish, I tell them, "Life is one IQ test after another." When someone else does something foolish, I'll say, "He may be incompetent, but he's very consistent." And when I bump into a person accidentally, I remark, "You probably didn't deserve that." [199]

It's fun to name cats, and visitors are often interested in how you arrived at their names. Sometimes you pick a name you think is clever, such as "Commie Rat" or "Crapalotl." Other times there is a characteristic which suggests a name. "Studebaker" was born in a car, "Thistle" had wicked claws, and "Oreo" was black and white like the cookie with that name. Sometimes you use a theme. "Intrepid," "von Hindenburg", "Sea Wolf," and "Amelia Earhart" were named after famous disasters. "Belladonna" and "Foxglove" are notorious poisons. Often you get to know a neighbor's cat before you learn what they've named it, and you give it a name of your own. We named one that always leaned out of the neighbor's window, "Gargoyle," and another that was always scratching itself, "The Flea Hotel." You can get in uncomfortable situations when neighbors learn what you've re-named their cat. [#200]

Even if a joke or remark is made at the expense of someone who is present, others who overhear it may be entertained.

The guys I hang out with like to make cracks about each other. The person we make fun of doesn't enjoy it, but it's often good for a laugh from the other guys. When we all got dressed up for an annual dinner, we insulted each other's suits. We said, "Did you forget to change your clothes after you did the barn work?" and "Those are the fanciest looking overalls I've ever seen." When we played in a golf tournament together, if someone hit a bad shot they'd be asked, "Do you golf much?" or the comment would be made, "That went so far I can't see it." When we went to a dance together, we said, "You dance like Donald Duck; flat-footed," "Where'd you learn how to dance? The army?" and "Don't you know that humans can't fly?" Those who didn't dance were called, "Chickenshit," and asked, "Is your ass stuck to the chair?" [#201]

A common way of entertaining others is to tell or read them jokes and stories.

Ronnie gets attention at a party because he always has lots of jokes to tell and a way of telling them that makes them funny. People gather around him to hear his jokes. [#202]

122

I asked Steve, "Why all the funny stuff?" He told me, "Listen, all through elementary school no one would pay any attention to me. Now I make them laugh and they pay attention to me." [#203]

Frequently off-color jokes receive positive reactions. Jokes and stories are made more entertaining by mimicking characteristics of those one is talking about. People mimic characteristics of various national, ethnic, and deviant groups, and individuals that the listener is personally acquainted with.

It's fun to make fun of others. My friends and I like to ridicule other people's appearance. One guy we went to high school with had a limp, and every time his name was mentioned someone would imitate his walk. We also make fun of the way people talk if they stutter or have trouble pronouncing words. A man came to fix our furnace one day, and asked, "Is your mudder home?" "Who?" I asked. "Your mudder, Rose." "Mom?" I asked. "Ya." So I went and got her. Now every time the man's name is mentioned, all I can think of is his question, "Is your mudder home?" and I feel compelled to say something with the word "mudder" in it. We also make fun of people's accents. There was a South American student in my school, and, the poor guy, we always made fun of the way he talked. Often when people mimic something about a person they also try to imitate their appearance. If someone is mimicking a fat person, he will stick out his stomach. We know a woman who has a neck problem, and every time my brother talks about her, he leans his head on his shoulder so he looks like her. [#204]

Also, people sometimes fabricate stories to get positive reactions from others.

My younger sister likes to invent stories in order to make an impression on my friends. One night she came running into my room to tell us my brother had been hit by a car and was in the hospital. There was no truth to this; she just wanted to get me going and make herself look clever. I wasn't amused, but my friend played into her hands by laughing at her little performance. [#205]

Another means of getting positive reactions is to sing, dance, act, and/or wear a costume. People perform informally, often in front of friends or relatives.

Mike gets lots of attention at a party because he's always clowning around. He sings funny songs, acts like a fag, and just generally makes a fool of himself. But he has a very pleasant way about him so people like to be around him. [#206]

Our family was on holiday in Spain, and we were all together in one of our hotel rooms. My daughter placed roses in her hair and began to dance with a shawl to Spanish music. We encouraged her and she loved every bit of attention she got. [#207]

I gave a talk in psychology class contrasting two theoretical positions. When I took the position of gestalt psychologists, I put on a golden bowler, and when I presented the experimental approach, I put on a rat mask. The props added a real flair to the presentation, and the teacher and several other students commented on them. [#208]

People also participate in formal productions, such as sporting events, music recitals, Christmas and Easter plays and concerts, and end-of-season performances of dance and ice skating. People use costumes and special items of apparel to get positive reactions.

Today there are many adults who wear costumes to the clubs on Halloween. Some of the costumes are just great. One man wore the classic outfit of a flasher. When he threw open his trench coat a flashbulb went off in your eyes so you couldn't see what he had on underneath. I think the best costume was the person who went as a Christmas tree. She looked exactly like one, and you couldn't see a person beneath the boughs. She kept her lights plugged into the wall socket, even when she danced. As for me, I wore a cap with GOD lettered on it, a bow tie which flashed on and off, and a T-shirt with "Have a nice day" on the front. I also carried a globe under my arm which I whacked with a spoon from time to time to cause earthquakes, and gave out animal crackers to people with the admonishment, "Don't say God never did anything for you!" The better your costume, the more attention you get from others. After midnight some clubs hold a parade, judge the best costume, and award prizes. [#209]

19. Giving others pleasure

People give others pleasure by a variety of means. Pleasure may be produced by pleasant tastes, affection, sex, and entertainment. (Also see Tactic 18, Entertaining Others.)

> My wife usually gives me a short back scratch when I go to bed at night. It is so relaxing, I'm in seventh heaven. [210]

Such acts are frequently rewarded with positive reactions.

> I spent a couple of hours preparing a dish of chicken in peanut sauce for a potluck dinner. It was a real hit. I saw people going back for seconds, and at least six people came up just to tell me how much they liked it. A couple of people asked how to make it, and my husband complimented it several times. [211]

20. Praising others

People frequently praise those they want to receive positive reactions from. Praise can be directed at anything associated with a person, including his endeavors, knowledge, interests, possessions, appearance, personality, character, taste, friends, and relatives. Thus one may tell others one likes a picture they painted, a talk they gave, their new car, their lawn, their hairdo, the jewelry they are wearing, their smile, their choice of a restaurant, a dessert they made, the person they are dating, their children's manners, and so on.

> There is a woman I find very attractive I would like to get involved with. She dresses exceptionally well, and when I run into her I tell her how great she looks. [212]

People also tell each other favorable things that others say about them.

> I went to see a local presentation of *Electra*. A girl I find quite charming did an exceptional job in the play and afterwards I congratulated her on her performance. I mentioned that three of my friends had felt the

125

same way I did, and pointed out that one of them is an actor and another directs productions herself. I could tell the girl was quite moved by what I said. [#213]

A girl told me that Brenda, a close friend of mine, has more poise than anyone she's ever seen. I made a point of repeating this to Brenda, because I knew she'd be quite pleased. [#214]

21. Acknowledging the accomplishments of others

People acknowledge the accomplishments of others in order to increase the chance of getting positive reactions in return. Thus one may take the time and trouble to a) go see others in sporting events, recitals, plays, choirs, or dance or skating performances, b) attend talks they are giving, c) read poems, stories, articles, or books they have written, d) go to displays of their work in art, craft, culinary, or science shows, e) witness their receipts of awards or honors, or f) attend their confirmations, graduations, weddings, promotions, retirements, anniversary parties, or any other events of special significance to them. When doing this one is likely to a) make sure the other person knows one is attending, b) applaud when appropriate, and c) compliment or congratulate the person afterwards.

I went to see the recital organized by my music teacher. I knew from past years that the performance would be awful. However, my teacher gives me a great deal of personal attention, and she charges me reduced rates for lessons. The least I can do is show support by attending her recital and telling her afterwards what I liked about it. [#215]

After we win a hockey game a lot of people congratulate us, which makes us feel good. Even when we lose, some fans say, "You'll get them next time." When I get a pat on the back I know my efforts in the game are appreciated. Knowing that people like me and are interested in me is very important for my self-esteem. People who say something to give others a little boost are really important. They are usually very outgoing people who are friendly and very nice, and they almost always get a positive response in return. I know when I give a person a boost, the person always thanks me, which makes me feel good. Also, I know I am likely to get a boost in return from them in the future. [#216]

One may also acknowledge a person's accomplishments by mentioning the accomplishments to the person's friends or relatives. Sometimes one acknowledges a person's accomplishments in order to develop or maintain a relationship with someone else one wants positive reactions from. Thus one may attend the wedding of a friend's daughter, or go see a performance by a friend's wife, because this maintains or strengthens one's relationship with one's friend.

> My best friend's daughter asked me to come see her volleyball tournament. I went, because I value my relationship with my friend and I knew she'd be pleased if I went to see her daughter play. [217]

22. Giving affection

Affection is another form of positive reaction. There are many kinds of affection, including touching and patting, rubbing or scratching a person, resting one's hand on a person, putting one's arm around a person, holding hands, hugging, and kissing. People often express affection toward others with the expectation or hope of receiving affection or other positive reactions in return.

> When I want affection from my girlfriend, I start acting affectionate toward her. I hug and kiss her and she hugs and kisses me in return. Sometimes I put my head in her lap and she rubs my back. I love giving and receiving affection, and I find the more I give the more I get. [218]

People frequently feel disappointed if they do not receive affection in return.

23. Developing and displaying physical attractiveness

People seek to increase and display their physical attractiveness in order to obtain positive reactions from others.

> If you are looking for a guy's attention, you have to make yourself attractive so he'll notice you. [219]

If you're not looking good on a day, it's best to avoid the guy you're interested in. You don't want him to see you look like a dog. [220]

I used to be a "ninety-pound weakling" until I started lifting weights. All my life I was picked on. But now I want to live. I want to be able to walk down the street and have people turn around twice to see who I am. I want to be able to date anyone I please. [221]

People use a variety of approaches to improve and display their facial appearance, physique, expressions and posture, dress, hair, and odor. In order to improve their facial appearance people frequently wash their face, try to remove blemishes and facial hair, apply makeup, and in some cases undergo plastic surgery. People seek to improve their physical appearance by exercising, dieting when they are overweight, eating more when they are underweight, tanning, and wearing clothes which emphasize their attractive traits and hide their unattractive ones.

Guys go to great measures to attract girls. Pumping up is one of the best ways to make yourself more appealing sexually. I have a membership in the local gym and spend ten to twelve hours a week in the weight room. It helps relieve pressure, but the main reason I do it is to look better. When I ask other guys why they lift weights, they give a variety of reasons, but always mention the opposite sex. One told me, "Well, I want my muscles to get bigger, and then girls will like me more." Another said, "I do it to improve my physical appearance, to be more confident around girls, and to turn the babes on." [222]

You frequently see people wearing clothes which emphasize their best features. If a woman has a small, cute ass she wears tight pants, and if she has big breasts she wears tight sweaters. If a male has a muscular physique he wears shorts and cutaway T-shirts. The opposite happens too. A woman who is flat chested will wear full blouses, rather than skintight shirts, and people who are overweight wear baggy clothes so you can't see where the fat is. [223]

People also employ certain postures and expressions to get positive reactions.

A guy in my high school gets attention because he walks around all day with his stomach sucked in and his chest pushed out. I mean this guy is good! My friends and I wonder how he can hold this position for the entire day. #224

I like to watch people and pick out the individuals who look really good. Once you figure out why they stand out you can adopt what they are doing yourself. Good posture is really noticeable and you can achieve this by focusing on the highest point on the top of your head and using your spine to push that point up as far as possible. Another thing is confidence. If you are confident you turn your head and look directly at people. If you lack confidence you often look at people out of the sides of your eyes and don't turn your head to face them. Another factor is presence. When you watch a group of performers on stage, usually the one you focus on has the most presence, and this is not necessarily the performer with the most skill. I think presence is based on the angle of your chin. Most people seem to keep their chin down. But a person with presence has their chin raised. Then there is the one feature which makes a person look either attractive and pleasant or unattractive and unpleasant. This is the direction of the corners of your mouth. If they rise, people will want to be with you, and if they fall, people will want to shun you. Also, the more upper teeth you show when you smile, the more appealing you are as a person. There is one thing that is very unattractive, and that is using mouth gestures which are not symmetrical. It's really ugly when you twist one side of your mouth in a different direction than the other side. These things are really simple, but they make so much difference I've tried to adopt all of them. #225

A primary way in which people try to attract positive reactions is in the way they decorate themselves with clothing and accessories. Many people spend a great deal of time and money selecting clothes and accessories which will obtain positive reactions. People often seek to wear clothing which is a) in style, b) complements their physique and their complexion, c) matches the other things they are wearing, d) was purchased in a status store, e) carries a status label, and f) is of quality construction.

My friends and I spend lots of time shopping for clothes. We often go with someone so we can get another opinion as to what looks good on us and what doesn't. The other day I went with a friend who found three dresses she liked equally well. I told her the blue one wasn't her color, the black one looked like she was going to a funeral, and the peach one really suited her. Then I reminded my friend that it was her decision, because she'd have to wear it. She bought the peach one. [226]

I like a really elegant look. I watch other people to see who looks really classy and who doesn't. I also get ideas by looking at the latest fashion magazines and noticing the models who have the look I want. I use these ideas when I select what I buy and wear. [227]

I was sitting in a doughnut shop having a coffee. A girl with a nicely made-up face, a stylish hairdo, and a very fashionable outfit sat down several tables away. My attention was drawn to her because she was so well dressed. Then I noticed that her hand kept going to her belt to check if it was still in place and her eyes kept darting down to make sure she wasn't showing too much cleavage. No doubt she wanted admiring glances from others, but she seemed very self-conscious about her appearance. [228]

People also use novelty to appear interesting and attract positive reactions. Thus they wear clothing which is somewhat different in design than that being worn by others, and they commonly change what they wear from one day to the next to achieve a more interesting appearance. They also buy and wear new clothing and jewelry which others have not seen before. Because other people are unfamiliar with the new items they are wearing, other people are more likely to notice them and comment on them.

I needed a large, everyday purse and got one from a shop which made them out of antique rugs from Afghanistan. The purse is brightly colored and has a really distinctive design. I've had dozens of compliments because it is so unusual. [229]

Lots of people buy their clothing out of province. They do this so they won't end up wearing the exact same thing as others who do their shopping here. Nothing is more embarrassing than going somewhere and seeing someone else wearing a carbon copy of what you have on. I bought a new coat I really liked in a local store. But after I wore it once, I saw two other people wearing the identical coat. So I never wore it again. It had just become too ordinary for me. [#230]

From time to time some people radically change their look in an effort to get the positive reactions they want. Another approach which gets positive reactions is to wear clothing which is more revealing than the clothes other people are wearing.

Darlene never says very much. It's just the revealing way she dresses, while keeping that sweeter-than-honey look on her face. She wants every man to notice her, and the maddening thing is they do. [#231]

I watched four guys standing at the bottom of the staircase at the library when a girl wearing a short skirt walked down the stairs. The guys nudged each other. One commented, "She must know we're looking. Why else would she wear a short skirt on a cold day?" [#232]

Every chance I get during the summer, I go to the beach. I grab a bikini and head out in the morning, and don't usually return home until five or six. That gives me lots of time to be noticed. A lot of good-looking guys hang out at the beach, and they're more likely to notice you if you have next to nothing on. [#233]

However, when one wears clothing which is more revealing than that worn by others, one is likely to get negative comments from those competing for positive reactions.

People also do other things to their appearance to get positive reactions. For example, they adopt hairstyles and hair colors which enable them to appear more attractive and interesting. They also attempt to remove unfashionable body hair. Thus women shave their legs and armpits, remove pubic hair which can be seen when they wear a bathing suit, and in some cases try to permanently destroy hair which appears on their breasts, upper lip, or chin. In addition, people try to remove body odors through bathing and using soap, deodorant, douches, toothpaste, and mouthwashes. At the same time they apply floral and other odors to smell more appealing.

24. Developing and displaying personality traits

In order to obtain positive reactions from others, people develop and express certain personality traits. Many individuals act friendly, pleasant, charming, nice, and giving. Others act confident, "cool," or assertive.

> In order to attract girls, most males make an effort to appear very polite and sweet. Many guys I know brag about how they fooled a girl into thinking they were superpolite and shy. This is all bullshit. They don't do it to be nice. They just do it to manipulate the girl. [234]

People also try to drop behaviors which alienate others.

25. Developing abilities

People develop a wide variety of abilities in order to obtain positive reactions from others. Individuals spend many hours and even years learning to do things at a high level of proficiency. This can involve strength, agility, wit, intelligence, knowledge, creativity, daring, and anything else that might impress other people. The areas in which they apply themselves include working hard, doing a job properly, playing a sport, giving a speech, organizing a meeting, playing a musical instrument, driving skillfully, holding one's liquor, fighting, dancing, and numerous other activities. People are willing to make this investment of time and energy in expectation of receiving positive reactions in the future. In many cases they develop the ability to perform better than others and to do things that others can not do.

> You should see the male kids in town practicing tricks with their skateboards. They jump over obstacles and do turns in the air. They work for hours on the sidewalks and plazas trying to master the latest stunts. [235]

> Have you seen synchronized swimming? People half drown themselves to get attention from others. Instead of keeping their head in the air, and their legs under water, they keep their legs in the air, and their head under water. [236]

26. Producing achievements

People also seek to produce achievements which will impress other people and obtain positive reactions.

> I know a girl who went through four years of high school and never missed a day of classes, even when she was sick. She told me this was so important to her. She received a plaque for her attendance and said afterwards that it was really nice to have the plaque because it made her feel like she contributed something. [#237]

> I entered a project in the science fair which showed that Polynesians have more fat than other races because fat helps them float in water. The Polynesians fish, travel on the sea, and have to cope with sudden high waves which strike the shore. People liked my project, I got a fourth place award, and my junior high science teacher gave me an A. One judge told people that my project was the one to see. [#238]

People try to take major roles in performances, study at prestigious schools, work for well-known companies, hold important positions, get work published by recognized publishers, produce better work than others, score higher than others at various endeavors, win competitions, and receive awards and honors.

> My eight-year-old sister says, "I plan to practice really hard in figure skating this year, so I can win a gold medal in every competition." [#239]

> There is a lot of competition to get a spot on a sports team. Everyone knows the best players will make the team and the others will be cut. Because we take this competition seriously we go at it pretty hard. Tempers sometimes get out of control, and I've seen fights break out because the competition is so great. Once on a team, practically everyone likes to get attention from their coaches, friends, and fans. There is a lot of competition to get to play as much as possible during games. When we make a good play or score a goal we want to be noticed. Everyone likes to see their name and face appear in the newspaper and on TV. It makes you feel good and gives you confidence in yourself. [#240]

Normally, the more a person excels, the more positive reactions he or she receives.

Tara is known throughout the school to be an excellent student. Last week she had two exams, one in biology and the other in physics, and made the top score on both. The teacher announced to the class that Tara received a ninety-eight on one of them. Her science project won the competition, and is on display in the school lobby. [#241]

Doug is one of the top scorers on the hockey team and gets considerable attention from the media, fans, opposing players, coaches, and his own teammates. Recently after a game in which Doug played very well, he was interviewed by a newspaper reporter. The next day his name was in the headlines of the sports page together with his picture and various quotations. Fans regularly come to see Doug play. Some have read about him in the paper, and young girls hope to be able to meet him. The opposing team pays considerable attention to Doug, because they feel if they can keep him from scoring they have a better chance of winning. They sometimes assign a player to cover him the entire game. Because Doug is one of the best players, the coach gives him more ice time during regular shifts and power plays, or when the team is short-handed or needs a goal. Players on Doug's own team recognize his scoring ability and frequently pass him the puck. In a close game with time running out they try to get the puck to him with the hope he'll be able to score the winning goal. When he succeeds he gets even more attention from his teammates, the coach, fans, and the media. [#242]

The expectation of receiving positive reactions is a strong motivator. Individuals try to have the best lawn, garden, or Christmas lights in the neighborhood; win a scholarship; get on the Dean's list; have the cleanest house; get a poem published in a recognized magazine; earn a law degree; enter the best preserves at the local fair; be the first to master a double tour en l'air in dance class; earn a larger salary than others; become a millionaire or billionaire; or win a political office. Often people select achievements to work for which will gain them much more recognition, instead of working for achievements which will not produce as much recognition. The more recognition one gains through one's achievements, the better.

My older brothers excelled at all kinds of sports and our living room is filled with about one hundred and fifty trophies, medals, and plaques which they won. When I was born, they were quite disappointed I was a girl and not a boy, because they had high hopes for a younger brother they could train to be an exceptional athlete. Nevertheless, at an early age they did show me how to catch a softball, throw a football, and hold a hockey stick. I soon realized that excelling at sports was the way to win their affection, and this became my goal. In the seventh and eighth grades I was chosen female athlete of the year in my school, but this went unnoticed by my brothers. No matter how well I succeeded in the sports I played, I wasn't able to please them. In high school I played on five different school teams. I was very proud when I won two trophies, and I expected at least a nod of approval, but the response I got from my brothers was, "Only two? Why didn't you do better?" As I continued to win trophies, I finally began to receive some praise from my brothers. For the first time they told me they were proud of me. But I wasn't going to stop there. In my last year of high school I received six trophies on awards night, including the one for best female athlete of the year. It took three people to carry my trophies into the house. My brothers were really surprised, and repeatedly showed how proud they were of me. I proved to them that even though I was a girl, I was just as good an athlete as they were. #243

Just as achievements can increase the amount of positive reactions one receives, losing or giving up one's achievements can cause a loss in positive reactions.

When I was ten years old I took the girl next door to see a movie. I was the first of my group of friends to have a date, and this gave me a position of influence. In grade school I hung out with lots of girls, and at one time was dating five different girls at once. In high school I was a member of the honor society and active in sports, and girls usually expressed an interest in me and I would take it from there. My parents thought I was quite the social being and enjoyed seeing me going out with some of the best-looking girls from socially prominent families. My friends and brothers envied my success. I was all caught up in the game of social status, and this gave me an incredible feeling of power.

Then suddenly in the eleventh grade, I just stopped dating. I was tired playing social butterfly and wanted a rest. I realized I wasn't dating to have fun, but because I thought I was supposed to, and because I wanted the social status. For the better part of the next two and a half years I remained single. I didn't think this would affect the status I had held for years, but I was very wrong. My parents thought I was strange, my brothers thought I was sick, and my friends looked at me differently, as though I had lost my golden touch. [#244]

27. Displaying achievements

People display their achievements to others in an effort to get positive reactions. They reveal their achievements by showing others what they can do, telling and writing others about their achievements, placing signs of their achievements in public view, and telling others how other people respond to them.

People frequently find opportunities to show others what they can do. This can range from displaying works of art and playing a musical instrument to performing various feats with skates, skis, cars, boats, and windsurfing rigs.

> When you go to the rink for a public skate, you see many people showing off what they do best. Some skate as fast as possible, some do jumps and spins on figure skates, and others produce clouds of spray with hockey stops. [#245]

> I've been pestered all week by my son to watch him blow out a candle with his "chi," or personal power. He makes a forward thrust with an open hand and stops a few inches in front of the flame. After watching numerous failures, I want to leave and do something else, but he keeps begging me to watch. Occasionally he succeeds and the flame goes out. No doubt the candle is frightened to death. He's been working on this a couple of hours a day, and now complains how sore his arms and shoulders are. [#246]

> Sometimes when I'm outside with friends, I'll go up to a vertical metal pole which is about four inches in diameter, grip it with both hands, and hold myself horizontal to it. This usually impresses the people I'm with. There is something of a trick involved. You bend forward at the waist, grip the pole with both hands beneath your waist, squeeze the pole between your right side and your right elbow, place your left

elbow into your stomach for support, and raise your legs. When I've tried this with a pole which is too thin, I've hurt my ribs, but I pretended I was fine. You'd look stupid if people knew you injured yourself while you were trying to show off. [#247]

People frequently tell others about their achievements.

When I drove the school bus today, one little girl kept telling me, "Jerry, Jerry, I threw up four times in school today." She was enormously pleased with herself. I told her, "Sit down and shut up!" [#248]

Do you bowl? I normally bowl 160, but last week I bowled a 270. It's the best I've ever done. I'll probably get a league trophy for most improved player. I'm telling all my friends. [#249]

Last weekend I was at Scottie's Lounge and picked up the daughter of a cabinet minister. What a looker. We spent the night screwing at my apartment. [#250]

Let me show you the flowers the head office sent me. They wanted me to know how happy they are with my success as office manager. It's the best year our local office has ever had. It's the first time we've actually made a profit since we opened. [#251]

People also write others about their achievements, both informally, such as in a personal letter, and formally, such as in a résumé. Large portions of local newspapers are dedicated to notifying the public of individual accomplishments through articles and photographs. The newspaper reports sports news; announcements of births, engagements, and weddings; news of meetings of organizations; announcements of awards, appointments, and promotions; lists of university honors and degrees; reviews of performances; and efforts on behalf of charities.

Some people also fabricate achievements in an attempt to be accepted and receive positive reactions from others.

I was standing outside my apartment when a young guy came by and started a conversation with me. As we talked he told me about winning lots of ski competitions, various trips he had taken, and numerous degrees he had earned. He had done too much, too fast, and I realized he was just a bullshit artist. [#252]

In addition, people display signs of their achievements to the public. They make sure others are aware of the degrees and honors they have received by using titles, wearing special jewelry, and hanging formal announcements on their walls. They place trophies, plaques, and medals in prominent places where others are likely to see them, such as on the mantelpiece, in a display cabinet, on a wall, or on their desk. They wear patches on their jackets to show the teams they played with, the positions they held, and the competitions they won. Sometimes they adopt distinctive styles of dress and behavior which remind others of their achievements.

A colleague spent a year at Harvard in the management program. Ever since, he wears Ivy League clothes and a Harvard tie. [253]

One of my professors is from Newfoundland and must have had a Newfie accent to start with. But since he attended Oxford, he's spoken with a British accent. [254]

Individuals frequently keep scrapbooks with photographs and newspaper articles about their achievements, which they show to others.

When I visited my cousin he showed me a newspaper article about the time he rescued a person from drowning. It happened when he was on vacation in Florida. The person he saved was a bigwig and my cousin had a letter of commendation from the governor of the state. [255]

People also notify and remind others of their achievements by talking about how other people respond to them. Thus they talk about other people who compliment them, copy what they do, mention or cite their work, ask them for advice, and follow their advice.

My brother always talks about how successful he is in university. He brings this up even when people are talking about something else. He tells us the positive things professors say about him, so everyone will pay attention and praise him. [256]

I had an interesting phone call today. A stockbroker from Halifax called me for advice on a stock he was considering. I was a client once in his office and he knows I know a lot about mining stocks. I guess he felt he could get better information from me than from other sources. [#257]

In some instances, the achievement that people notify others about is simply the fact they attract positive reactions.

A friend of mine who is no longer married likes to tell me about all the males who call her up. She'll say that one called this morning and another this afternoon. Then she'll add that her son remarked, "Mom, I don't know how you do it. I wish girls called me that way." [#258]

When people inform others of their achievements they run a risk of being viewed as bragging or boasting. If so, they may be criticized for putting on airs, letting it go to their heads, "acting big," or thinking they are better than others. Therefore people usually try to tell others about their achievements in ways which do not suggest they are bragging or boasting. Nevertheless, other people frequently see through them.

There's nothing wrong with complimenting yourself or being proud of yourself. But when you get out of hand, that's bragging. People brag mainly about how good they are at sports or how smart and beautiful they are. It's really no fun being around people who brag a lot, because you get sick listening to them. [#259]

The way Don talked to his new friends, you'd think he was the world's greatest drinker. Several times he raved about how much he had drunk the previous weekend. His friends began to doubt him, and finally the day came when Don ran out of excuses and had to go drinking with them. They proved he was just hot air. [#260]

Charlene makes me sick. She's got a real good body and can wear lots of the newest styles. The guys all gawk at her and she loves it. She'll go on to me about how many guys asked her to dance the last time she went out. She even has the nerve to say stuff like, "I can't seem to get out of the car without having guys turn around to look at me and whistle." She tries to make it sound like it bothers her. Can you imagine saying stuff like that about yourself? It's a wonder her parents aren't in the poorhouse trying to keep her in the best clothes. [#261]

The best way to let people know about an accomplishment is not to spill your guts about it right away. This bozo came up to me and my friends and started going on about his trip the previous weekend when he had hiked ten miles a day with fifty pounds on his back. We weren't impressed at all. What he should have done was mention he'd been on a weekend trip. Then as we asked him questions about it, the story would have come out and we'd have been impressed. [#262]

28. Displaying achievements of one's family members

People seek positive reactions by informing others about the successes of their family members. For example, adults like to tell others about the achievements of their children and grandchildren. People also like to mention a spouse's or parent's occupation when it carries status.

> When I visit my neighbors, they frequently boast about their daughter. They make comments like, "Bethany can color really well for her age," "She has a great sense of humor," "She speaks very clearly for a two year old," and "Bethany has many more words in her vocabulary than other children her age." I catch myself bragging about my daughter too. I'll say, "Molly's riding instructor says she has real talent. I think she could go to the top if she wants to." [#263]

> Some wives brag about their husband's job. They say, "My husband's a lawyer," or "Steven, my husband, is a doctor." [#264]

> When I brought home my first painting from kindergarten, my parents hung it on the refrigerator door and showed it to everyone who entered the kitchen. My younger sister was jealous of the attention I was getting, and bit me hard. Now that my sister is older, she seldom acts violent to get attention. Instead, she gets good grades, which really wins my parents over. They post her best tests on the refrigerator door where others can see them. [#265]

People sometimes notify newspapers and radio and TV stations about the achievements of a family member. They make written submissions and often include photographs. When these are published or aired other people become aware of the family member's achievements, talk about them, and comment on the achievements to the person and the person's family.

29. Acquiring and displaying possessions

People acquire possessions and display them in an attempt to get positive reactions from others. They seek to obtain objects which impress themselves and others. Consequently others are likely to notice their possessions, be envious of them, and talk about them. People consider these possessions to be extensions of themselves. Therefore when a person's possessions receive positive reactions from others, the person feels that he is receiving positive reactions. Possessions which often receive positive reactions are cars, houses, furnishings, property, clothes, fur coats, jewelry, money, art, boats, antiques, pets, lawn mowers, sporting gear, toys, recreational vehicles, stereos, computers, and other electronic equipment.

> A good-looking vehicle makes a difference when you're trying to attract females. Many guys I know get an attractive car for the sole purpose of picking up chicks. I know guys who are not nice and don't look like much, but do have a good-looking car. Every time I see them around town they have a girl in their car. [#266]

Sometimes the location of a possession produces positive reactions. For example, a house may be desirable because it is in a good neighborhood or on waterfront property.

The uniqueness of a possession increases the positive reactions it receives.

> Everyone in my community knows Angela. She always has the best of everything, and whatever it is, it has to be different from everyone else's. Her clothes really stand out, and she drives a pink car. She would do anything for attention, and believe me she gets it. [#267]

The more expensive a possession, the greater amount of positive reactions it generates, because few people can afford to get it. When few people have a possession, it attracts attention and positive reactions. However, as more people acquire the possession, it attracts fewer positive reactions. Then in order to get positive reactions one must obtain new possessions that others do not have yet.

Last summer I worked at a day camp for about twenty children. Most of the children already knew each other and got along quite well. One nine-year-old boy, however, was new to the community. He brought expensive toys with him, such as computerized games and remote-controlled cars. As a result he attracted the attention of other children, who became interested in him. He soon made friends and joined in their activities. #268

The family that lives next to us has a family business. They live in a nice house and every member of the family has a brand-new car. In the summertime it's almost a ritual for the whole family to go outside and wash their own cars. When the father bought a brand-new Cadillac, their son was over at our house right away giving us the full particulars. Every time they make a purchase, whether it's a new stereo, TV, or even a piece of clothing, they feel compelled to boast about it to anyone who'll listen. They usually tell everything about the price, make, and so on, and always end their spiel with the comment, "It's one of a kind." #269

When I first bought a computer for word processing, computers were very expensive. The first couple of years, I found myself constantly mentioning it to others, and frequently inviting them over to see it and try it out. Now that I've had the computer for a number of years, I rarely mention it to people. Maybe it's because it doesn't seem so special anymore. Computers are cheaper today and more people have them. However, I'm planning to buy the latest laptop computer to use when I'm traveling. It's quite snazzy, and I'm sure I'll show it to all my friends. #270

Sometimes one acquires possessions simply to establish or maintain relationships with others who have them too. As a result one obtains positive reactions from those one wants to receive positive reactions from.

I bought my first Mistral windsurfing board this past summer. Before that, I was left out when all my buddies went to the beach. I'm one of the guys now, even though I don't know how to windsurf. The boards are pretty expensive and I like telling people that I own one because they look at me like I'm special. It's worth the money. Now I'm part of the beachfront crowd and can party with them too. #271

30. Displaying experiences

People also display their experiences to others as a means of getting positive reactions. These experiences may have occurred in connection with work, trips, investments, relatives, mates, colleagues, friends, neighbors, hobbies, performances, organizations, school, church, sports, gambling, accidents, crimes, natural disasters, wars, and other dangers. People bring up their experiences, tell others about them, and show them pictures of them. They also wear articles of clothing, place items in clear view, and give gifts which reveal the fact they have had the experiences. By these means they communicate to others that they have had interesting and worthwhile experiences and therefore are interesting and worthwhile people who deserve positive reactions.

People commonly talk about their memorable experiences in order to get positive reactions.

Brian usually gets lots of attention at parties because he always has so many interesting stories to tell. He was a cop in Montreal for eleven years and his supply of stories is endless. [272]

It's fun to go away and ski at big mountains and meet new people. It's easy to get attention from girls on the slopes if you have good equipment of your own and are a good skier. After you've been skiing there's a great social life at the lodge. But the best part of skiing is coming home and telling everyone about the fantastic time you had and making all your friends jealous. [273]

In addition, people use many methods other than talking to display their experiences.

When people go to Florida or the Caribbean during the winter, it is an absolute must to get an outstanding tan. Then when you get back home everyone notices the tan and asks about it, and you have a chance to tell them where you were. [274]

At the gym people frequently wear T-shirts which announce where they've traveled, sporting events they've competed in, and other gyms where they've been members. [275]

One of the neatest parts of travel is that you encounter so many things that you haven't seen before. Every place you visit has some things which are much better than what you get at home, and I like to take the time to find out what they are. I always end up bringing back music cassettes, wine and liqueurs, clothes, weavings, carvings, and prints for myself and my friends. It's really fun to show and give others things they've never seen before. #276

This spring I went white-water rafting in Maine. The companies that organize the trips place photographers on the shore and in kayaks to take photographs and videos of people in each raft as they go through the wildest rapids. After the trip everyone goes back to the company headquarters to view the photographs and select the ones they want to buy. It's big business selling photos which will impress your friends and family. #277

31. Associating with people who attract positive reactions

People seek to get positive reactions for themselves by associating with people who attract positive reactions. This may be someone who is recognized for a certain ability or accomplishment, such as a star athlete; someone who is particularly attractive, such as the winner of a beauty contest; someone who is known to be particularly wealthy; or someone who holds an influential job. Individuals also show others photographs of themselves with well-known people.

In high school girls were always boasting about who they were going out with, especially if it was the captain of the hockey team, the class president, or the handsomest boy in school. #278

I'd rather be seen with one of the guys on the hockey team than with somebody who curls at the curling club every Wednesday night. Not that there's anything wrong with curling, but it's so much cooler to be with a guy who is recognized, and is on TV and in the paper all the time. #279

I would never date a guy who worked at Burger King. It would be embarrassing to go out with someone who fries hamburgers, no matter how gorgeous he is. But I do like some guys who work at Ted's.

Ted's is a classy club which plays 1950's music, and the staff do dance routines together. A lot of the girls like the guys who work there because they have such cool jobs. [#280]

Tony is the piano player at the resort where I work as a bartender. Whenever business is slow in the bar, he sits and gossips a bit about the resort. Tony likes to drop names. He'll lean across the bar, lower his voice, and tell me what Edward, the general manager, or one of the other managers said to him in confidence. "Edward asked me about that. He put his arm around my shoulder and said, 'Tony, what do you think I should do?'" Tony is proud he is asked for advice by the managers. Regardless of what we talk about, Tony constantly emphasizes how important he is to the resort. [#281]

I'm taking a course with a professor who likes to drop names so he can look important. He spends most of his time talking about Harvard, the UN, and knowing Joan Baez, Martin Luther King, and others. He told us how special the house was that he stayed in in Geneva, and how he called up Liz Taylor and Richard Burton in Geneva and asked them over for a drink, but they replied, "Sorry, we're going to be married on the Nile tomorrow." The younger students are impressed, but I just feel so embarrassed for the man. [#282]

People who associate with those who attract positive reactions, often succeed in obtaining positive reactions for themselves.

I knew a boy in grade school who was from England. He had a very high voice, and was constantly teased about it until he told us he was a distant relative of the Queen. Some of the kids believed him and he made some new friends. [#283]

When a girl walks around with a guy's hockey, football, or baseball jacket on, everyone knows that she's his property. This usually leads to more invitations to parties and other activities. When a friend of mine started wearing the jacket of a local hockey star her popularity shot up. After they broke up she didn't get the invitations she used to get. So she started going out with his teammates to restore her popularity. Often girls will choose an ugly boy who is popular over a cute boy who is not. [#284]

I was in junior high at the same time as my older brother, and he was very popular with the girls. The older girls sought me out and wanted to spend time with me. They hoped if they paid attention to me, my brother would pay attention to them. [285]

32. Being influential

One reason why people take influential positions and roles is because of the positive reactions they receive from others. When they hold such positions they are usually treated with more respect. They are less likely to be argued with or interrupted, and serious attention is paid to what they say and to their creature comforts.

> I'm amazed at how much effort and money people devote to getting elected to the city council. The candidates spend thousands on their campaigns, and the money comes out of their own pockets. If they're elected their salary is just nominal, and not much more than they've spent on their campaigns. But they do get their names and pictures in the newspapers and on TV, and lots of attention from people in the community. [286]

33. Controlling desirable resources

People also seek to get positive reactions from others by controlling desirable resources. Such resources include information, money, equipment, and jobs. Often other people want to obtain access to these resources in order to use them to get positive reactions for themselves.

> My younger daughter keeps tantalizing my older daughter, "I know what your Christmas present is. Do you want me to tell you?" She drops hints about the present, such as, "Well, it's sort of big," and gets lots of attention from her sister. [287]

> An elderly man in the village where I live constantly reminds his children about his will and how quickly he can change it. This has worked quite well and they don't neglect him. [288]

34. Acting upset

When people act upset they frequently get positive reactions from others. Often they are genuinely upset. However, in many cases they want others to know that something is wrong, and they hope to get sympathy or to have things set right. Depending on the person and the circumstances, when people are upset they may sigh, hang their head, act moody, sulk, look discouraged or depressed, become quiet and withdrawn, go off by themselves for a walk or a drive, or give others the silent treatment.

> When my sister wants attention, she sits on the couch hugging a pillow all day and sulking. My friend's father also sulks. When his family asks him what's wrong, he won't say unless they coax him. If you go around with your lip hanging down, people are sure to notice. [289]

> I get lots of attention from my friends when I'm in a bad mood, won't talk, and won't drink with them. Everyone wonders about me. They ask what's wrong and if I'm going to be all right. [290]

> My parents hate when I suddenly go quiet. They want to know what's wrong, because they think I'm mad at them. [291]

> A popular way to get attention at summer camp is to withdraw and make sure others know you've done so. One thirteen year old, Tina, waits until everyone is assembled before moving away from them. When she does so, she stays close enough to be seen by the other campers. This never fails to work. Someone always goes over to find out what's wrong. [292]

> My dad's retired. If we're really busy and Dad thinks we aren't paying enough attention to him, he'll start ignoring us and giving us the silent treatment. Sometimes he does this for days. [293]

Individuals also complain, whine, act nervous, cry, yell, slug the wall, slam doors, and stamp their feet in order to get attention.

The most common method the people I know use to get attention is complaining. My mother complains all the time that in addition to working part-time, she has to do all the shopping, cooking, dishes, cleaning, and laundry. This makes the rest of us feel sorry for her and guilty about not helping, and as a result we act nicer to her. My father complains about his allergies and asthma. He really plays them up to everybody in order to get sympathy. As for myself, I'll complain about having two midterms and a paper and a presentation to do in one week, while having to work all weekend at my job. This gets me sympathy from my parents. When my friend's sister got pregnant, my friend thought his parents would kill her. But she complained so much that her life was ruined and acted so depressed, her parents ended up feeling sorry for her and giving her almost constant attention. [294]

Some teenagers complain all the time about their problems at home, how horrible they are doing in school, and the fact they don't have a boyfriend or girlfriend. They complain to anyone who'll listen to them. [295]

I work in a restaurant and staff use various ways of getting attention when they're upset. One employee is usually happy, but when she's upset she wants everyone to know. Then she breaks lots of dishes. But you don't have to go to this extreme, because it's easy to get attention. When I have a large amount of work to do, I make small gestures to show I'm displeased, and I act panicky. The supervisors notice and ask me how things are going. This gives me the chance to tell them I'm overworked. [296]

People also run away from home and threaten suicide to get positive reactions.

On his first night at camp, Carl packed his little suitcase, and took off. However, he made sure other kids saw him leave, and they reported him to the counselors. This was a great way to get attention, because we ran after him when he did it, and talked to him at length afterwards. After we brought him back the third time, we had him sleep with us. However, he got more attention than he wanted. When we reported all this to his social worker, she came and took him home from camp. [297]

My sister attempted suicide by taking an overdose of sleeping pills. She suspected Jim, her husband, was fooling around and that their marriage was falling apart. She told me later she didn't want to kill herself. She just wanted Jim to notice her and stop his cheating. #298

35. Revealing misfortune

When people reveal personal misfortunes to others they are very likely to get positive reactions from them.

I ran into a woman I know in the grocery store. Usually we just say hello to each other and go on our way. However, this time she was right behind me waiting in line at the checkout counter. When I asked how she was, she told me she had cancer and was not as strong as she used to be. I told her I was really sorry and squeezed her arm to show support. I waited for her to pay for her groceries and for a taxi to come take her home. I like her, but if she hadn't told me she had cancer, I wouldn't have waited around. #299

In order to get positive reactions, people frequently inform others when they are ill or have experienced some other mishap or calamity.

Gordie wasn't feeling well, and cried and whined while no one paid attention to him. But the minute his mother sat down next to him on the bed, he stopped fussing. #300

My daughter is absolutely fearless and throws herself into any activity with a vengeance. As a result she accumulates many cuts and bruises. She makes a point of showing me each one to get my sympathy. #301

I get regular letters from my mother in England. Dad has had a serious cold for months now, and he recently fell and hurt his leg. He and Mom are also having trouble maintaining their large house. This is the primary focus in all her letters. She recently reprimanded me when I wrote back because I didn't mention my father's ailments. #302

Sometimes people fabricate misfortunes because they have learned this produces positive reactions from others.

At camp, Stephanie told one of the male counselors she had been raped and was worried about being pregnant. He brought her to the female counselors, and we spent many hours talking to her and trying to help her solve her problem. Then when we'd done all we could, we phoned her social worker. The social worker told us Stephanie made up wild stories and used the one about rape on almost every new person she met. [303]

36. Acting differently than others

Another method of trying to get positive reactions is to act differently than other people. Often this involves going to greater extremes than others do. Examples include dressing differently than others; cutting or coloring one's hair differently; acting more exuberant, rambunctious, or scatterbrained than others; using more gestures; taking off items of clothing; dancing in an unusual fashion, such as by oneself, or in an inappropriate place, such as on a tabletop; starting a fight; taking greater risks than other people; drinking more liquor and/or acting drunker; talking more or louder than others; and expressing weird ideas.

My mother is a grammar school teacher. She has a girl in her class who walks like a robot and talks out loud when students are supposed to be quiet. The girl certainly succeeds in getting attention. [304]

I wore any strange outfit I could come up with just to see my parents' reaction. I realize now it was stupid, but it certainly kept them on their toes. [305]

My little brother has always dressed a little different. The other day he shaved two big X's onto the side of his head. He says, "It's cool. Everybody likes it." [306]

A girl in my high school class always wore the most fashionable clothes, talked the loudest, and had the most ridiculous laugh. One day she came to school with so many gold chains around her neck you couldn't see the top she was wearing. People would walk up to her, pick out a chain they liked, and ask where she got it. But after a while people started whispering about her when she walked past and teasing her about her neck being sore, which wasn't what she wanted at all. [307]

Perry does anything when he's dared. He'll chug six beers in a row or straight rum. For some reason people like to stand around and watch him do it. #308

37. Failing to do what one is supposed to do

People also attempt to get positive reactions through failing to do what they are supposed to do. However, they frequently receive negative reactions for this. Examples include not going to bed on time, not getting up on time, not eating one's vegetables, not sharing one's toys, not doing one's homework, not going to school, not doing one's chores, and not following rules.

> As a grade school teacher I've found that some students who fail to do their homework are perfectly capable of doing it. They aren't trying to be bad; they are just trying to get someone to pay attention to them. #309

> Cliff is an only child and has always gotten lots of attention at home. When he entered the first grade he became just one of thirty-six children in the class. This was a difficult transition for Cliff. At first he refused to let other children play with the toys he was using. Then he began to push other children around and was verbally abusive. He also refused to do his schoolwork or take part in group play. #310

There are other reasons why people do not do what they are supposed to do. These include conserving energy, assigning the task a low priority, and forgetting to do the task.

38. Doing something not approved of

People sometimes behave in ways which are not approved of in order to get attention. Often they receive negative reactions instead of positive reactions. Thus people may try to elicit a reaction through spilling food or drink, wetting the bed, playing with matches, throwing knives, writing on walls and doors, breaking objects, mistreating animals, roughhousing, running and screaming in the house, making faces, teasing siblings, making rude remarks, talking back, staying out late, disrupting class, skipping school, making bad grades, intentionally making mistakes, hanging out with the "wrong" crowd, dating unacceptable people, dressing in a different manner, acting reckless, breaking rules, drinking and getting drunk, smoking, using drugs, swearing, fighting, using obscene gestures, lying, stealing, destroying or defacing property, gaining or losing too much weight, flirting, and infidelity.

Albert is old enough to talk, but it's difficult to understand everything he says. He tries to get your attention by talking constantly. If he notices he doesn't have your full attention, he pokes you while he talks. He also tries to talk louder than everyone else in the room. If this doesn't work he begins poking and screaming. And if this fails, he runs at full speed through the house screaming at the top of his lungs. This usually gets him a swift slap across his rear end from his father. [311]

My younger sister is ten, and when she has friends over at the house she likes to show off by acting rude to me. I think she does it to let on she's cool. Impressing her friends is important to her. [312]

When I was younger I would steal things and deliberately get caught, because I knew my mother would have to come and get me. [313]

When I was a child I had two older sisters. Because I was the youngest child, I received a lot of attention. One of my sisters doted on me, but then she developed a terminal illness. As a result she couldn't pay attention to me anymore and my parents gave most of their attention to her. I needed some way of getting my attention back, and I began to eat. I was originally skinny, but I began to sneak food into my room whenever possible. I put on weight until I became twice as fat as I should have been. It seemed that any attention, even if it was negative, was better than no attention at all. My other sister tried to get more attention by making bad marks, and she failed a year in school. She ran around with a rough crowd, and did everything possible to displease our parents. [314]

My boyfriend and I double-date with another couple, Bob and Linda. When we go out to a dance or pub, if Linda starts to feel neglected she will dance and flirt with other guys. This gets Bob's attention, and usually produces a heated argument between them. But I think this is what Linda wants. She doesn't seem to care whether they are fighting or talking, as long as she has Bob's undivided attention. [315]

39. Being a nuisance

A common way of obtaining reactions from others is to do something which bothers them, i.e., to make a nuisance of oneself. In many instances in which people become a nuisance, they do so to try to get positive reactions.

A guy in my science class in high school was the standard class clown. He would frequently make rude remarks and use any excuse to leave class. He made paper airplanes and threw them at the bald spot on the teacher's head. When the class was completely quiet he would drop a book on the floor just to watch everyone jump. This got him the attention he wanted. His friends would laugh and the teacher would expel him. [#316]

I watched two teenage guys sit down behind a group of six girls waiting for a movie to start. The girls responded to greetings from the guys and continued talking among themselves. Then one of the guys put his legs over the seats right between two girls. A couple of minutes later he reached over and took the drink one girl was holding. She demanded it back in a joking manner and he returned it to her. Then he asked to see a pin she was wearing. She asked why, but seemed to appreciate his interest. Then one of the other girls passed a box of popcorn back to the two guys. [#317]

My younger sister is ten years old, and when I am on the phone she listens in on the extension and throws in her two cents worth. One day I was talking on the phone to a guy who is a good friend, and she declared, "My sister loves you!" I don't know whether I was more embarrassed or mad. She wanted to get a reaction from me and make an impression on my friend. [#318]

I worked at a day camp for children, and there were two brothers who were eight and ten years old. They were quite rude and often bullied other children, who didn't like them very much. When we went on outings the two had more money than the others. They would buy things the other children couldn't afford and then ridicule them for being poor. [#319]

My eleven-year-old daughter uses whatever means she can to get attention from me. She knows lots of ways to get on my nerves to make sure I react to her. Sometimes she sings at the top of her voice when she's near me; or she goes through a noisy song and dance routine, "I'm Standing On Heels," repeatedly; or else she'll claim that what I'm eating has gone bad, because she knows this makes me feel sick to my stomach. [320]

Terry is a pain in the butt. The other night we were playing Ping-Pong and he was playing pool. He kept trying to hit our Ping-Pong ball with his cue stick. He's awful when you go to the drive-in movie. He'll start complaining that he's too hot, then he's too cold, then he's bothered by the window steaming up. No one wants to sit in the back seat with him because he starts picking on them. When he's in the front he'll start playing with the radio or shove in a tape to drown out the sound of the film. You would swear he's a child. [321]

I teach in a high school and one middle-aged teacher acts very immature in the staff room when he wants attention from female teachers. He pinches our arms and steps on our feet. [322]

40. Asking for attention

People also ask others outright to give them positive reactions. This usually takes the form of a direct request, such as "Watch me, Mom!" "Give me a kiss," "Can I mooch a back scratch?" "Aren't you going to tuck me in?" "Why don't you call me?" and "Drop by my office sometime."

Daphne, a four year old, was playing with her blocks on the floor while her mother peeled vegetables for dinner. Daphne suddenly jumped up, ran to her mother, and wanted up in her arms. "Why don't you build a tower?" asked her mother. "I want you to play with me!" Daphne pouted and walked slowly back to her blocks. A few minutes later she returned. "Can you play now, Mommy?" "Not yet, dear." [323]

People also request positive reactions in other ways, as in the case of a child who carries a book to an adult in order to be read to; a person who asks others to attend their performance, sporting event, art show, graduation, or wedding; or someone who reminds others that their birthday is fast approaching.

> Sports are definitely not my thing. As fate would have it I have two female friends, one in high school and the other in university, who keep asking me to come see their basketball games. Both of them are considered the best player on their team, and both want me to see what they do exceedingly well. [324]

41. Accusing a person of not paying attention

People also try to get positive reactions from others by accusing them of not paying attention to them. Thus a person may inform another that he is not listening, or ask why he does not call or write more often.

> If my parents aren't paying attention to me, I tell them, "OK then, don't listen to me. See if I care." That usually brings them around. If someone at school ignores me, I tell them, "Alright, be a snob. See if I give a damn." [325]

> I got out of bed early Saturday morning and started to straighten up my apartment. My girlfriend, who was still in bed, said, "If you are going to get up and fuss about, then I might as well go home." She was telling me she expected my full attention. [326]

Feelings

There are two feelings connected with seeking positive reactions from others. These are loneliness and pleasure. Loneliness encourages people to seek positive reactions. Loneliness occurs when people do not get the positive reactions they want from those they want them from, and when they are separated from those who regularly provide them with positive reactions. The second feeling is pleasure. When people do get the positive reactions they want from the individuals they want them from, they feel pleasure.

Loneliness

Loneliness is a punishing feeling. Loneliness means a variety of things to people, including feeling alone, having no one to share things with, missing someone, and feeling no one cares. People describe loneliness in very negative terms.

> It's feeling you are facing the world all alone, without anyone to lean on. You feel empty and incomplete. [327]

> When I feel lonely I keep wanting to cry. I feel really sorry for myself and unhappy. [328]

> The more I think about the fact I'm lonely, the more depressed I get. [329]

> I hate it. It has to be the worst feeling in the world. I don't feel it often, but when I do, I really get down in the mouth. [330]

> Loneliness has to be the worst feeling there is. I don't understand how old people can cope with being alone all day. How can they stand it? I would go crazy. [331]

> Loneliness brings on other feelings in me, like rejection and depression. It makes me remember painful times in the past, such as a long period of grief after a very close friend was killed. These feelings just make me feel more lonely. Sometimes I'm so preoccupied with loneliness I can't get through the day without breaking into tears. [332]

> It's a terrible feeling and I despise it. I actually get to the point that I think of suicide. [333]

Some people also experience physical effects in connection with loneliness.

> When I'm homesick I feel helpless and drained of energy. When it happens to my roommate from Ontario, she gets severe headaches. [334]

Feelings

My husband and I moved from England to Canada when I was twenty-two. I was pregnant at the time, and we'd been in Canada for six weeks when my husband started work. Our furniture and our dog hadn't arrived yet from England. The day my husband left for work it really hit me. Suddenly I felt all alone. I realized I was permanently away from home, and for the next two weeks I had panic attacks. It wasn't clear what I was scared of, but my heart would pound, and I felt clammy all over. I was just heartbroken and cried every day for a week. I felt so terrible. I really needed to be with someone, and dreaded the time my husband would leave for work. As soon as he left I would call a woman I knew, and by 8:30 AM, I would be at her house. She wouldn't even be dressed yet, and I'd stay at her place all day. My landlady also took me under her wing. One day when I felt really bad she had me go with her to her place of work. I said hello to the people she introduced me to, but I was unable to talk to them. I was just so panicky. I also kept having irrational ideas. I said I'd give my baby up for adoption when he was born, because I wouldn't be able to cope with him. I also hated the house we'd rented, although it was really quite nice. I was frightened to go out of the house, find my way around the neighborhood, or go downtown. I really didn't want to speak to strangers. It helped to talk to my husband about how I felt. But the day our dog arrived from England was the day I started feeling all right again. #335

Despite the strength of these feelings, many people hide them from others. They do not want others to think they are too emotional and not in control of themselves.   .

None of the members of my family like to talk about their feelings of loneliness. My mother has found it very hard to adjust to her children leaving home. As each child left, her feelings of loneliness increased, and her marital and health problems have only made her feel more lonely. However, she's not a person who shows her feelings, and she makes every effort to hide her loneliness from others. She considers any display of loneliness a sign of weakness. When she feels lonely, she engages in a flurry of activity and attempts to keep as busy as possible. Only those who know her well know she is upset at all.

As for my grandfather, his wife is dead and his children have moved away. He lives by himself and feels left alone. He is a relatively quiet person who would never complain to anyone about his loneliness. He tries to hide his feelings by diverting his own and other people's attention to his physical condition. He frequently complains about his health problems.

My grandmother on the other side of the family felt lonely from time to time for a number of years when she was still in her home. Loneliness has become her constant companion since she moved into an old people's home four months ago. Although she tries to be cheerful and witty with visitors, loneliness never completely leaves her. She attempts to hide these feelings from others, and succeeds with strangers. But regular visitors and staff can see the unhappiness and loneliness in her eyes and hear them in her voice. However, she doesn't want to be a burden on anyone by complaining. She feels everyone has their problems, there are always people worse off than she is, and she doesn't want anyone's pity.

I'm the same way as the other members of my family. When I get lonely I try to get rid of the feeling through activities, although mine consist of school, sports, and work. I make every effort to conceal these feelings from others. It would embarrass me to express them, and I don't want others to know I have them. [336]

People believe others will interpret loneliness as a weakness. Homesickness, for example, is generally considered immature, both by those who see it in others and by those who experience it.

It's maddening how people think homesickness isn't serious until they go through it themselves. When my friend and I left Prince Edward Island to attend a university in Halifax, friends from the Island would call and tell us to enjoy ourselves and not to be so foolish about wanting to come home. When we tried to explain we were homesick, they would laugh at us. One told us, "Halifax is the place to be." But when you're homesick, the place to be is with familiar people. [337]

Also people do not want others to feel sorry for them, or to tell third parties about their apparent weakness. Males have to be particularly careful because these feelings are often considered effeminate.

When I feel lonely, I try to hide the fact from my friends. It isn't cool for guys to feel lonely. [338]

If people do tell someone they are feeling lonely, that person is likely to be one of their closest friends.

When people feel lonely

Loneliness occurs in a variety of circumstances. These include the following:

1. Being alone
2. Being aware that unlike oneself, other people are not alone
3. Being with people that one does not receive positive reactions from
4. Not getting the positive reactions one wants from those who are present
5. Being separated from those one has relationships with

People are least likely to feel lonely when they regularly receive the kinds of positive reactions they want from the people they want to receive them from. They are most likely to feel lonely when they receive indications that they do not matter to those who matter to them.

1. Being alone

Many people experience feelings of loneliness from time to time when they are by themselves.

> I get really lonely when I'm walking home from somewhere, such as school. I can't wait to see a familiar face. When I can talk to someone I know, the feeling passes, and I don't feel lonely. Then when I'm alone again, the feeling is there once more. I just hate being by myself. [#339]

> When I'm alone, I near go out of my mind. I hate it. [#340]

> I'm loneliest on weekends when many of the local girls go home from residence. I can't do the same because I'm from Montreal. I only get to see my family two times a year, and I really miss them. Sometimes I sit around my room for hours on end feeling sorry for myself. More than once I've actually gotten sick to my stomach because being alone bothers me so much. Occasionally I get tired of moping around and feeling lonely and depressed. Then I go talk to some of the other girls who stay here over the weekend. [#341]

Feelings of being alone can be intensified by the awareness that one may appear alone and lonely to others. Consequently, people can be too self-conscious and embarrassed to go places alone where most people will be with others.

> I know it's foolish, but when I'm in a crowd or a room where I don't know anyone, I'm afraid people will think something is wrong with me because I don't have any friends. #342

> When I was a teenager, I was absolutely petrified of having no friends. I guess I felt if I was alone people would think I was weird or something, and I'd be laughed at all the time. #343

> It's not very often that someone goes to a movie alone. I've commented to friends several times how sorry I feel for a person sitting by himself and how lonely he must be. I watched one man in a row ahead of me who seemed to be embarrassed to be seen alone. His friends had left to get some popcorn and there was no one on either side of him. He began throwing pieces of popcorn at some other friends a few seats away. It seemed to me he was showing everyone that he did have friends and wasn't alone. #344

2. Being aware that unlike oneself, other people are not alone

When one is alone, feelings of loneliness can be brought on by the awareness that others are not alone and one is not included in their groups.

> I feel hurt when I learn that some friend is having a party and hasn't invited me. I really get to feeling sorry for myself. #345

> When I was living in an apartment house, the woman downstairs came home late one night with a group of people. They stayed in her apartment for half an hour, then went back out to their car. As they drove off the woman ran to the door and cried, "Wait for me!" in a really pitiful, forlorn voice. Maybe they forgot to take her along. I felt sad for her. #346

> I feel most lonely when I'm not out with the guys. If they go to a club, and I'm not home in time to go or I don't get invited, I feel left out. One night I had to study and they all left without me. I got to thinking about them being at the club and me being at home by myself, and I

felt all alone and couldn't concentrate on my studies. When they got home I felt a lot better. [347]

3. Being with people that one does not receive positive reactions from

A person can also be with others and feel lonely. Often this occurs when the others present are not those the person receives positive reactions from.

Sometimes when there are people near me, I feel lonely. I only feel secure when those who are close by are friends and family I can talk to. [348]

I don't mind being alone if I'm waiting for someone, or if I'm there for a purpose. But I get uncomfortable if I'm just sitting there with no one I know. [349]

This is my first year at university and I don't know many people. Every time I walk into a classroom I see all the students I don't know and I feel lonely. [350]

4. Not getting the positive reactions one wants from those who are present

Feelings of loneliness can also occur when one does not get the positive reactions one wants from those who are present.

It is strange how loneliness can hit when you least expect it, and not appear when you most expect it. There have been times when I have been out with friends for a good time, and felt extremely lonely because I realized I couldn't communicate with any of them. [351]

The lack of a suitable response from the other person in one's relationship, raises doubts that the person still cares. Frequently one seeks reassurance that he or she does care by making further attempts to get positive reactions.

I can be in the apartment with my fiancé and be lonely. If he's busy reading or working at something and not paying attention to me, then I feel he's not actively with me. I don't feel lonely when we talk, he holds me, or we make love. [352]

161

Often when I reach over and put my hand on my wife or pat her, she doesn't respond. It makes me feel ignored. I want to do something else so I can get a response, but usually I just remove my hand. #353

When my daughter leaves for school she shouts, "Bye!" from the front door. I'm usually in the bedroom, and I shout, "Bye, sweetheart!" Then she'll shout, "Bye, Mom!" And if my wife doesn't answer, she repeats, "Bye, Mom!" I know when my wife leaves for work and doesn't say goodbye, I feel forgotten. #354

In a relationship, if person A shows signs of being upset with person B, person B immediately wants to see signs that person A still feels positive towards him. Often B does not want to leave to do something else until he can obtain such signs from A.

5. Being separated from those one has relationships with

One of the most common "causes" of loneliness is being separated from those one has relationships with, i.e., those one receives most of one's positive reactions from.

I often feel lonely when I look at pictures of my family and friends and remember happy times in the past. #355

My brother and sister were in university with me, but they graduated and moved to another province. I get lonely when I think about the years when they were here, or when I go to a sporting event that I used to attend with them. #356

When me and my girlfriend arrived at the residence hall on the mainland, we figured like OK, we're Islanders, it's impossible not to like us. But were we shocked. All the rest of the girls in the residence were bitches. Like we're both from large, friendly country families and it hurt. Finally we just couldn't take it any more, like it was just so lonely. So we said to each other, "The hell with it! Scholarship or no scholarship, let's go home." And we did. #357

Many children get anxious when they are separated from their parents. Some cling to their parents in a new place or in the presence of strangers. One woman told me her son can't bear to be left alone inside the car for even the shortest time. When he doesn't get his way at home he tries to run away, but always returns crying. Parents use this fear of being alone when they want to leave a place and their child doesn't. The parents pretend to leave the child behind, and the child becomes upset and runs after them. Some children will crawl into bed with their parents, if the child they normally sleep with is absent. [#358]

I was recruited from Ontario to come to the university and play hockey, and just couldn't wait to get on the plane. I felt like an eight year old on Christmas Eve. I was going to a distant place where the only person I knew was my hockey coach. Images of stardom, girls, pubs, and fun kept going through my mind.

When the airplane landed it was a dreary, rainy day. As I waited for the coach to pick me up, I watched people meeting each other and leaving together. I started to get an empty feeling and wondered whether I was making a mistake coming here. Later, after two weeks on campus, the excitement I felt for university life disappeared. The whole situation was really frustrating. I tried to be friendly with people, but they were reluctant to open up to me. It hurt a lot. I wasn't used to trying to make friends, because back home I knew everyone and always had someone to hang around with.

All I thought of was home. It got to the point where I started feeling sorry for myself, and this made the situation all the worse. There wasn't a day that went by that the thought of leaving for home didn't cross my mind. The only thing that kept me from doing so was the fact it was my decision to come here in the first place. My parents had wanted me to go to a university close to home. So I couldn't just quit and go home. It would be admitting I was wrong. When I called home, I would tell my family everything was fine. It was so great to hear their voices and be filled in on happenings around home. They would tell me all my friends and former teachers were asking how I was doing. Then Mom would tell me how proud she was of me being out here on my own, doing well in school, and also doing well in hockey. It made me happy to know my family were all proud of me. But when I hung up the phone I was all by myself again.

The biggest problem was I had no one to share my burden with. It seemed everyone around was happy except me. I didn't know anyone well enough to talk to about it, and I didn't want to upset anyone at home. I tried to hold all my anxiety inside and didn't display how I really felt to anyone. I spent a lot of time thinking and trying to convince myself I would get over it soon. It felt like I was in jail. At night I would just lie in bed and wait for morning. The weekends were the worst. Everyone else in the dorm went home and I usually wandered around doing mindless things. I actually started playing games with myself, although I didn't realize it at the time. I tried to keep myself from calling home for over a week, but I usually failed. After a while all I wanted to do was stay in my room and do homework. Looking back, this was a mistake.

About two weeks ago I finally started to come out of my shell. I realized no one was going to come and rescue me. I had to face reality and learn to do things on my own. No one else was going to feel sorry for me. These past three months have been one of the hardest times I've gone through in my life. [#359]

People normally experience a great deal of loneliness after a relationship or family breaks up.

My fiancé and I separated last weekend, and I've been so upset I haven't been able to sleep for four nights. All I've been able to consume is one glass of eggnog. I just feel nauseous. I really don't want to have to deal with the pain of being alone again. It took me years to get over the last man I was in love with, and it's disheartening to think I'll have to go through that again. [#360]

I feel lonely when I watch a TV program about a family. Even though my parents have been divorced for many years, I remember our times together. [#361]

People usually undergo considerable loneliness when the other person decides to end the relationship. They often get rid of items which cause them to feel hurt, such as photographs, clothing, household items, and travel souvenirs associated with the other person.

People experience considerable loneliness after someone dies that they were in a relationship with.

A neighbor has three grown children and has been a widow for five years. She was married for twenty-six years, very attached to her husband, and very dependent on him. She tells me it was difficult to adjust to being alone. After his death she felt empty and abandoned.

Some days she didn't even get out of bed. With time and the aid of her children she managed to cope with loneliness. She still feels lonely from time to time, but as she says, "I have accepted he's gone, and I must get on with my life. I don't want loneliness to control me." #362

A few years ago I lost a close friend in a car accident. I felt very alone and depressed. At first I wanted to be by myself to deal with his death, and I spent six months reminiscing about the times we spent together. I realized this wasn't helping and turned to my friends and family for support. The loneliness did not go away. But somehow being around others made it easier to deal with. Still, even when I was surrounded by friends and family, there were many times I felt completely alone. #363

Several years ago my dad died a few days before Christmas. I still feel lonely for him, and I'm sure the rest of the family do too. Even with our family at home and lots of friends around, Christmas is the most difficult time to cope with. It's when I feel loneliest. I get so depressed over the loss of Dad, I can't get excited over Christmas. #364

Loneliness occurs even when one knows the separation will be temporary. Thus people can get quite lonely when they travel or visit away from home.

My grandmother lives by herself in the States. When she had to go to the hospital, I went down to stay in her place and visit her each day. I really didn't know anyone else well. Every evening I would go over and visit the next-door neighbors who are good friends of hers. I really didn't feel lonely until the neighbors left for their summer vacation. Then I got very lonely. #365

The last time I went to a professional convention, I got really lonely. The people I knew there had already made plans to get together with others, and didn't have time to do things with me. I felt awful. So I called up a good friend of mine who lived in the next province, and left the convention early to spend a couple of days with her and her family. She and I had a nice time talking and doing things together. Otherwise the trip would have been a real bummer. #366

Probably my greatest love is for travel and adventure. I long for it when I'm tied to a single place for a period of time. But there are times when I'm traveling that I really feel lonely. Once I wrote in my diary, "This morning I had a wonderful breakfast with family, relatives, and friends before boarding the plane. The goodbyes were difficult, but I felt exhilarated knowing my adventure was about to begin. Now I'm lying on a fold-out bed unable to sleep. What the hell am I doing, leaving everyone behind to go off by myself to Europe? All of a sudden I don't feel so excited anymore. I feel scared and lonesome. Why didn't I stay where I was with friends and relatives? I just wish I could stop this aching feeling that fills my stomach. Whatever lies ahead, I hope I don't feel this lonesome again." Another time I wrote, "I feel afloat in a sea of humanity as I sit on the balcony of my room in downtown Cairo. Horns are honking, people yelling, and tires screeching. The center of the city is full of people, some rushing by and others poking along. The streets, sidewalks, and overpasses are a mass of humanity. Outside my closed door there is a continuous bustle of people, rushing to catch buses and trains, or entering the hotel to rest and escape the crowds. Here I am, surrounded by thousands of people, yet I feel so apart from everyone. I can't help feeling all alone, and thinking how far I am from friends and loved ones." Whether you are by yourself or surrounded by lots of people, there are always times you feel lonely. [367]

One result is that many people do not like to go on a trip by themselves, and if they do so they often join other travelers they meet.

I take my vacations in Mexico and the Caribbean, and I go back to the same places again and again. I stay in my regular hotels and hang out at my favorite bars and nightclubs and listen to my favorite bands. I like the fact people recognize me and call me by name even if I haven't been there for a year. Because I'm by myself, I tend to stay put. If I were with someone else I would travel around with them and see more things. [368]

When I went to Europe I liked the freedom of traveling alone and going to the places I wanted to see. But once I got to each place I would find other travelers to do things with. That way I didn't get lonely. [369]

I was in Bali by myself and feeling pretty lonely. When I stopped in a tourist office in Ubud I struck up a conversation with a Dutch girl. We decided to take a walk in the Monkey Forest at the edge of town. She didn't have much money, so I volunteered to pay her way on a day trip around Bali that I was going on. It wasn't a sexual interest, I just knew I'd have a much nicer time with company. That's what we did, and we had a pleasant time. #370

The person who is left at home is likely to feel equally lonely.

My boyfriend is leaving to go to Africa for a month. He'll be gone on his birthday, and I'll feel really bad we aren't together. I'm going to be very lonely. So I'm trying to get my girlfriend to go to Montreal with me to spend a weekend shopping and clubbing. #371

People also feel lonely when they are separated from relatives and friends on days which are customarily spent with them. These include birthdays and holidays such as Christmas, Thanksgiving, New Year's, and Easter.

I have a friend who is attending university here from Alberta. She likes living on her own, and has no difficulty fitting in and making new friends. But she says, "It started to bother me around Christmastime because I couldn't be with my family. It was really hard and I'm still a little homesick." #372

People often invite relatives and friends to Christmas or Thanksgiving dinner who would otherwise be alone, because people realize they are likely to feel lonely.

This year my fiancée and I fixed Christmas dinner together. I called up a couple from Scandinavia and a woman from Halifax who had moved here, to invite them too. I thought they might not have anywhere else to go and would really feel all alone. However, they'd already been invited to Christmas dinner by others. #373

My best friend is separated from her husband, and their children are living with him. He's so nasty at times I expect him to refuse to invite her over for Christmas dinner. I'm inviting her to eat with us if he doesn't come through. #374

Many people also undergo increased feelings of loneliness after close relatives and friends from out of province come to visit and leave again.

When people are separated from those they have had a relationship with, they often try to maintain contact with them. A person may write or telephone, sometimes as often as once a day.

> When I went off to British Columbia to get a professional degree, my boyfriend had to stay in Prince Edward Island. I was terribly lonely. He would call me every Sunday morning and I would lie in bed and not get up until he called. Getting that call was really important to me. Once he didn't call and I got really worried and called him that afternoon. #375

Frequently people try to rejoin those they are separated from.

> About a week before I left Prince Edward Island to attend a university in Nova Scotia, I began to think about all the people and things I was going to miss when I was away from home. My family drove me over to the university. When we arrived, I began to wonder what I was doing there. Nevertheless, I decided to make the best of it. After my family left, I wandered around campus and decided it was a fairly nice place. However, when night came I sat in my small room, stared at my friend who was attending the same university, and was overcome with homesickness. This feeling became more frequent as the week went on. I felt miserable. I was unable to do my tasks and think coherently. There was only one thing on my mind, which was getting home around familiar people. It makes you realize how big a part your emotions play in your daily life. My friend was suffering from the same feeling. We were living on a floor with thirty other girls, and thought we were the only ones who felt this way. When we were with the other girls, we felt like idiots for being homesick, and this made us feel worse. I began to wonder what I was doing attending a university in Nova Scotia rather than at home. My mother called on a Sunday and I told her I wanted to go home for good. My parents tried to talk me into staying. I really considered it, but I decided if I could get into the Island university, I would go there. So on Thursday I returned, registered at the local university, and haven't regretted it since. #376

My fiancé is the most important thing in my life. We had to live apart for eleven months while I was attending graduate school in Quebec. I didn't want to stay in Quebec and he came up for a week after I arrived because he was scared I'd quit and come home. I had a really hard time being apart from him and I was terribly lonely much of the time. However, being in Quebec was the best thing that could have happened to me professionally. I got excellent training, and experience I couldn't get at home. I've recently returned to Prince Edward Island, and professionally this has been a disaster. There's no employment in my specialty, and I have to take a job in some other area and at a lower rate of pay than I would have in Quebec. But I really don't have a choice. My fiancé has his own business here and not in Quebec, and I want to be with him. #377

Michael went with Debbie for two years. They had a good relationship and she was very special to him. Michael explains, "I felt content and happy with her." Although they broke up several months ago, they're still friends. Michael says, "There are times when I think I'm losing everything. I feel very lonely." He states he still loves Debbie and would do anything to get her back. "She is on my mind a great deal of the time." When he wants someone to talk to, he looks for Debbie. "I can confide in her and tell her anything that's on my mind. She understands how I feel." When Debbie spends time with others, Michael feels rejected. He tries to make her feel guilty by telling her she's rarely there when he needs her. He also argues with her about the people she spends her time with. He tells her he'll never speak to her again if she goes ahead and dates certain guys. But this doesn't stop her. #378

Five years ago my family returned to PEI (Prince Edward Island) from Victoria, British Columbia. My father was very happy with the move, because PEI is his home and his relatives live here. Although PEI is also my mother's original home, she became inactive and depressed as a result of the move. The twenty years she had spent in Victoria were the most enjoyable years of her life. She says, "Even today I would return to Victoria on an hour's notice. Yes, I'm very homesick." One of my two sisters was ten years old at the time of our move. She told me, "I'm no longer homesick. I'd always wanted to be the new girl in school. Also, much of my growing up has been on the Island, so if we went back to Victoria, I'd be homesick for here." My second sister was twelve when we moved back to PEI. She was very homesick for six months and rebelled against my parents. She got into trouble, and says, "I did everything I could to make them pay." Now she speaks very highly of the Island. My two brothers were quite enthusiastic about the move because they had always dreamed of living on a farm. However, both really missed their friends, but hid it well. One, who was thirteen at the time of the move, returned to Victoria three years later for two months. The other brother, who was sixteen when we moved, would not go back to visit for fear he would stay. He told me, "I could not tell Dad how I felt, because I was supposed to be strong and I knew it would hurt him." As for myself, I was fifteen when we moved, and I became so depressed that my parents sent me back to Victoria on our doctor's orders. When I left to return to Victoria, I was the happiest I'd been in six months. But once back in Victoria I really missed my parents, sisters, and brothers. I developed real problems with asthma and was unable to stay. To my surprise I was very happy to return, not to PEI, but to my family. I realized then I would have to make PEI my home because I belonged with them. Our family now lives on PEI and we are basically happy. All of us were affected by homesickness, because it was homesickness that brought my father back to PEI in the first place. [379]

When children become adults, move away from home, and establish new families, one or both parents are often willing to move where their children are in order to regain sources of positive reactions.

Reunions between people who have been apart are often very pleasant experiences.

Being away from your family makes you appreciate your home better when you come back. It makes you realize how nice certain things are that you just took for granted before. It's nice to know you can pick up the phone at any time and just talk to someone you know. It's strange how being around familiar people is so comforting. Even the small things people do and say are more noticeable to you than before. Being away also brings you closer to the people you left at home. Even brothers and sisters are glad to see each other again. My brother and I fight constantly, but when I returned home we got along great for about two weeks. After that there was the same old bickering again. But how much can you ask for? [380]

My girlfriend and I are really happy to see each other when we've been apart. We sure have great sex when we get back together. [#381]

When people are separated from those they have a relationship with, they frequently seek new relationships. Normally new relationships supply sufficient positive reactions that the old relationships are no longer needed and are ended.

It's hard to keep a relationship together when you live in different cities. You need day-to-day contact to maintain a good relationship. When you're apart you'll eventually meet someone else who can spend more time with you than the person you're separated from. [#382]

My first love was this cute little chick in my high school class. We developed a very close and understanding relationship, and loved spending every free moment together. Then I told her I was going away to school in Vancouver for four years. Well I thought she was going to die. She cried for a week. After I left, we kept in touch every day for the first month, but then we began to move further apart. It wasn't the same. We couldn't hang on to each other without seeing each other and being together. Everything we'd built together fell apart with the blink of an eye. It didn't work because we were so far apart. [#383]

When people know that an existing relationship is likely to dissolve, they sometimes start looking for a replacement ahead of time.

When I get worried that my girlfriend and I might break up, I start getting anxious. I begin feeling I'm all alone in the world, and that no one cares about me. I also start going over in my mind who else I could get involved with. [#384]

Loneliness and relationships

People need positive reactions on a regular basis in order that they will not feel lonely. Positive reactions provide concrete evidence that one is liked, one matters to others, and there is no need to feel lonely. People are least likely to feel lonely when they regularly receive the kinds of positive reactions they want from the people they want to receive them from. Normally this is obtained through relationships. Therefore, in order to deal with loneliness, people try to establish relationships or use those they have already established.

I started university this year, and when my dad left me at the dorm I understood I was here for good. The first couple of weeks, going back home crossed my mind many times. But I started meeting all kinds of new people and forgetting about being homesick. I discovered most of the other girls were homesick too. Not many of them liked to admit it, but they talked about home a lot, and when you talk about something a lot you must miss it. Now we all watch out for each other. When you have a problem, someone is always there to talk to you. [#385]

When I'm not involved with someone, I can really feel lonely and miserable. The only effective way for me to deal with these feelings is to get out and start finding someone else to get involved with. I've learned to start looking immediately after a relationship breaks up. When I'm involved with someone I almost never go out to clubs. But when I'm not involved, I go to clubs and bars practically every weekend hoping to meet someone. [#386]

Having loved ones and friends around keeps me from feeling lonely. If I start feeling lonely, I'll go to any length to get together with someone I know well. I need to feel wanted and cared for, and this only happens when there are relatives and friends around. [#387]

When I feel lonely, I can get really desperate to get together with a close friend. There is one friend I feel I can talk to about anything. I'll try repeatedly to call her, and if I can't get her, I'll call her friends to see if they know where she is. Often she's already made other plans, so we arrange to get together some time in the future. Then I start trying to think of someone else I can get together with right away, and I start trying to call them. [#388]

When I get lonely, I call up my boyfriend and we go for a drive or for something to eat. [#389]

I feel most lonely when my boyfriend isn't around. I start feeling I'm not cared for. To get rid of this thought I go see my other friends. They reassure me they care through the things they say and do. [#390]

Sometimes I've been involved with someone, and it becomes clear they expect more from the relationship than I do. One girl offered to support me if I would stay with her, but I went ahead and moved where I had a job waiting for me. Another girl really felt I was the one for her. I didn't feel as strongly, and I know she was quite hurt. Then there was a girl I told that I wanted to continue dating other people. She kept seeing me because she hoped with time I'd fall in love with her. When it didn't happen, she really hit the tranquilizers hard. It seems you can't have relationships without hurting people. Because I really don't want to hurt others, I sometimes feel bad about it and ask myself if it would be better if I just quit getting involved. Then I realize there is no way I'll stop, because my need for a relationship is too great, and a relationship that's less than ideal is sure better than none at all. #391

I'm elderly and retired. When I'm lonely or bored I usually go visit my relatives and stay anywhere from a couple of days to a week. While I'm there I do some cleaning or baking, or take care of the little ones and give their mother a break. If I want to go to bingo, I'll call a friend to go with me. #392

My grandmother is in her eighties and lives by herself. A lot of times she claims she is more incapable than she really is. She does this so her neighbors, who are also her friends, will drop in regularly to see if she's all right. Her neighbors bring her meals and fix things around her house. I worry she's making excessive demands on her neighbors. So I've tried to get her to use a local organization for the aged, which delivers meals and does repairs for a nominal fee. But my grandmother isn't interested. She thinks if she uses the organization's services, the neighbors won't come by very often and she'll lose her personal contacts. #393

Based on my personal experience, friends and family are the only cure for loneliness. #394

The knowledge that one is in regular, daily contact with people who provide one with the positive reactions one wants, enables one to better deal with periods of being alone.

I can study all day by myself if I know I'm going to see my girlfriend that evening. It's really different when I don't have a girlfriend, because I'll be lonely and I'll work by myself as little as possible. I'll go where other people are hanging out and try to study there. I'll be much more likely to walk around and hope to see someone I know. I'll also stay out late at night barhopping. I feel this same need to get out around people when my girlfriend goes out of town and I can't be with her. #395

People who are in satisfying relationships often forget that loneliness exists.

The great thing about being involved with another person is that you've always got someone to share things with. You can go to a movie or read a good book or get an idea, and then talk to them about it. When things go poorly at work they are there to listen and commiserate with you. When I'm in a good relationship, I forget what feeling lonely is like. #396

Feelings of loneliness can be satisfied through positive reactions from very few individuals. People do not require positive reactions from everyone or large numbers of people to satisfy this need.

When I draw something I am fairly content with, I show it to a friend or family member. I want the person to like my drawing. If she does, then I'll show it to someone else to get additional approval. I'll do this with three or four people before I'm satisfied. I also do this with things I write. In my senior year at university I wrote a couple of papers I felt very satisfied with, and asked a couple of friends and a family member to read them. I did this because the work was an extension of myself, of my views and feelings at the time, not because I felt that my work would alter how other people look at life. I'm not looking for widespread recognition; I merely want some people I know to approve of my work and me. Once my work has their approval, I no longer need to show it to anyone. I do this two or three times a year with something I've invested a lot of time and energy in. #397

Frequently one person, such as a mate, provides a large percentage of the positive reactions one needs.

I find I really need a mainline relationship which provides mutual love and emotional support. In addition to that I like to flirt around and have an occasional affair, and this interest in extra people is purely sexual. However, when I lose a mainline relationship, I lose all interest in playing around and concentrate on finding another mainline relationship. At such times I can't be bothered with women who are not available for a mainline relationship, such as those who are currently married. But once I get another mainline relationship going, I'm ready to play around again. #398

When one does not have a single, regular source of positive reactions, such as a mate, one attempts to obtain positive reactions from a variety of people. People who are without a mate, or single, devote more time and energy to getting positive reactions from people outside of their home than do married individuals. These may be people they meet at work, in school, in bars and clubs, and in activities.

Although some relationships provide a high percentage of one's positive reactions, they may not provide certain kinds of positive reactions one wants.

When I go to a party or dance, I often see friends there and sit with them and talk to them. But I'm usually hoping to find someone to get involved with and so are my friends. When I don't connect with someone, I start feeling lonely and often go home early. #399

A friend of mine decided to have a child without marrying. Her child brings a lot of love into her life. However, she says there are times when she wishes she had someone close to talk to and be there for her. She misses not having someone to comfort her after a long, hard day. #400

I find friends almost always let me down. Often, when you need them the most, they've already made plans to go to meetings, parties, out of town, or to be with other friends or relatives. They are frequently involved with their boyfriend or girlfriend and have little time for you. It's rare that you get to see a particular friend more than once a week. Sometimes they'll promise to call you back and won't, they'll borrow money and not return it, or they'll make clear they disapprove of the things you are doing. But no matter how unsatisfactory things are between you, or how pissed off you get with them, you still need them when you've got problems and have to have someone to talk to. Still, if you want emotional closeness on a steady basis, you've practically got to get a girlfriend or boyfriend you can see every day. [#401]

Nevertheless, relationships which are far from ideal can still help one avoid feelings of loneliness.

The reason I seek out men is that I feel no one loves me. I'll go out to bars just to pick up a man, and he'll make me feel special and unique for a few hours. [#402]

There are the girls you're willing to get involved with. Then there are the girls you're not willing to get involved with, but are willing to screw. When you're out at a bar, if you can't get together with the first type, a night with the second type makes you feel a lot better than being all alone. [#403]

People will frequently become involved with someone who is less than ideal in their efforts to deal with loneliness. Thus individuals will establish a serious relationship with someone who is older, less attractive, or less successful than they desire, and they will become involved with someone who is divorced, currently married, or alcoholic rather than continue waiting for someone more suitable. People also frequently remain in relationships which are unsatisfactory or destructive rather than face loneliness anew, and they are often unwilling to leave a relationship until they have developed a new relationship with someone else. When relationships break up, loneliness frequently pushes both parties back together.

Various other factors are related to feelings of loneliness. For example, people often feel a need to get together with someone they receive positive reactions from when they have an experience which is significant to them.

The loneliest I ever felt was when I was in the hospital having an operation and my boyfriend and my family couldn't be there to comfort me at night. [#404]

> I think one of the things that shakes me up most is when I get stood up on a date. It makes me feel quite undesirable, and I don't want to believe it's happened. Afterwards I feel a really strong need to talk to a good friend about the hurt I feel. #405

> I have a good friend and whenever anything traumatic happens the two of us get together to drink, be consoled, and talk about incidents from our childhood. We've done this when we've broken up with girlfriends. Recently we got together after his brother was in a serious car accident. #406

In recognition of this need, friends and relatives often take the initiative and show signs of support and caring when a person has a bad experience, such as a death in the family or a serious illness.

Another factor which is related to loneliness is increasing age. As people become older they tend to lose many of their relationships. Their children move out of the house and to other locales, and their mates, closest friends, and relatives die. At the same time, retirement and physical infirmities, such as arthritis and poor hearing, curtail their participation in activities which would take their minds off loneliness and enable them to meet others. As a result many older people experience a great deal of loneliness.

> My grandfather lives by himself. He feels very lonely and sad since the death of a close friend a year ago. They had been friends since childhood. He often suffers from severe depression and loneliness during winter. In winter he can't shovel snow and use his car. His spirits lift in summer, when he can get outside and garden and use his car to visit others. #407

> I always looked forward to the day when my children would be grown and out on their own. Harry and I were going to travel, relax, and just enjoy each other's company. But my Harry died only one year after our youngest got married. We never got to do all the things we'd planned. Now, I'm just lonely. Most of my children have families of their own, so I don't get to see very much of them. Actually I volunteer to baby-sit with my grandchildren just so I don't have to be alone. #408

Coping with loneliness

People are frequently able to forget about being lonely while they are active. Working, cleaning house, looking at television, eating, reading, pursuing a hobby, and watching other people all help in this regard. Doing things with other people can also help take one's mind off one's desire for a close relationship. People also frequently turn on the radio or television while they are doing other things, and this can substitute for having other people present. In addition, people develop their own individual tactics for dealing with loneliness.

> When I feel lonely I try not to think about it, or else I go to bed and sleep. #409

> My grandmother is much more lonely since she moved from her home into a nursing facility. She sits and stares out of the window for hours. She is more sensitive now and cries easily and often. When she feels lonely or that she's going to cry, she sings or recites lengthy poetry she learned as a child in school. #410

Another way in which people cope with loneliness is through trying to talk to others about what they are feeling.

> When I feel lonely, I can't hide it. It has too large an effect on me. I find it helps me to talk to someone, but I don't like involving them in things they might not want to be in. But if they offer, I'll talk to them. It helps me get over it. #411

> With the statement, "If you need anything else, dear, just call," my parents drove off and left me to begin my freshman year at university. I was all alone with a hundred and fifty strangers who all seemed to know each other. I had come to play basketball and my coach introduced me to several girls on the team who lived in my dorm. They were nice, but it wasn't home where I wanted to be. However, I did my best to get involved in all the orientation activities. While riding on the bus to the freshman barbecue I had a chance to talk to the other girls and was astonished to learn I wasn't the only one feeling homesick.
>   At the beginning of the semester girls in the dorm exchanged

many letters and phone calls with loved ones and friends at home. The daily mail played an important part in many girls' lives. The first two months away from home were the hardest. The few girls who were from off the Island, like myself, found it particularly difficult. Most girls went home to various Island communities on the weekends and the dorms were almost vacant. Also many roomed with their best friend from high school and it was hard for newcomers to break into existing cliques. Males, on the other hand, did not show signs of homesickness. They projected an image of finally being free from their parents and in control of themselves. They did not go home as often as the girls on weekends, but they did seem to appreciate letters, phone calls, and the odd care package just as much. Many students attended the Thursday night pub at the student center. With the help of good company and entertainment many forgot their woes. Others, however, found the alcohol encouraged them to reveal their inner feelings.

Most members of the girls' basketball team were from off the Island and they found the adjustment very hard. Homesickness is a mild description of what they felt. But with a busy schedule of practicing seven days a week, no one ever had a free weekend or much spare time. By the end of the season the girls all knew each other's problems and were always there for moral support. By the second semester most freshmen had made friends and were well established in dorm life. There was still the occasional person who showed signs of not fitting in. Usually they were spotted and helped by the resident assistant on their floor and sometimes professional counseling was recommended. It wasn't easy, but I managed to survive my first year in the dorm. With help from new and old friends, I got through.

My next two years went well and all too fast. Because of the enormous amount of homesickness I experienced my first year, I was extremely sympathetic toward others in the same boat. My fourth year I decided I would become a resident assistant and help freshmen with problems like homesickness. The first piece of advice I would give anyone feeling homesick is get involved. The busier you are, the less time you have to daydream and feel lonely. Homesickness is the worst feeling in the world. The quicker it is dealt with, the better off you are. Because of my great yearning for home, I could have easily quit anytime during my first semester. However, today I'm in my final year and very glad I stayed. Now when I'm home, I feel homesick for the Island. #412

Choosing to be alone

Despite the need that people experience to be with those they receive positive reactions from, there are times when many people desire to be alone. They may seek privacy in order to concentrate on their work, think through a problem, deal with their hurt, or engage in behavior which could be criticized or ridiculed.

> If I'm in the right frame of mind, I can be alone for days and be perfectly happy. #413

> I'd go crazy if I had somebody by my side every minute of the day. Being alone, even for a little while, gives me time to clear my head, sort out my problems, and just sit down and have a good cry. #414

> When I get upset, I need to go for a long, quiet walk by myself. #415

> When I'm alone, I don't have to worry about what I look like, or that I might say something wrong to someone. #416

Often when people are in relationships and receiving positive reactions, loneliness disappears, and they feel free to pursue other interests by themselves.

> When there's no one around to distract me, I work a lot better. At such times I can put in long hours working by myself. But I can only do this when I've got a good relationship going and don't feel lonely. Otherwise, I'd be hanging around other people and getting very little work done. #417

Loneliness and unacceptable behavior

When people can not get positive reactions in order to satisfy loneliness, they sometimes engage in unacceptable behavior. Unacceptable behavior does succeed in getting the attention of others and reactions from them. Both positive reactions and negative reactions provide attention and reaction. A negative reaction may be a poor substitute for a positive reaction, but when one is lonely, a negative reaction is sometimes better than nothing at all because one is not being ignored.

Pleasure

When people receive positive reactions they experience pleasant feelings. They feel happy and pleased, which frequently produce a glow, or feeling of warmth. Positive reactions are an important source of pleasure for people. People frequently seek out others who give them positive reactions, spend time with them, and obtain as many positive reactions as they can.

> Friends help make happiness in your life. They make you feel good. You spend time with them and enjoy yourself. That's why the more friends you have, the happier you are. My friends always help me forget my problems. They can talk about anything, it's just fine with me. #418

> When my wife gives me a hug, I feel very happy. #419

> When Kent and I are at a party or entertaining, we glance across the room at each other several times during the evening. Kent will wink at me and blow me a kiss. It gives me a nice, warm feeling. I usually mouth back, "I love you," and he mouths, "Me, too," in reply. I always smile for some time afterwards because I feel like we're young again and dating or honeymooning. It's a wonderful feeling, especially when many of our friends have unhappy marriages, because you know your marriage is secure. #420

When one receives positive reactions one feels good about oneself, and that one is a significant, meaningful, and worthwhile person. One also feels appreciated and quite often liked or loved. The positive reactions provide actual evidence that other people think well of a person, and that the person matters to them. They act to validate the person's sense of worth. Pleasure also enables people to provide others with positive reactions. When a person shows signs of experiencing pleasure, such as by smiling, he provides the person he is looking at with a positive reaction.

An important point is that the feelings of pleasure which one experiences from positive reactions are temporary in duration. They quickly disappear. Then in order to experience the same feelings again, one has to seek and get additional positive reactions. Because the feelings are so pleasant, people want to experience them again and again and are willing to go to considerable effort to do so. People are drawn to those who have previously given them positive reactions and caused them to experience pleasure, and often seek to continue associating with them.

> I've been taking business courses from a correspondence school. The thing I like about this school is that they don't just send you a printed mark at the end of your course. Instead, they write comments on your assignments, such as "Keep up the good work" and "You've done a fine job." #421

> I saw an actor do an outstanding performance and told him so afterwards. Ever since then he's been unusually friendly, and every time he sees me he comes over to talk. I think he's hoping I'll praise him again. #422

An individual who provides another with positive reactions, provides him with pleasure. People value those who provide them with their positive reactions and pleasure, and frequently want to do things to give them pleasure in return. People think if they give these individuals positive reactions and other resources, the individuals will continue giving them pleasure. People learn that the more positive reactions and other resources they give a person, the more positive reactions and pleasure they receive in return. In contrast, if people fail to give these individuals positive reactions and other resources, they risk losing their sources of pleasure. Normally people feel like conserving time and energy, and do not feel like exerting themselves to give an individual positive reactions, but do so anyway because the individual is an important source of their pleasure. In a sense, a relationship is an arrangement where both parties are willing to expend the energy to give the other person pleasure in order to continue receiving pleasure from the other person.

Pleasure from positive reactions can be understood in terms of tension and release, and this is outlined in Model 2. In regard to tension and release, one normally wants a specific type of positive reaction from a specific person or type of person, and approaches that person to obtain it. Therefore, one has a particular model in mind that one wants to satisfy. This model produces tension. One's model is not consistent with reality because one is not receiving what one wants (Situation 1). If one receives the type of positive reaction one wants from the person one wants it from, then reality changes to be consistent with one's model, one's tension is released, and one experiences pleasure. The release of tension is experienced as pleasure (Situation 2). When one receives a positive reaction from a person that one does not want it from, no tension is released and one does not experience pleasure (Situation 3). Also, if one receives a positive reaction from a person one usually wants it from, but this occurs at a time when one is busy doing something else, then the positive reaction does not release tension and produce pleasure. Because one is doing something else, one has a different model in mind that one is trying to fulfill, which the positive reaction can not satisfy. As a result this positive reaction can even be a nuisance because it interferes with what one is doing (Situation 4). Also, if one wants a particular type of positive reaction from a particular person and receives a different type of positive reaction from that person, then one is often disappointed because one is unable to execute the model one had in mind. Because the other person does not provide the type of positive reaction one wants, reality remains inconsistent with one's model, one is unable to release one's tension, and one does not feel pleasure. For example, if person A wants to talk about her problems at work, and person B does not want to listen, but wants to be affectionate instead, then person A remains unsatisfied (Situation 5). The reason that the pleasure from positive reactions is temporary and quickly disappears is that when one successfully executes a model, one's tension is released and pleasure is produced. Afterwards no tension remains to be released, and therefore no means remain for obtaining pleasure. One has to decide to try to execute a new model, before one can have fresh tension to release.

When people do not get the positive reactions they want, they experience negative feelings. They feel disappointed and unhappy. When they are neglected or ignored they feel forgotten, worthless, lonely, and depressed. (See also the preceding section on Loneliness in this chapter and the chapter on Avoiding Those Who Reject You in this volume.)

Love

The individuals that people have relationships with are quite meaningful to them. Because these individuals provide most of a person's positive

Model 2: Pleasure from positive reactions

The relationship between reality, model, tension, and pleasure

Symbols:

=	is equivalent to	↑	an increase in
≠	is not equivalent to	↓	a decrease in
→	produces	Δ	a change in

A. When reality is inconsistent with one's model, one experiences tension.

Reality ≠ Model → ↑ Tension

When reality is not equivalent to one's model, tension is produced, or increased.

B. When one changes reality to be consistent with one's model, one releases tension.

Δ Reality = Model → ↓ Tension

When reality is changed to be equivalent to one's model, tension is reduced, or released.

C. The release of tension is experienced as pleasure.

↓ Tension → Pleasure

A decrease in tension produces pleasure.

Positive reactions, tension, and pleasure

Situation 1:

Model:	I want Positive Reaction (type 1) from Person A.
Reality:	I am not receiving Positive Reaction (type 1) from Person A.
Result:	I experience tension.

Situation 2:

Model:	I want Positive Reaction (type 1) from Person A.
Reality:	I receive Positive Reaction (type 1) from Person A.
Result:	I release tension.
Result:	Therefore I experience pleasure.

Situation 3:

Model:	I want Positive Reaction (type 1) from Person A.
Reality:	I receive a Positive Reaction (any type) from Person B.
Result:	I do not release tension.
Result:	Therefore I do not experience pleasure.

Situation 4:

Model:	I am busy trying to execute a model which does not involve seeking a positive reaction.
Reality:	I receive a Positive Reaction (any type) from Person A (whom I normally want positive reactions from).
Result:	I do not release tension.
Result:	Therefore I do not experience pleasure.

Situation 5:

Model:	I want Positive Reaction (type 1) from Person A.
Reality:	I receive Positive Reaction (type 2) from Person A.
Result:	I do not release tension.
Result:	Therefore I do not experience pleasure.

reactions, they eradicate most of the person's feelings of loneliness, and they are a major source of the person's pleasure. People associate the feelings of pleasure they receive from positive reactions with those who provide the positive reactions. Therefore, people tend to have pleasurable, or warm, feelings when they think of those they have relationships with. They speak of liking, loving, caring about, and needing them. People use endearments, such as dear, sweetheart, honey, baby, love, and darling, to remind their mates and children that they are meaningful to them.

Love can be defined as associating the pleasure one feels from positive reactions with the individual who provides the positive reactions. The amount of love people feel for another person is based on the kinds and amounts of positive reactions they receive from that person. Thus people feel more love for the relative or friend who provides them with a greater number of positive reactions, than they do for the relative or friend who provides them with fewer positive reactions.

> When our son left home for university, I didn't miss him. In fact, our home life became much more peaceful. My son is always moody and unfriendly and often won't speak or respond to the rest of us. He constantly argues with his mother and yells at her. He spends most of his time with his friends. My daughter is a different case altogether. She doesn't spend much time with her friends, but devotes her time to her homework and various activities. She is pleasant and talks to us and seeks our advice, and we often do things together. I know her mother and I will miss her a great deal when she leaves for university in a couple of years. #423

People are quite interested in maintaining their regular sources of positive reactions. They may establish good supplies of positive reactions from relatives, adopted family members, mates, friends, neighbors, colleagues, supervisors, employees, customers, acquaintances, and pets. People have considerable vested interest in protecting their sources of positive reactions from harm. It is expensive to identify, establish, and maintain good sources of positive reactions. When these are lost a person must invest considerable effort in establishing new sources, while being punished by the feeling of loneliness. People express considerable distress when individuals who provide them with positive reactions leave them, or are lost or destroyed. They experience grief because they have lost an important resource. People rarely experience grief when those who do not provide them with positive reactions leave or die. The loss of a source who presently provides positive reactions is usually more upsetting than the loss of a source who previously provided positive reactions.

> When my favorite cat was killed by a car, I was more upset than when my parents died. I think it was because I saw my cat every day, and she would climb on my knees and hold on and purr while I rubbed her. She was full of mischief and always entertaining. In contrast, I only talked to my parents on the phone a couple of times a year. They lived on the other side of the country and I rarely visited them. [#424]

Functions of seeking and providing positive reactions

Positive reactions come from people, and are obtained through contact with them. The two feelings, loneliness and pleasure, encourage individuals to associate with other people in order to get positive reactions. As a result, humans are not solitary beings, and actively seek the company of others. Loneliness reoccurs when people are separated from those they regularly receive positive reactions from. In addition, the pleasure from receiving positive reactions is very short-lived. Therefore individuals are forced to continue to associate with others to avoid loneliness and to get a regular supply of pleasure. People spend time with others; converse with them; develop relationships, or exchanges of positive reactions, with them; remain with those they have relationships with; return to them as soon as possible when separated; and when they encounter difficulties remaining together, seek out and form new relationships.

> I listened to a religious sermon on the radio which dealt with loneliness. It stated that nothing is more devastating. Loneliness paralyzes us, and is the ultimate pain, even worse than physical pain. According to the sermon, there are two types of loneliness. One is the loneliness of those who live solitary lives without meaningful relationships with others. They may keep loneliness at bay through working hard,

partying, and acquiring possessions. But sooner or later they have to face their emptiness, because God created us to be social beings. The other type of loneliness occurs when you lose someone, for example through divorce or death, or something like a very satisfying job. When this happens, time can be so heavy that one starts drinking. The theme of the broadcast was that God gives us families to spare us from the curse of loneliness. Moreover, it is the standard family model and proper family relationships which best protect us, and if we tamper with these we are just inviting the bitterness of loneliness into our lives. Millions of people are lonely today because they did not take these relationships seriously enough. They have disregarded the way God has designed human nature. The broadcast stated that Psalm 68:6 tells us, "God sets the lonely in families." #425

There are a number of reasons why it is advantageous for people to be together with others. People are potential resource centers for each other. When people are with other people they are more likely to be exposed to their knowledge and to acquire it themselves. By watching others and listening to them, people learn to identify additional resources and how to obtain them. They also learn to recognize sources of danger and how to avoid them. However, when one is only in contact with others one gets a very limited amount of positive reactions. In order to get more positive reactions, there are several things one can do. One can provide others with positive reactions, one can identify the activities that others consider meaningful and participate in them, one can act in ways which favorably impress others, and one can do things for others that they want done. If one does not do such things, one gets few positive reactions from others. Therefore, in order to obtain a sufficient quantity of positive reactions, one has to coordinate one's activities with the needs, desires, interests, endeavors, and expectations of other individuals. The better one does so, the more positive reactions one receives. The more positive reactions one receives, the more likely one is to receive shares of the resources others obtain. Many of these resources would be difficult to obtain on one's own. In addition, when people are with other people they are able to form cooperative ventures. Dealing with the same individuals on a continuous basis is much more efficient than dealing with strangers. People know what they can expect from the individuals they are familiar with, but not from those they are unfamiliar with. Ongoing experience with the same individuals allows people to predict the nature and degree of their cooperation, and to plan and act accordingly. When individual humans cooperate and share with each other, they obtain a greater quantity and variety of resources than they could get on their own. Furthermore, as a group changes its focus in order to obtain new resources, the individual has to change with the group in order to continue receiving positive reactions. The more successful the individual members are in coordinating their behavior with the behavior of the other members of the group, the more successful the group is likely to be, and the more resources the group and its individual members are likely to obtain.

> Guys who play on the successful sports teams in university report they get all kinds of advantages. These include discounts on equipment in sporting-goods stores, entrance into lounges when they are underage, the nicest-looking tail on campus, and good summer jobs. [#426]

The quest for positive reactions from others is synonymous with a quest for resources from others. People can detect positive reactions from others well before it is clear what others are willing to do for them. People get immediate rewards in the form of pleasure from positive reactions. Indications that one will receive rewards of other resources are less obvious and usually follow later. Those who are willing to give a person positive reactions are frequently willing to give the person additional resources. Therefore receiving positive reactions from a person is an early indication that one is likely to obtain resources from that person.

> One of my elderly customers was friendly with me when he came to my store. He asked me about myself and we talked. As time went on he and his wife would drop by to talk and bring small gifts, such as flowers from their garden or a cake. During the summer they invited me and my children to their house in the country for meals. When he and his wife spent the winter in town, I invited them to dinner. Then his wife had to go to the hospital, and I had the man over for meals several times a week. When I was remarried he acted as a witness in the civil ceremony. I was out of town one week, and they invited my daughter to visit them. Last winter when they moved to town, they had a problem finding a home for their pets, and I kept their cat at my place. I'll probably keep the cat every winter from now on. In

the summertime we still go to their house in the country for lunch, and they drop by with flowers when they are in town. [#427]

When people alter their behavior in order to get a larger number of positive reactions, they effectively alter their behavior to get more resources. The resources they receive may be food and water, sex, or stimulation, or the means to obtain them, such as time, energy, materials, jobs, money, information, and relationships. When one works to obtain a greater quantity of positive reactions, one is working to obtain more resources. The amount of positive reactions one receives from a person indicates the extent to which the person is likely to provide additional resources. Those who provide individuals with a greater amount of positive reactions are likely to provide them with a greater amount of resources, and those who provide individuals with fewer positive reactions are likely to provide them with fewer resources. When the programmed feelings of loneliness and pleasure encourage people to seek positive reactions from others, these programmed feelings are in effect directing people to go where they have a greater chance of receiving resources. The programmed feelings are keyed to an early indication of resources, i.e., receiving positive reactions, rather than to the later uncertain outcome of whether or not one is actually given resources. Therefore, the programmed feelings enable one to act faster and receive the resources sooner, and increase the chance that one will receive the resources oneself rather than see them go to someone else. The better a person is at detecting and getting positive reactions, the more resources he is likely to obtain.

A similar situation occurs with the person who provides positive reactions. People provide others with positive reactions in order to be able to get positive reactions for themselves. When a person does not provide positive reactions, fewer people approach him and remain in his presence who want positive reactions for themselves. When a person does provide positive reactions, more people approach him and remain in his presence who want positive reactions. Therefore, the better a person is at providing positive reactions, the larger the number of people who will approach him and remain in his presence to get positive reactions. The more voice inflection, positive facial expressions, smiles, warmth, laughter, enthusiasm, and animation that a person provides, the more successful his positive reactions are, and the more attractive he is to those seeking positive reactions. Also, the more appropriate his responses are and the more interest he shows in the other person, the more successful his positive reactions. Activators such as smiling and humor also encourage a person to provide others with positive reactions. People who come to a person for positive reactions often give him a share of their resources, and they often use additional resources to get additional positive reactions from him. Therefore providing others with positive reactions in order to get positive reactions for oneself, leads to getting more resources for oneself. The better a person is at providing positive reactions, the more resources he is likely to receive.

It is significant how quickly one experiences the feelings of pleasure and loneliness. Feelings of pleasure occur immediately after receiving positive reactions. Similarly, one feels lonely as soon as a relationship ends, or as soon as one receives indications that a relationship may end.

> I was talking to my girlfriend on the phone and she mentioned she was thinking about going to a graduate school on the West Coast. The moment she mentioned this I started feeling very lonely. [#428]

When one is separated from the individuals who provide one's positive reactions, one is separated from the individuals who provide much of one's resources. The speed at which the feelings of loneliness and pleasure occur, provides one with a maximum amount of time in which to establish new sources of positive reactions and new relationships. The faster one can respond to new sources of positive reactions and establish new relationships, the faster one regains access to resources. The two feelings, loneliness and pleasure, are tied to the availability of resources. Loneliness serves as an indicator that one needs to gain access to resources, and pleasure serves as an indicator that resources are probably available.

At the same time, the pursuit of positive reactions is an expensive process. People expend considerable amounts of time, energy, and other resources seeking positive reactions. Often they have to provide others with positive reactions in order to get positive reactions and additional resources for themselves. They frequently fail to get the positive reactions they want or to get these positive reactions from the people they want them from.

I put a great many years into my marriage, and worked very hard helping my husband with his business. Then I found out he'd been having an affair for years with a younger woman. He decided to move in with her, and I was left with nothing. [#429]

I do everything I can for my son, but you wouldn't believe how rude he is. When I want him to help around the house, he yells and swears at me. When he's watching TV and I want to watch too, he tells me to go away. The other day I started to tease him and he told me, "Shut up!" [#430]

I believed my research was quite original and solved an important problem. When it was published, I sent reprints to others working in the area. But the research was ignored and never cited. [#431]

There's the loveliest woman who goes to the same bar I do after work every Friday. I've gone over and talked to her a couple of times, but she isn't responsive. It's clear the interest isn't mutual. My loss. [#432]

On the other hand, when people succeed in getting positive reactions, they may gain access to a source of additional resources which lasts for the remainder of their lives. We should not forget that the pursuit of resources other than positive reactions also involves considerable wasted effort and numerous failures.

Excess behavior

Excess behavior is behavior in response to feelings which results in one acting contrary to the purposes the feelings are designed for. As a result, one loses resources rather than gains or protects them. For example, the feelings of loneliness and pleasure encourage people to seek positive reactions, and when people obtain positive reactions they normally gain other resources. However, there are situations in which people expend time and energy seeking and obtaining positive reactions when there is little chance of their gaining other resources.

People spend an enormous amount of time and energy obtaining and providing positive reactions. A high percentage of talk is dedicated to this purpose. A great deal of this effort fails to obtain additional resources. People spend time every day getting positive reactions from and giving positive reactions to people they are unlikely and unable to get other resources from.

> On my way back from lunch today, a woman I know stopped me to tell me about her experience in law school. She spent half an hour telling me about the problems she encountered, while I tried to explain why I think they occurred. I run into her about once a year. [#433]

> I have a friend I enjoy being with, but she can never pay her own way. So when I want to get together for a coffee or dinner, I always have to pick up the tab. [#434]

Frequently people seek positive reactions to such an extent that they are prevented from obtaining resources.

> When I'm not in a relationship, I don't get any work done. I spend all my time out looking for someone I want to get involved with. [#435]

> This is my son's last year in high school, and suddenly he's discovered girls. He was never religious before, but he's joined a youth group at a church, because "That's where the girls are." He spends so much time going to church activities and talking to girls on the phone, he has little time left for studies. I don't look forward to seeing his grades. I think his chances of getting in a good university are just about zip. [#436]

> My daughter was the top student in her graduating class. I'm sure she'd have no trouble working into a high-paying career. But she's happiest when she's performing on stage. She just loves the attention, and wants to be an actress. It's such a hand-to-mouth existence, she'll probably have to get part-time jobs on the side to survive. [#437]

> If you spend years trying to write a great novel, you won't produce the quantity of work which helps you pay the bills. [#438]

Also, once people establish ongoing exchanges of resources in relationships, additional efforts to obtain and provide positive reactions within those relationships serve no purpose. However, people expend huge amounts of time and energy in their relationships continuing to obtain and provide positive reactions.

One also wastes energy when one smiles and laughs in situations where one is unable to provide others with positive reactions. This is the case when one reacts with pleasure to something one reads, sees on television, or remembers.

A total loss of resources occurs when a person commits suicide in response to loneliness or the loss of a relationship.

Society and positive reactions

A number of practices are established in society to help individuals receive positive reactions. These include identification systems for individuals; norms of giving positive reactions during interaction with others; recognition of large segments of the population on specific days each year; and recognition of certain changes in an individual's age, family, religion, and job. Society also provides numerous opportunities for individuals and groups to work for and receive positive reactions. In addition, activators are used in various ways to get people to respond favorably to people, products, and services.

Individuals are identified as such and this makes it easier for them to receive positive reactions. Individuals are assigned names which help people distinguish them from others. Individuals use their names when meeting other people, filling out forms, and gaining recognition for the work they produce. Names allow other people to talk and write about specific individuals. Individuals identify with their names and correct those who mispronounce or misspell them.

There are norms of behavior during interaction which promote both giving positive reactions to others and acknowledging positive reactions from them. Good manners include recognizing the presence of people, greeting them, introducing people to each other, using names and titles, thanking people for their efforts on one's behalf, listening to people, using compliments, recognizing the achievements of others, including people in activities, avoiding topics which would make others uncomfortable, and apologizing for one's failures to do the preceding.

Large segments of the population are honored on specific days each year. This is the case with family members at Christmas, mothers on Mother's Day, fathers on Father's Day, soldiers on Memorial Day, children on Easter, and sweethearts on Valentine's Day. Presents, flowers, feasts, parades, and ceremonies are used to provide positive reactions.

In addition, certain changes are recognized in an individual's age, family, religion, and job. Individuals receive positive reactions when they have a birthday each year, attain adulthood at eighteen years, and reach their one-hundredth birthday. Each individual also receives special recognition when he or she is baptized, confirmed, graduated, promoted, retired, married, and married for a specific number of years; and also when he or she produces children or dies. Applause, presents, parties, and ceremonies are often used to provide positive reactions.

Society also provides numerous opportunities for individuals to work for positive reactions. Not only is participation in organizations and activities encouraged, but instruction is often provided in how to become a more successful participant and win positive reactions. An enormous variety of specialized organizations and activities are provided within which individuals can obtain positive reactions. These involve sports, exercise, hobbies, community service, education, work, investments, entertainment, the arts, religion, politics, nature, sex, pets, and many other subjects. Individuals are also recognized for service to the society. Displays and competitions are regularly organized for individuals to show their expertise and receive recognition. Individuals are awarded differing amounts of recognition based on their ability to outperform others.

Society also provides the means for giving positive reactions to individuals. Newspapers, newsletters, the radio, and TV are all used for this purpose. In addition there are performances, talks, competitions, graduations, and award presentations. At such gatherings individuals display their abilities and/or have their achievements acknowledged. The audience is expected to pay attention and applaud. Afterwards, people frequently remark on the number and status of those who attended, i.e., the quantity and quality of the positive reactions received.

I have two young nephews who play hockey, and at the end of the hockey season our family attended an awards night. They gave every boy who played on the team one kind of award or another. #439

I went to hear a colleague give a talk about his research in South America. My attendance was expected as head of his department; otherwise, I wouldn't have bothered. At the end of his talk another colleague and I asked questions to indicate our interest. I wanted to show him that what matters to him, which is his research, matters to me too. Then the other colleague and I left before the end of the question period. I felt somewhat guilty about leaving early, but I rationalized that attending his talk and complimenting him later would make up for this. #440

Last week I went to my daughter's high school to meet her teachers. They gathered all the parents together in the gymnasium and the principal introduced the president of the student council, who introduced the council's vice president, treasurer, and secretary. As each was introduced, we all applauded. The student council president asked parents to volunteer to chaperone dances. Then the principal introduced each teacher, made a few comments about each one, and asked the teacher to walk up front so we could see what they looked like. He asked us to hold our applause until the end. When he was finished he proclaimed, "Ladies and gentlemen, our teaching staff," and we all applauded. Then the parents went to talk to the appropriate teachers about their own child. #441

Positive reactions which are given to individuals are often accompanied by additional resources. Such resources include jobs, higher salaries, advertising roles, roles in movies, invitations to private and public events, and subsequent interest by the public.

At the same time there are organized limits on the amount of positive reactions a person receives. For example, time and space limitations are frequently placed on political speeches, coverage in the mass media, and presentations of papers at scientific conferences. In addition, the threat of losing one's sources of positive reactions is a common form of social control. A person who acts in an unacceptable manner may be expelled from social organizations, lose jobs and relationships, and be prevented from seeing family and friends.

Positive reactions are also accorded to organizations and institutions within society. Organizations, institutions, and even societies compete with each other for recognition. Businesses, universities, communities, government agencies, and nonprofit organizations all receive recognition based on their success in their various areas of expertise. They also compete for positive reactions through advertisements, displays, presentations at conferences, charitable contributions, support for educational and environmental causes, meals, parties, the appearance of their facilities, participation in parades, and fireworks displays. Often they are ranked relative to similar organizations, and the population is informed of the ranking. Such recognition is often followed by additional resources, ranging from new investors in a company's stock to additional funds for university research.

Individuals, groups, and organizations use activators to get others to respond the way they want. Smiles, humor, and laughter are used in personal contacts and the mass media to attract an audience and promote people, products, and services.

Society also uses positive reactions to protect itself and pursue its military aims. Members of a military unit train together and are frequently isolated from civilians. Therefore, they depend on each other for their positive reactions. Members of a unit are placed into a combat situation together, and fight the enemy to protect themselves and their sources of positive reactions, i.e., the other members of their unit.

Environmental impact

Often people are not content with making do with what they have, because what they have fails to generate sufficient positive reactions from other people. Other people pay attention to things that they wish they had too and to things they have not seen before. When one has things that others already have or that others have already seen, then other people pay little attention to them. Therefore in order to obtain the attention of others one has to obtain a) things that others don't have and wish they did, and b) things that others have not seen before. Because people need positive reactions several times a day, they must constantly

try to find ways to obtain them. A major difficulty in obtaining positive reactions is that most people are so involved trying to get positive
reactions for themselves that they have little time and energy left over
to provide others with positive reactions. As a result positive reactions
are a limited resource, and people must compete with each other to
obtain them.

People obtain various items in order to attract attention, win praise,
and/or produce envious comments. They acquire new clothes, houses,
furnishings, cars and other vehicles, electronic equipment, boats, cot-
tages, jewelry, antiques, music, and art. Often they already own something comparable. Thus they may replace a car or set of living room
furniture with a new car or set of furniture. At the same time a major
source of a person's positive reactions is the person himself. People
frequently praise and congratulate themselves. In order to feel good
about themselves, individuals seek evidence that they are doing as
well as or better than other people. One way they try to do this is by
acquiring items which are as good as or better than other people are
getting. Because others are constantly adding to their material goods,
people must do the same just to stay even. If people fall behind, they
will receive fewer positive reactions from others and from themselves.
The more items they acquire and replace, the more impact they have on
the environment.

Theoretically, one could try to obtain positive reactions by con-
suming less resources and obtaining fewer material goods than others.
However, this is not a popular strategy, perhaps because it does not
work. If you see a person walking down the street and a person driving
an expensive sports car, other things being equal, which one are you
going to pay more attention to?

AVOIDING EMBARRASSMENT

Brief contents

Detailed contents

Detailed contents

continued on next page

Introduction

People do not want others to view them in a negative way, or to react negatively to them. People are supersensitive to negative reactions and the possibility of receiving them. A person feels embarrassed when others are likely to react negatively to him. He may do something unintentionally, he may do something intentionally and others may find out, or others may do something to him. The common factor is that regardless of how it happens, the person finds himself in a situation that can cause others to react negatively to him. As a result, he feels embarrassed. Embarrassment is an early warning system. It notifies a person that he is in a position in which he may receive negative reactions from others. When a person does something embarrassing, other people respond by staring, laughing, teasing, and by gossiping about him. An important factor in embarrassment is that others witness what the person does. A person rarely feels embarrassed when he does the same thing in private that embarrasses him in public.

Embarrassment is a very punishing experience, and a person tries his best to avoid doing things which could cause him to feel embarrassed. The great discomfort that a person feels when embarrassed helps the person protect his resources. People are likely to react negatively if a person does anything that they feel negatively about. When people have negative feelings about a person, they are less likely to provide that person with resources, or to value that person's resources highly enough to be willing to trade their own resources for them. Other people provide a person with most of his resources. Therefore it is in each person's interest to learn what others feel negatively about and to carefully avoid doing these things. One way a person learns this is through being embarrassed and by watching others be embarrassed. Embarrassment is a sensitive detector of the possibility of getting negative reactions from others, and the memory of embarrassment is a strong, painful reminder of a) the fact one does not want to be embarrassed again, and b) precisely what one should not do again. When a person avoids embarrassment, he protects his resources.

A person feels embarrassed as soon as he realizes others know he has done something that they disapprove of. This provides the person with a maximum amount of time in which to change his behavior, stop doing what others disapprove of, and protect his resources. This also allows a person to make an immediate association between the punishing feelings of embarrassment and the specific behavior which was responsible.

The nature of embarrassment

A person wants to receive positive reactions, not negative reactions. Therefore a person wants to present his best side to others. A person does not want others to view him or react to him in a negative way. People do not want to give others any grounds on which to view them negatively. They do not want to do anything which will reflect badly on themselves and cause others to think poorly of them. People do not want to differ from others in any negative way. They do not want to give any indications that they are absurd, careless, clumsy, dishonest, a failure, fallible, foolish, forgetful, "a fuck up," ignorant, ill-mannered, ill-prepared, immoral, imperfect, improper, inadequate, inappropriate, incapable, incompetent, inconsistent, incorrect, inept, inferior, irresponsible, "a joke," lacking in common sense, lazy, ludicrous, mistaken, negligent, ridiculous, silly, sloppy, stupid, uncoordinated, uncouth, unreliable, unsound, unsuccessful, worthless, wrong, less than ideal, not in charge of themselves, or wanting in any other way. People dedicate an enormous amount of time and energy making sure that none of these labels can be applied to them. They expend a great deal of effort taking precautions and ensuring that their appearance, actions, and what they say can not be ridiculed and criticized by others.

> I can't wear my hair like that, because I would look stupid and feel embarrassed. [#442]

> I don't mind wearing a dirty sweatshirt, no makeup, and not fixing my hair when I'm around the house. But I'd be embarrassed if someone outside the family saw me this way. When someone comes over, I put on something clean, apply some makeup, and fix my hair. [#443]

> I'm very embarrassed when someone visits and the house is messy. If I know they're coming, I'll straighten up beforehand, even if I have to leave work early to do so. [#444]

When I use a toilet in someone else's house, I always make sure the door is locked or latched so no one can walk in and see me. In many homes the bathroom door doesn't lock properly and anyone can push it open, so I hurry as fast as I can. If the door is close to the toilet, I sometimes brace my foot against it. #445

Many people who eat steak in a restaurant would like to pick up their bone and chew on it to get those last bits of meat. But they'd be too embarrassed to do so, because other people would stare and think they were eating like an animal. #446

When I got in the taxi I told the driver I wanted to go to the convenience store in the Brighton neighborhood of Charlottetown. Everyone in town knows where this store is, and it's the only store in that residential neighborhood. But the driver couldn't remember the name of the street the store is on. He told me, "I'd better find out the name of the street before I tell the dispatcher where I'm going. I don't want to look stupid." Then he got out his map and studied it for the next two blocks as we drove through some of the heaviest traffic in town. "It's on Park Terrace," he finally announced. We could easily have had an accident, because cars around us were changing lanes and entering the street from shopping malls as he searched for the name. But it was more important to the driver to make sure he didn't embarrass himself and look stupid. #447

People give meticulous attention to washing; shaving; cleaning clothes; being neatly dressed; wearing the right clothes; fixing their hair and applying their makeup in an acceptable way; saying the right things; sitting, standing, and walking properly; greeting others; acting properly in public; selecting the right possessions; and keeping their possessions neat and clean. People also undergo many discomforts in order to avoid negative reactions and embarrassment. They frequently wear uncomfortable clothes, do not scratch themselves in certain places when they itch, go without food when they are hungry, force themselves to stay awake, undergo increasing discomfort until they can get to an acceptable location to eliminate, stand in uncomfortable postures, and sit and kneel on uncomfortable surfaces rather than place their bodies in positions which are more comfortable. In addition, they try to ensure that those they associate with, such as their families and friends, do not do things which can be ridiculed and criticized either, because this would reflect badly on themselves.

A person is quite aware of how he appears to others. When he is in a position which could cause others to react negatively, he feels embarrassed. Embarrassment is based on the ability to anticipate negative reactions. It is a warning system which responds instantly, like a sensitive smoke detector, when one realizes that one qualifies for negative reactions. One feels embarrassed even before others respond to the situation, and even if there is no evidence of a negative reaction, such as staring and laughing, from others.

Anything which can cause a person to be viewed negatively by others is a possible source of embarrassment. It does not matter how the person got into that position, he still feels embarrassed. Therefore, it makes little difference whether the person put himself in this position, whether someone else put him in this position, or whether there are circumstances beyond his control that put him in this position. Regardless of how it happened, others have a reason to respond negatively to the person, and the person feels embarrassed. In addition, a person's actions may be entirely proper, but they may be misinterpreted by others and looked at in a negative way and the person can feel embarrassed. Even if a person is a victim of an accident or a practical joke, he may be presented in a negative light and feel embarrassed. If a bucket of water is spilled on a person, or someone hits him in the face with a lemon meringue pie, it is clear to onlookers that the person himself is not responsible for his improper appearance. Despite this, the person feels embarrassed. This is because, regardless of how it happened or who is responsible, the person knows he looks foolish to others when he is soaking wet or covered with meringue.

People avoid embarrassment by not doing the things that are ridiculed by others. People learn what these are as a result of being ridiculed for specific actions. When one recalls a situation in which one was embarrassed, one usually feels embarrassed anew. One often remembers embarrassing situations for long periods of time, and frequently for the remainder of one's life.

When my friend was sixteen, she went for her driving test. She passed with flying colors and spent the rest of the afternoon driving a friend around. About five o'clock she dropped off her friend and headed for home. On the way home she ran into another car. As ridiculous as it seems, the driver of the other car was the man who had given her the driving test. That was a few years ago, and when anyone mentions the accident, she still gets very upset. I don't blame her, because it makes you look pretty bad. #448

When I was in junior high, a friend and I dropped by our old elementary school to see our fifth-grade teacher. At we were leaving the school, my friend mentioned the teacher was amused that my fly was open. I was quite embarrassed. That was over forty years ago, and since that time I always check my fly when I leave my home or office. If I'm nervous about going somewhere or meeting someone, I check it several times. #449

Alice, a friend of mine, got together with a group of friends to celebrate a person's birthday at a local lounge. Alice is one of the quietest people you would ever meet at a lounge. While Alice was dancing, a girl she didn't recognize kept bumping into her. Alice considered the girl quite pushy, and assumed the girl had been smoking dope and was drinking to hide the smell. When Alice left the dance floor, the girl seemed to follow her. Alice was standing at the bar talking to her boyfriend when the girl came up to Alice and ripped Alice's shirt. Alice was terribly confused over what was happening and went to the washroom. The girl followed Alice into the washroom and Alice entered a booth and locked the door. The girl began kicking the door of the booth and screaming profanity at Alice. The girl was so upset she was crying, and claimed she was going to get Alice back for the time Alice made fun of her when they were six years old. This had happened almost twenty years before, and Alice couldn't even remember doing or saying anything to the girl. #450

People also learn what can produce embarrassment by seeing and hearing other people ridiculed for specific actions. Embarrassment is so punishing, people want to minimize the amount of embarrassment they go through. Therefore they are quite attentive to what could cause them to be embarrassed in the future. As a result, people closely monitor their appearance and behavior in order to remove potential sources of embarrassment.

There are different degrees of embarrassment, ranging from a slight twinge to devastation. A number of factors are related to how much embarrassment one feels. These include a) what one does, b) who witnesses it, c) how many witness it, d) how others react, and e) how long ago it happened. One is likely to feel more embarrassed when a) one does something major, b) one wants to make a good impression on those present, c) many people witness the incident, d) other people react strongly, they mention what happened, and they remember what happened, and e) the incident happened very recently. One is likely to feel less embarrassed when a) one does something minor, b) one does not care about the impression one makes on those present, c) few people witness the incident, d) other people do not react, they do not mention what happened, and they forget about what happened, and e) the incident happened a long time ago.

There's a woman I know named Sheri. Today when I passed her in the hall, I called her Shelly by mistake. I felt momentarily embarrassed, but that was all. [#451]

I feel really humiliated when others hear me fart, especially when I do it at my boyfriend's house. One time we were having dinner at his house, and I knew I had to fart and got up to leave. But as I walked away from the table, I farted. You want to see a person's face turn red. They all thought it was funny and laughed. But I just wanted to get out of there, and fast. [#452]

It's embarrassing when you carry food and drinks into the bleachers at a ballgame and slip and spill them on someone. It's even more embarrassing when the person you spill them on causes a big scene. [#453]

People often experience fear and anxiety when they are faced with a situation in which they might receive negative reactions. People hate negative reactions because they hurt so much, and are apprehensive when they might receive them. Therefore people try to avoid situations in which they might be embarrassed. Many people do not want to perform in public, such as give a speech, sing, or dance, for fear someone might react negatively.

When I read out loud to a group of people and make mistakes, I get embarrassed. I try to hide my embarrassment by making a joke and continuing to read. [#454]

Simply having others realize that one is anxious or embarrassed constitutes a negative reaction.

> I am very self-conscious when I'm in front of a crowd and everyone is watching me. I can feel my face getting red, and I say to myself, "Everyone knows you're embarrassed." This makes me twice as embarrassed and twice as red. [#455]

People worry about how they appear to others, and this often dominates their attention and interferes with their concentration on the task at hand. Because they have a single-focus mind, they can not focus on what to do, how they appear to others, and how others are reacting to them, all at the same time. As a result they are less likely to perform well. When their anxieties interfere with their concentration, they may stammer, stumble, or forget things, and their nervousness becomes apparent to others. Some people even shy away from attention from others for fear it may include negative reactions. Having others look at them or consider them, makes people anxious that there might be something about them that others will react negatively to.

What embarrasses people

When something happens which places a person in a negative light in front of others, the person feels embarrassed. The person may do something which makes him appear improper, or others may do something to the person which makes him appear improper. As a result, those who see the person have a reason to view the person negatively, and this is the one thing the person does not want. Even if others tease a person about something everyone knows did not happen or everyone knows the person did not do, the person still considers it a negative reaction and can feel embarrassed.

> One day my biology professor talked about sex-change operations. He mentioned how they are done and what they cost. He also told us that the first successful sex-change operation in the United States took place

in the 1950's and was done on a man named Richard. The operation was a success and Richard is now named Christine. Unfortunately, my name is Christine too. So half the class turned to look at me. Students gave me compliments, like "Oh, they did such a nice job on you Chris. You can't even tell." Well I dislike attention, especially from twenty or more students. I blushed and felt really uncomfortable even though I shouldn't have, and that really bugged me. Students continued to make comments about this all day to me. But by the time class was over, I was able to laugh about it. I think I was embarrassed more by all the attention than anything else. [#456]

An important feature of embarrassment is that a person is embarrassed when he thinks other people know what has happened. A person can do something privately and have no feelings of embarrassment, but do the same thing in a public setting and feel embarrassed. The person engages in the same behavior in both instances. The only difference is whether he thinks that others know about it or not. When a person does something embarrassing, the less attention he receives from others, the better. If he could escape the attention of others altogether, there would be no need to feel embarrassed.

When I slip and fall on ice, I'm more concerned about other people seeing me fall, than I am about whether I've injured myself. The more people who see me fall, the more embarrassed I am. Once a man came over and asked if I was all right. This is a sensible question, but I didn't think so at the time. When he offered me a hand to get up, all I wanted was for this angel of mercy to disappear from the face of the earth. [#457]

There are a great variety of ways in which people embarrass themselves or are subjected to embarrassment by others. These include the following:

1. Being the subject of unwanted attention
2. Having a different appearance or behavior
3. Appearing improperly oriented
4. Having less than others
5. Making mistakes
6. Revealing one's ignorance
7. Forgetting

8. Neglecting to do something
9. Acting clumsy
10. Doing something inappropriate for one's age
11. Discovering one is in a different situation than one thought
12. Having one's private life exposed
13. Revealing one's emotions
14. Failing
15. Doing something bad
16. Lying
17. Revealing one's biological nature
18. Being associated with something improper
19. Being associated with someone who acts improperly
    Model 3: Embarrassment by the actions of others
20. Receiving negative reactions
21. Being questioned about things that might receive negative reactions
22. Recalling or being reminded of embarrassing incidents
23. Unintentionally causing another person embarrassment
24. Seeing another person embarrassed

1. Being the subject of unwanted attention

Many people do not want others to watch them or stare at them. If no one watches them, then no one can think or say anything bad about them, and they do not have to worry about making any mistakes or about receiving any negative reactions. In contrast, when people are subject to public scrutiny, they have to be on guard and often become more tense. If people think others are watching them or staring at them, they become self-conscious and wonder if they are doing something wrong or if something is wrong with the way they look. Sometimes they blame one of their physical features or something else they feel self-conscious about.

> I think people laugh at me. I think they look at my hair and laugh at it because I'm going bald and I'm only twenty years old. [#458]

Many of the embarrassing things that people do cause others to stare at them. Therefore a person who is being stared at may be right in assuming there is a reason why others are doing so.

People want attention when it is the right kind, at the right time, and comes from the right person. They can feel embarrassed when they receive kinds of attention that they do not feel comfortable with. For example, they do not want to look like they are still immature, or that they are trying to get praise and compliments from others.

I get very embarrassed when one of my relatives says how much I've grown and that I'm becoming such a nice gentleman and everything. Then my parents start bragging about me and tell them everything I've been doing. #459

Sometimes when I'm walking with my teenage daughter, I run into someone I know. If I start to talk to this person about how well my daughter is doing in school or about a prize she's just won, my daughter gets embarrassed. After we leave the person, my daughter says, "C'mon, Mom. Don't! Why do you tell everybody that?" It's clear she wouldn't say such things about herself. #460

My mother embarrasses me when my friends are around. She tells them that a lot of guys like me, and that I turn down dates. #461

I left my hometown to get an education and to find work. But I had to return to my hometown when my relatives died to deal with their effects. As I was going through their papers I discovered they had sent my picture and an article about me to the local newspaper every time I earned a degree or got a promotion. I didn't know they were doing this, and I was embarrassed. It seemed so tacky, like I wanted to boast about my success. I would never do anything like that myself. #462

People are also embarrassed when someone is romantically or sexually interested in them whom they consider inappropriate.

I'm not even eighteen, and I keep running into middle-aged men who want to start a relationship with me. It's the last thing I need. I can't get away from them fast enough. #463

Another guy and I went to Moncton on our motorcycles. It took some time to find a camping site that wasn't full. So when we got to the nearby restaurant, it had just closed. We knocked anyway, and an elderly woman told us to come in and she would serve us dinner. She said she wouldn't do this for anyone else. When we went to pay our bills, she explained she was divorced, but her ex-husband didn't want her to go out and enjoy life. She asked what we were doing the next night, and said she wouldn't mind helping two young men with a drive. We laughed when we got back to our tent, but we felt humiliated that an elderly lady had tried to pick us up. [#464]

It's embarrassing when a gay shows an interest in you. You sure don't want anyone you know to see it happen, because you'd be kidded about it for years. Also, you have to wonder what's wrong with the way you look and act, that makes him think you're gay too. [#465]

People also do not want attention which is designed to make them feel embarrassed and produce a reaction.

When people reach their thirtieth, fortieth, fiftieth, and sixtieth birthdays they often feel they are getting appreciably older and become somewhat sensitive about their age. Many people have friends and relatives who try to get a rise out of them at this time by drawing as much public attention to their birthday as possible. Some anonymous person will try to embarrass them by putting an announcement in the newspaper with their name, birthday, and age, and often a picture of them when they were much younger. Sometimes at work they'll put up notices at the entrance to the building, decorate the area with balloons, and hang up a banner announcing "Happy Birthday" and the person's age over the person's office door. Another thing people do is hire a local service which decorates the person's front lawn or place of work on their birthday with numerous plastic flamingoes, penguins, skunks, and cows, and a sign announcing their name and birthday. The person this happens to tries to figure out who is responsible and vows to get them back at the first opportunity. [#466]

2. Having a different appearance or behavior

People are frequently ridiculed for looking or acting differently than others. They may be stared at, talked about, called names and given nicknames, joked about, laughed at, and/or mimicked. They may be singled out because they are big, small, thin, or fat; or because their nose, chin, ears, teeth, or breasts are distinctive in some way. They may have freckles or a birthmark, or they may wear glasses or braces. They may have an unusual name, or one that is easily made fun of. They may have a different hair or skin color, or their walk, voice, or manner of talking may be distinctive. They may be handicapped, injured, or have a physical problem or disease, and they may use a wheelchair, crutches, or a hearing aid. They may not be intelligent or successful. They may dress differently than others. Also, they may have their own mannerisms or expressions. Any difference at all can be subjected to teasing and other kinds of ridicule. Because such differences often generate negative reactions from others, they are a source of embarrassment.

> I'm very self-conscious when everyone else is seated in an auditorium and I stand out because I arrive late or leave early. If I have to leave early, I put it off as long as possible, because I don't look forward to having everyone watch me leave. #467

> Sometimes I'll be walking by myself and not be aware that I'm talking out loud. It's embarrassing when you realize others can hear you. #468

Many children have no reservation about ridiculing differences, because they can get a stimulating reaction from the person with the difference, and they can get positive reactions from their friends who see them do this. Most children, and numerous adults, look for things about others which will enable them to ridicule them. Those who are ridiculed learn just how punishing embarrassment is, and they often learn this while they are growing up and dealing with other children.

> All the kids in school are teased by other kids. One may be teased because she has "dirt across her face," or freckles, and another may be teased about a boyfriend. #469

> Kids who have a severe acne problem are the most likely to be abused. Other kids call them names like pizza-, crater-, or shotgun-face. #470

> A kid who is considered a nerd or dork can be laughed at from elementary school all the way through high school. Other kids find it a lot of fun to say and do things that upset him, and no one really wants to be his friend. #471

> A young guy who lives near me is verbally abused by the other guys. He usually keeps to himself, because when he is with the other guys,

they make fun of the way he looks and the clothes he wears. He just takes it and doesn't try to defend himself. The other guys like it when he's around because he's good for a laugh. [#472]

A student at school remarked I have a big nose, and this really bothered me. I know I have a big nose, but a comment like that makes me painfully aware of it. I kept wondering if that's what other people think too. For weeks, every time I looked in the mirror, there I was, all nose and nothing else. [#473]

One of my classmates in grade school, Wayne, had two very large front teeth. The class had no qualms about pointing this out to him, and called him a variety of nicknames, like Bugs Bunny, Incisor Man, and so on. One day a student at the back of the class made a pair of huge buck-teeth out of rolled-up sheets of paper. The rest of the class followed suit and everyone put them on. Wayne was well aware of what was happening, but he refused to acknowledge it. When the teacher entered the room, she only made it worse by making each student apologize to Wayne. None of the apologies were sincere. [#474]

However, children are not the only ones who ridicule differences in others.

People were taking photos at the party last night, and a guy called out, "Come on, Dave, show us your rotten teeth." [#475]

Decades afterwards, some people still find it difficult to talk about the things they were ridiculed for in the past.

3. Appearing improperly oriented

People are embarrassed if they think they appear improperly oriented to others. This happens if their appearance is marred or inconsistent, if they have a pimple or a tiny piece of paper over a shaving cut on their face, if they have an inside label sticking out of a piece of clothing, if their clothes are out of alignment, or if they wear the wrong combination of colors or designs. (See the chapter on Employing Orientations in a later volume in this series.)

It's embarrassing when you find out you've got some food on your face, teeth, or clothes, or some lipstick on your teeth. You can't get it off fast enough. [#476]

215

There are all kinds of embarrassing situations involving clothes. Have you ever been all dressed up and looking really sharp, only to find out that your slip has been showing all afternoon, the hem of your dress has fallen, or you have a run in your pantyhose? Of course, nobody tells you until it's too late to do anything about it. #477

My parents are Vietnamese, and my father says that my mother caused him to be very embarrassed. It happened when he and my mother were eating in a restaurant in California. My father decided to go to the washroom, and when he looked in the washroom mirror, he saw that one side of his shirt collar was properly arranged, but the other side was tucked down inside his shirt. He was quite embarrassed and stated it was all my mother's fault because she didn't tell him. I asked if my mother was sitting across from him in the restaurant, or at his side where she couldn't see his collar. He replied that it didn't matter where she was sitting, because even if she was sitting behind him, it was still her responsibility to let him know and not embarrass him. He felt that because his clothes were not properly arranged, people would have less respect for him. #478

4. Having less than others

People are often embarrassed when it is apparent that they have less than others. They may have less or inferior clothes, possessions, education, achievements, success, money, connections, or status.

I won't use small change to buy things at a store. I don't want people to think that's all I have to spend. #479

I'm embarrassed when others see that the clothes I'm wearing are worn-out or need repair. I don't want others to see I have holes in my socks or shoes. I'm always careful to put on a fairly new pair of socks before I go to someone's house where I might have to take off my shoes, or before I go to a shoe store to try on new shoes. If I do get a hole in my shoe, I'm careful to keep the sole of the shoe on the floor when I'm seated, so others can't see it. I try to get the shoes repaired right away, and I wear another pair until I do. If I'm missing a button on a shirt, I won't wear the shirt unless I put a sweater over it. If I go somewhere where I'll be seen in my underwear, such as to the doctor, I make sure the pair I have on doesn't look worn. #480

A young man I know has been living on his own since the age of seventeen. He has had no one to help him, and lives on the little money he earns from a job. He has a run-down apartment in the worst part of town. He is ashamed that he doesn't have much furniture and that his apartment is infested with roaches. His friends think his place is disgusting, but good for a laugh. #481

One of the families in my neighborhood had only enough money to make ends meet. They were the talk of the neighborhood. People said the father was on welfare and a bum, and that their children wore sloppy clothes and smelled. A highly respected family in the neighborhood held a neighborhood picnic and this family showed up. They didn't wear the best clothing and most of the people there just stared at them. A month or two later the family moved to another neighborhood. #482

5. Making mistakes

People are embarrassed when others are aware they make mistakes. People may do something incorrectly, such as use the wrong buttonholes when they button their shirt, wear their T-shirt or sweater backwards or inside out, put on two socks which do not match, call the wrong telephone number, not know they are talking to the wrong person on the phone, open the wrong side of a milk carton, arrive for an appointment late or on the wrong day, hand someone too little money to cover a bill, fail to catch an error in something they write and distribute to others, step on someone's foot when dancing, cut themselves when shaving, call someone the wrong name, or drive the wrong way on a one-way street. They may also have to turn around and go in the opposite direction because they change their mind as to where they want to go.

Sometimes you aren't thinking, and you call the person you are dating by the name of the person you used to go with. You can even call your spouse by the name of your previous spouse. It's embarrassing, because it looks as though you don't consider the person you are with different and special. #483

I was working as a bartender one afternoon. A couple sat down at a table and the woman ordered a glass of white wine and the man a rye and water. I took them their drinks and collected the money. The man called me back to the table and pointed out I had served the woman a glass of water and given him a rye mixed with white wine. I was quite embarrassed. That is one mistake I'll never forget. #484

When you go to a church service, it's difficult to remember when you are supposed to stand, sit, or kneel, and when you are supposed to say something or sing. It's embarrassing when you get it wrong, and particularly embarrassing if you are the only one who messes up, because you stand out like a sore thumb. Most people play it safe and watch and listen to others and follow what they do. #485

Two sisters, Joan and Patricia, went to a party, where the hostess introduced them to her brother, Tom. Tom talked quite a bit to Joan during the party, and hardly talked to her sister at all. When the two sisters returned home, they told their parents about the party, and the family teased Joan about Tom. The next day Patricia got a phone call from Tom inviting her out to dinner. No one could understand why he would ask Patricia instead of Joan. That evening when he came to the door, Patricia was all dressed up and met him at the door. "Hi, Joan," he said, "is Patricia ready?" It was very embarrassing for both Tom and Patricia. #486

In addition, people may make mistakes in pronunciation and grammar, and get their facts, interpretations, and predictions wrong.

People also make mistakes in regard to recognizing people. They may not recognize someone who recognizes them.

It's always embarrassing when someone calls you by name and you don't recognize them. Obviously they recognize you or they wouldn't know your name. But there's no way you'd remember their name, because you don't even remember their face. So you have to fake it and try to act friendly. But you don't know what to say to them, and you just hope they won't realize you don't know them from Adam. #487

People may think they recognize someone they do not know.

When I was five years old my family went on a trip. We had stopped at one place, and I was standing next to my mother, wondering where my father was. Then I saw him. I ran up to him, wrapped my arms around his leg, and gave him a big hug. But when he looked down at me, I realized the man wasn't my father at all. Even though I was only five, I remember being very embarrassed and everyone laughing at me. #488

I was walking through the mall with my little brother right behind me. He started thumping his feet loudly and I yelled, "Cut that out, will you? You sound like a horse." I turned to face him, but he was nowhere to be seen. Instead, there was a young woman in high heels walking just behind me. I didn't stay around to hear what she'd say. #489

My family were visiting a national park, and my brother and I were sitting in the outdoor amphitheater late at night watching a film. My brother made up an excuse to go back to the cabin. At the cabin, he took a long black coat and tied the sleeves so that the coat looked like a cape. Then he came back to the amphitheater, sneaked up behind me, and said with a fake accent, "I vant to bite your neck." But it wasn't me who screamed. It was some other girl he'd never seen before, because he'd gone to the wrong row of people. Was he ever embarrassed. #490

On my way to class I saw my boyfriend talking to a bunch of guys. I walked up behind him, goosed him, and put my arm around him as he turned to face me. To my horror, it wasn't my boyfriend. Instead, it was a guy who sat near me in one of my classes. Even today, I can't look at the guy without turning red as a beet and feeling like a fool. #491

My most embarrassing experience happened in junior high. I was dancing with a girl at a school dance when a friend came up and kicked me in the rear. I chased him all over the school and finally caught up with him drinking at a water fountain. I sneaked up and kicked him as hard as I could in the rear. But it wasn't my friend; it was some girl I'd never seen before. I got out of there as fast as I could. #492

People may mistakenly think that someone is smiling, speaking, waving, or honking at them.

I always embarrass myself when someone waves or smiles at me whom I don't recognize. I don't want to embarrass myself by showing I don't recognize them. Therefore I don't dare turn and look around me to see if they are looking at someone else. So I wave or smile back, because I don't want to let on that I don't recognize them when they seem to recognize me. Invariably someone else behind me knows them and responds. Then I feel embarrassed for acting like I know someone who doesn't know me. [#493]

I was in a reception line to meet the former Prime Minister of Canada. After he finished shaking my hand, he said, "You're looking good." He was facing in my direction, and I replied loudly, "Thank you." That same moment I realized he wasn't speaking to me at all, but to the person whose hand he was presently shaking. I was terribly embarrassed and turned red as a beet. I felt very foolish for answering the Prime Minister when he wasn't even talking to me, and I thought I must look conceited to think the Prime Minister would tell me I was looking good. [#494]

People may also make a mistake regarding the kind of person they think they are dealing with.

Sometimes I am in a store and need to talk to a salesclerk. But when I ask one a question, the person tells me they don't work there. It's embarrassing, and I always apologize. [#495]

I went to a dance and spent most of the night watching an attractive girl. I finally got up enough courage and went over to ask her to dance. When she looked up at me, I got the shock of my life. It wasn't a girl at all, but a guy with long hair. After that I swore I would never ask anyone to dance again. [#496]

People also make mistakes about specific objects and locations.

When I finished buying my groceries, I wheeled the grocery cart out to our car and loaded the bags on the back seat. Then I sat down in the front seat to wait for my husband. Fifteen minutes later I realized I was sitting in someone else's car instead of our own. I jumped out and rushed to get everything out of the car before the real owner got back. [#497]

My husband and I were shopping in the Eaton's store in Halifax, and I realized I had to use the women's room. I found the restroom and entered a stall. As I was about to sit on the toilet, I looked down and saw that the person in the next stall was wearing men's shoes. I realized I was in the men's room by mistake, and just flew out of there. When I re-joined my husband he said I was as white as a ghost. [#498]

People may also do something stupid. This may be something they should know better than to do, or something that does not appear stupid until one sees what happens afterwards.

My brother and I were sitting in his car waiting until it was time to go to the movie. His steering wheel has spokes which are decorated with holes of various sizes. As we talked he poked his fingers in and out of the holes. Then one of his fingers got stuck. We tried everything to get it out, but failed. A friend of his came over to the car and the friend was able to take the wheel off the steering column. So all of us climbed in his friend's car and he drove us to the hospital. My brother had to sit in the waiting room until it was his turn to see the doctor. We could hear everyone snickering and laughing at us, and I don't blame them, because how often do you see a guy sitting in a hospital with a steering wheel attached to his finger? Half an hour later the doctor saw him and was able to extract the finger after he gave it an in-jection to take the swelling down. My brother let out a big sigh of relief. Needless to say, that was the last time he poked his fingers in those holes. If it had happened to me, I would feel so humiliated, I would never want to face anyone again who knew about it. [#499]

6. Revealing one's ignorance

People feel embarrassed when their ignorance is revealed to others. They may not know what to do, know what something means, or understand what others are talking about. They may think they know and find out they do not. Or they may try to act as though they know, and be forced to reveal that they do not.

I was in Toronto and bought a ticket to ride the subway. I stuck the ticket in the slot on the gate, and started to walk through. But the gate didn't move and I almost fell over it. I had put the ticket in backwards. I was embarrassed, and a security guard came over and showed me what to do. [#500]

I was excited about my first date, because it was with a guy I'd been interested in for a long time. When he asked me where I'd like to go,

I told him to take me to see the submarine races. My date asked if I was joking, but I told him I was serious. I'd heard about them many times, but never seen them. He drove me to a local park at the edge of a bay, which is a popular place where couples go to park. I hopped out of the car and ran down near the water and stood looking around. My date followed me and asked what I was doing, and I told him I was looking for submarine racers. When my date explained that this was just an expression for making out, I felt humiliated. I couldn't face him or hardly talk to him for the rest of the date. #501

I was actually looking forward to my first period so that I could use tampons. Well the time came and I was excited to finally use one. I felt like such a mature woman. But after I inserted one and went downstairs, I was in such pain I couldn't believe it. I couldn't even sit down and I thought there must be something wrong with me. I told my mother about my problem, and she asked me what I'd done. I told her I'd taken the tampon out of the paper wrapper and put it in. Mom started laughing to kill herself and I felt my newfound maturity slipping away from me. When she stopped laughing, she told me to go back upstairs and get another tampon, but this time to take it out of the cardboard tube. I felt so stupid, but I was kind of relieved there was nothing wrong with me. However, if I ever have a daughter, I'm going to tell her how to use tampons so she won't have to go through the humiliation that I did. #502

7. Forgetting

People are often embarrassed when it is obvious to others that they have forgotten something they should remember. For example, they may forget what they are supposed to do; forget what they were going to say; forget where they put something; forget to take something with them when they leave; forget where they bought something; or forget something they are supposed to remember, like a person's name, a telephone number, an identification number, a combination on a lock, or where they parked their car.

I applied for a job and made an appointment for an interview. Later they called me up and told me I had missed the first appointment and asked if I was still interested in the job. I was terribly embarrassed, because it just isn't like me to miss an appointment. #503

I went to introduce my date to my parents and for the life of me could not remember his name. I was so embarrassed that I didn't know what to say. My date was so humiliated he never asked me out again. #504

My boyfriend called me up and I didn't recognize his voice. I didn't know who it was and guessed several names, but not his. He got very upset and hung up the phone. It was very embarrassing. #505

I get embarrassed when I have to go back into a restaurant or store and retrieve something I left behind. Often it's my gloves or overshoes or a package. I feel everyone is looking at me while I make crystal clear that I really don't have my act together. #506

8. Neglecting to do something

People feel embarrassed when it is obvious to others that they have neglected to do something they should have done. For example, people may not have enough money when they attempt to pay a bill, or they may fail to bring something that is needed.

I took my girlfriend parking, but ran out of gas on the way. It was so embarrassing, and I felt so stupid. Can you imagine telling a girl that you ran out of gas? That's the oldest excuse in the book. My friends won't believe that I really did run out of gas. Thank God my girlfriend believed me, but she still made fun of me. Believe me, I got that gas gauge fixed the next day. #507

I've filled out a withdrawal slip at the bank, taken it to the teller, and been told that I don't have enough money in my account to cover it. Even worse, other people hear the teller say this. I feel like crawling out of the bank. #508

Tuesday I wore some corduroy pants that I had had on the day before and a thick pair of pantyhose. When I got home from work about eight o'clock Tuesday night, I changed into something more comfortable and discovered the pair of pantyhose I wore on Monday were still inside the pants. I was shocked. I worked all day and ran around town with an extra pair of pantyhose wadded up inside my pants, and never noticed them. At one time I was waiting at the head of the line in the bank and people should have noticed the bump in my pants. It's awful to think someone saw it. It's scary. I guess I didn't notice because the clothes I had on were pretty thick. I feel terrible. Just imagine, the pantyhose might have slipped down my pants leg and I would have dragged them along the street. Oh God, that would have been awful. If people knew about this, it would change my image in Charlottetown for the rest of my life. I think of myself as neatly dressed. But others would see me as sloppy and think badly of me, and I would see myself as others see me. I would have to hide, and couldn't go around town again. #509

People are also embarrassed when they are placed in a position in which they appear negligent.

It's embarrassing when my husband invites people for dinner and I have nothing prepared. #510

9. Acting clumsy

People are embarrassed when others see them act clumsy. They may trip, stumble, or fall; run into something; fail to catch an object; drop something; break an item; or spill something or knock it over.

I embarrassed myself by running into a glass door. #511

When I was twelve, I was showing off and riding my bike with no hands and crashed into a telephone pole. That was embarrassing. #512

When they take collection in church I get out some change. Sometimes it falls on the floor, and I have to hunt around for it while everyone watches me. #513

I was playing basketball when a teammate gently passed me the ball. I missed it and was embarrassed. #514

Often I have a stack of quizzes or reprints and want to give one to each student in class. But the sheets of paper stick together and I have trouble separating them. I may stand there making several attempts to get one separated while the student waits expectantly. I realize I must look incompetent, and I start to feel self-conscious. #515

My friend, Terri, decided she would make spaghetti for her new boyfriend, a group of his friends, and me. We offered to help, but she insisted on doing it herself. While she cooked upstairs we sat around the recreation room and joked about her cooking, because she is definitely not a domestic person. She wanted to impress her boyfriend and his friends, so I knew she was nervous. Then when she carried a tray with four plates of spaghetti downstairs, she tripped on the third step and fell to the bottom. Spaghetti was everywhere, but mostly on Terri. It was matted in her hair and hanging from her face. All we could do was crack up laughing. Terri ran crying to her room. Despite our coaxing, Terri would not come out of her room for the rest of the night. Whenever I think of that night, I laugh. But Terri still gets upset when someone mentions it. [#516]

The day I was scheduled to have my high school photo taken for the yearbook, I spent the entire morning primping to look my very best. I drove to the school and parked near "the smoking doors," which are the doors where the kids who smoke hang out. I parked close by so there would be less time for the wind to mess up my hair. Then I jumped out of the car, but tripped over the curb. I could tell what was happening, but it happened too fast for me to save myself. I landed flat on my face and knocked myself unconscious. The guys who were watching from the smoking doors must have nearly wet themselves laughing. When they saw I wasn't moving, two of them ran over to help me. I came to and one guy was carrying me and another had my books. There were teachers all around and I started to cry. I fell asleep in the health room with a severe headache. When my mother arrived, she woke me up to take me home, and it really sank in what had happened. I wanted to die. I couldn't go to school for two days because of my swollen face. Needless to say, I never went in the smoking doors again. [#517]

My husband and I traveled to another town to see a play. It was a stormy night and after the play most people were unable to travel home. The motels were full and local residents let people sleep in their homes. We were able to stay with an elderly couple, and when I entered their house and took off my boots, I tipped over a plant, which hit a glass vase and broke it. So there was soil and glass all over the floor. When the elderly lady of the house saw what had happened, she looked very angrily at her husband and blamed the mess on his dog. I hardly knew where to begin. When she heard what had happened, she was as embarrassed as I was. [#518]

10. Doing something inappropriate for one's age

People also become embarrassed when others see them do something inappropriate for their age.

> When I was fifteen years old, my two little sisters believed in Santa Claus. Before Christmas they each wrote Santa a letter and they wanted me to write one too. I did so and by mistake my father took all three of our letters to the radio station where Santa read them over the air. All of my friends heard about my letter. It was humiliating. [519]

> Yesterday when we went for lunch downtown, my wife and I had to stop and stare. An elderly man walked by us wearing a pair of black tights with large neon letters printed on the sides of the legs. It would have been acceptable on someone one-third his age, but on him it just looked ludicrous. I don't think he had any idea how absurd he looked. I'm much younger than he is, and I would be too embarrassed to dress that way. [520]

11. Discovering one is in a different situation than one thought

People are often embarrassed when they discover they have acted inappropriately because they thought their situation is different than it actually is. For example, they may be embarrassed when they discover they are not alone, someone is present they thought was absent, or someone is absent they thought was present.

> Sometimes you think no one is around or no one is looking and you pick your nose or try to get some food from between your teeth. But just then someone comes by or looks over and sees what you are doing. It's embarrassing. [521]

> I went to collect my date and her mother let me in the house. While I was sitting there, my date came downstairs with a mudpack on her face to ask her mother if a pair of pants and a sweater went together. She didn't know I was sitting in the living room watching this. I wanted to be friendly, so I said, "Why don't you ask me?" She was very embarrassed that I saw her wearing a mudpack. [522]

I put some toast on a plate, took it into the dining room, and went back to the kitchen to get something else. When I returned to the dining room I found my dog eating the toast. I started swearing at my dog, and went back to make more toast. I entered the kitchen saying, "You stupid bastard!" only to discover my grandmother standing there. She'd dropped by for a visit. It was one of the most embarrassing moments of my life. [#523]

Sometimes you make a move on a girl all night at a club, like dance with her and buy her drinks. But when you ask to take her home, she tells you she has a steady boyfriend. It's embarrassing. Your friends never let you forget it, and she gets quite a laugh. [#524]

I ran into an old friend from school that I hadn't seen for a few years. While we were talking, I asked if she was seeing anyone. She named a guy she'd been going with for the past two years, and I nearly died of humiliation. It was the same guy I'd been going with for the past four months. He was cheating on both of us. [#525]

While I was in nursing school there was some construction work on our floor in the nursing residence. When my roommate and I cleaned our room we swept the dirt out the door and into a hole in the floor. We thought it was a temporary hole created by the construction work. However, the hole was above the administrator's office and all the dirt landed on her desk. When they determined where the dirt came from, my roommate and I were punished. It was embarrassing, because as professionals we were expected to be clean, neat, and responsible. [#526]

Part of my job involves dealing with overdue accounts. Yesterday I was calling overdue accounts and delivering my set speech. One man I called was named Jeremy Brown. I told Mr. Brown that if his account wasn't paid within two weeks, the collection agency would pay him a visit. After I finished my presentation, he asked, "Is this Vickie?" I replied, "Yes." I had no idea who I was speaking to until he told me. It was the same man who was dating my cousin. My husband and I had been doing things with them all summer, but I only knew him by his nickname, so I hadn't recognized his name when I'd called him. I was highly embarrassed to have talked to him in this way. Even though I was on the phone, and there was no one else in the office at the time, my face was as red as it has ever been. [#527]

Julia went to visit a male friend of hers, and when she walked into his apartment he had just gotten out of the shower and had nothing on. She was so embarrassed she turned around and walked right back out. I think she was more embarrassed than he was. #528

People also become embarrassed when they are not aware of local customs and learn that they have acted inappropriately.

When we were vacationing in France we used a public washroom and a female attendant handed us towels to dry our hands. We thought this was a nice custom, and when we returned the towels to the woman and went to leave, she started talking away in French. We didn't understand her, but she got very annoyed and as we left she chased after us shouting in French. Later we learned it is customary to tip her. We were embarrassed and made sure we always tipped afterwards. #529

12. Having one's private life exposed

People are quite embarrassed when certain aspects of their private life are made public. They do not want their romantic interests, sex life, relationships, disagreements, failures, deviant activities, bad behavior, personal problems, addictions, cosmetic surgery, health difficulties, embarrassing experiences, or their criticisms of others to become public knowledge. When they share details of these with a friend, they expect that this will not be repeated to others. People tell others, "Promise you won't tell," "Don't tell you-know-who about this," "This shouldn't be mentioned to anyone," "Nobody is supposed to know," and "You are not supposed to know this, but . . . " People get upset when someone tells their secrets, reads their personal letters or diary, and listens in on their telephone conversations.

Occasionally when I'm talking with my friends on the phone, people at home listen on the extension. Then they bring up what we said in front of everybody. It's so embarrassing. #530

People love to tell their secrets to their friends, because they think they can trust them. But I know different, and learned the hard way. When you are getting along with your friends, they keep your secrets. But when you have a disagreement with them, they use your secrets against you and tell other people. #531

When people have knowledge of a person's private life, they have ample grounds to react negatively to the person, and no person wants this. The reason people keep a large portion of their lives private is in order to avoid embarrassment, criticism, and loss of resources.

My parents embarrass me the most. I hate it when they bring out the photo albums and show people all those embarrassing snapshots of me when I was a baby. #532

It embarrasses me when we are with other people and my wife brings up whether or not we're going to have kids. #533

An individual does not want others to stick their noses into his business, and to ask him uninvited questions about personal matters or to discuss his personal life with others.

I get embarrassed when my parents follow me around the house asking lots of questions before I go out with my friends. #534

No one likes to be the subject of critical comments, jokes, and gossip, even if they occur behind his back. The more embarrassment a piece of information will cause, the greater the effort to keep it private. The fact a person wants to keep his private life secret, enables others who know various details of his private life to get an entertaining reaction from the person by embarrassing him when they make these details public or threaten to do so.

My father was driving and my brother and I were in the car. We were passing the home of the guy who doesn't know I like him, when my brother announced, "That's where the love of her life lives." My father turned into their driveway. He started talking to the guy's father and told him I was in love with his son. I said, "Dad, I'm going to kill you. I am so embarrassed." #535

Other people are quite interested in the private lives of individuals. When they repeat this information to those who have not heard it, they can obtain positive reactions from them. People are particularly interested in the private lives of individuals they know. Not only is this information a source of stimulation, but it also indicates in what ways and to what extent an individual can be used as a resource. Information on a person's private life helps to determine the person's reputation, and to identify that person as a desirable or undesirable resource. Changes in an individual's situation are of considerable interest, because they indicate changes in that individual's usefulness as a resource. Gossip can be viewed as the current quotation on an individual's value as a resource. Also, many people want to obtain information on an individual which will elicit negative reactions toward the individual from others. Knowing this information enables them to a) show that they are superior and more deserving of positive reactions, b) express their envy and "cut the person down to size," and c) repay negative reactions they have received from the person or the person's family in the past.

13. Revealing one's emotions

People are often embarrassed when others see them express certain feelings, such as hurt, loneliness, anger, envy, and anxiety. People may have been teased or criticized for revealing their feelings in the past, or they may be concerned that others will consider them weak or immature. As a result, they often try to hide many of their feelings from other people.

> One time when I was in junior high I was upset by a bad mark on a history test, and the teacher sent me out of the room. When the students asked later why I'd been sent out, I told them I didn't know. Then one student said it was because I was starting to cry. This was true, and I was very embarrassed that the other students knew. The teacher had sent me out to spare me this embarrassment. [536]

> When something sad happens in a film, I don't want others in the theater to see me cry. I try to hide my tears, and don't wipe my eyes or blow my nose. Other people must feel the same, because I don't hear anyone else crying out loud. [537]

14. Failing

People also feel embarrassed when others know or believe they have failed at an endeavor. In sports, they may fail to make the team, fail to make a play or score a goal, or fail to win the game or tournament. In education, they may fail an exam, course, or year of school; fail to be admitted to a program or university; or fail to get a degree.

> One day a bunch of us guys, who are in the same high school English class, sat in the cafeteria and talked about our marks on our last exam. Those who got a good mark claimed the test was very easy and that you'd have to be pretty stupid to fail. While everyone talked about their marks, Eric sat in his chair and said nothing. Then one guy who'd done well asked, "Eric, are you going to tell us your mark?" Eric replied, "I'd rather not, because I didn't do well." Someone else continued, "Eric, is it because you failed?" Eric said nothing and there was an embarrassed look on his face. Then he got up and quietly left the cafeteria. [538]

In business or employment, people may fail to get a job, meet an objective, win a contract, get a raise, or get a promotion. They may also make bad investments or go bankrupt. In politics, they may fail to win a nomination, an election, or an appointment. In their social life, they may fail to get a date, have sex, establish a relationship, get married, produce children, or keep a mate. As a parent, they may fail to provide what their children need or want, or fail to raise successful children.

People are also embarrassed over other types of failure. For example, people may fail to do what they said they would do, such as take a trip, make a purchase, or meet a commitment.

> If you plan a big trip and tell everyone, they're impressed and jealous. But if you end up not going, you look foolish. It's a lot better to take a trip and have other people find out afterwards. They're still jealous. [539]

People may also fail at a specific action, such as hitting a target, obtaining a specific grade, or getting something to work right. Often this is something that they and others think that they are able to do.

I get embarrassed when I crack a joke and nobody laughs. #540

Sometimes you try to unlock your car door and can't get the key to work, or else you can't get your car to start. You feel incompetent and frustrated, and you feel embarrassed when others watch. #541

It's embarrassing when you have to show a film to a group of people, and can't get the movie projector to work. Everyone sits there while you try one thing after another without success. #542

A number of times I've gone into a booth in a public washroom, locked the door, used the toilet, gotten ready to leave, and can't get the door unlocked. I fidget with the lock and push and pull the door. I don't want anyone to come into the washroom and see me stuck in a public toilet booth, because I'd look foolish. Usually I get the door open. But once I didn't and had to crawl out under the door of the booth. #543

15. Doing something bad

People are embarrassed when others think they have done something wrong or bad. This may be an act which is considered rude, dishonest, unjust, immoral, deviant, or criminal.

I've been unable to get my key to work in my car door, and finally realized I'm trying to unlock someone else's car. I get embarrassed because I don't want people to think I'm trying to steal the car. #544

One evening I took a girl out on a first date and we went to the movie and then had a quick drink. The police stopped the car on a routine check and asked me to take a Breathalyzer test, which I failed. I explained I'd only had one drink, and they had me wait in the police car for fifteen minutes to retake the test, which I passed. During this time my date had to wait in my car, and several of my friends drove by and honked their horn. I was quite embarrassed and felt like five cents worth of shit. #545

I was at the mall and bought a large bedspread at the department store. The checkout girl said she didn't have a bag big enough to hold it, so I carried it in my arms. After I left the store, I was stopped by a security guard who asked me where I thought I was going with the bedspread. I turned fifty shades of red. It was a busy night at the mall and some of my neighbors were nearby. When I showed the security guard the receipt, he apologized. I felt very humiliated, and was bothered for days wondering if the neighbors thought I was shoplifting. [#546]

One night I was out drinking with three of my buddies, two of them picked up two girls, and we all went back to my house. The two guys got it on with the girls on the floor and the couch in the living room. The other guy and I were pretty drunk by this time. We started making catcalls at the busy couples, and the two girls yelled insults back at us. This went on for some time as we got more and more plastered. Later, the two of us danced nude on the living room tables and taunted the girls with various parts of our anatomy, but their minds were on other things. Finally, I pulled on some clothes and went upstairs to bed.

Upstairs, my girlfriend was in my bedroom waiting for me. When I got undressed for bed, she saw I didn't have any underwear on and asked where it was. I made up an excuse and told her all my underwear was dirty and needed washing, so I hadn't worn any that night. She accepted this. But the next morning she went downstairs to get some juice and saw the two girls lying half-dressed, passed out on the floor. One of the girls was wearing my underwear on her head. I had a hell of a time explaining what it was doing there. That was embarrassing enough, but think how embarrassing it will be if I run into those two girls again. [#547]

16. Lying

People feel embarrassed when others accuse them of lying, or catch them lying. They also feel embarrassed when they are put in a position where they feel they have to lie.

My sister got pregnant, but in order to protect her reputation, she told people she wasn't. I was embarrassed because I had to lie about her condition too. [#548]

It's humiliating when someone asks you an embarrassing question and you have to lie to protect yourself. If you have a chance, you don't hesitate to get back at them afterwards. [#549]

17. Revealing one's biological nature

People also embarrass themselves when they reveal their biological nature in socially disapproved ways. Thus they may show signs of a) nudity, b) urinating or defecating, c) producing other bodily fluids, gases, and phenomena, or d) their sexuality. People are also embarrassed when they do not actually reveal their biological nature, but others think they do.

When people reveal too much of their body to others who are not supposed to see it, they become embarrassed. This may happen when they forget to wear an item, take off too much clothing, have an item become unfastened or fall off, rip something they are wearing, hold themselves in certain positions, get their clothes wet so others can see through them, or do not know that others are watching them. In addition, someone else may intentionally or unintentionally pull off an item a person is wearing.

> I was at the beach, and when I took off my sweater I accidentally pulled off my bikini top too. The beach was crowded, and lots of people saw what I did. They also saw how embarrassed I was. #550

> One Friday night my friends and I were going to a club and decided to get some cigarettes at the department store first. I was sitting in the back seat of the car and they stopped at the main door to let me out. As I entered the department store, they began honking the horn. I turned back and could see them sitting in the car pointing at me and laughing. I figured they were just trying to embarrass me, so I flung back my head and strode confidently into the store. Because it was a Friday night, everyone and their dog were shopping there. Everywhere I went in the store people seemed to stare at me, but I thought it was because I looked pretty sharp in my new dress. After I finished roaming through the store, I went to the checkout counter. As I was getting out my money I realized there was a large lump along the back of my waistband. When I investigated, I found that the entire back of my skirt along with my slip were tucked into my waistband. Therefore every shopper and worker in the department store had seen me walking around in my panties. Worst of all, they were my bright pink and white polka-dotted panties. I felt like I was going to pass out. When I got back to the car my friends were killing themselves laughing. I was so devastated I started crying. I had them take me home and go to the club without me. #551

People are also embarrassed when they draw attention to their urination or defecation. They may soil themselves or their clothing, wet the bed, or they may produce noises, odors, or other signs which suggest they are eliminating.

> When I was ten years old my mom took me to say confession during Lent. I was very nervous and scared. When I entered the booth, I wet my pants and made a puddle of pee. Mom told people, "Oh Lord, nobody go in there until I clean this mess up." She sent me to the car. I was just mortified. #552

> It's embarrassing when you use a toilet and then can't get it to flush. It's really embarrassing when you are in someone else's home or when someone is waiting to use the toilet right after you. It's ten times worse when you've crapped instead of peed. #553

In addition, something may happen which suggests to others that people have eliminated, when they actually did not.

> It's embarrassing when you spill some liquid on your pants and it looks like you didn't make it to the toilet in time. When it happens in a club, people don't think you spilled a beer on yourself, they assume you were too drunk to control yourself. #554

People are also frequently embarrassed when others become aware of their bodily fluids, gases, and phenomena which are not involved in elimination and menstruation. This includes belching, coughing, drooling, farting, hiccuping, shivering, sneezing, spitting, vomiting, and yawning; having bad breath and other body odors; scratching private areas; getting cold sores, pimples, or warts; and having one's stomach growl.

> It's embarrassing when you're talking to someone and tiny pieces of spit fly out of your mouth on to them, or somewhere else where they can see them, like on their desk. After it's happened, there's nothing you can do about it. #555

> I was sitting in a business meeting listening to a speaker when I got the hiccups. They didn't bother me at first, because they weren't loud and continuous. But as the lecture proceeded the hiccups got worse. I tried

holding my breath, but that didn't work. Then I hiccuped so loudly that the speaker and everyone else turned and looked at me. I was quite embarrassed. [556]

Have you ever been talking to someone and suddenly had to sneeze, and then snot starts dripping down your nose? It's happened to me a couple of times. I can't hide it and feel humiliated. [557]

Often the only way to tell that your shirt or sweater needs to be washed is to smell it. But you don't want others to see you sniffing away at the armpits. It would be really embarrassing. [558]

A female friend of mine stopped by my apartment so we could go somewhere together. As we were leaving, the landlord's dog ran up and started smelling her crotch. She became quite agitated and tried to wave him away. She exclaimed, "Oh, oh, I just hate when this happens." I tried to push the dog away and teased her that she should bathe more often. [559]

People are frequently embarrassed when they or others draw unwanted attention to their sexuality.

Sometimes I have to walk by a bunch of guys who are standing around, and I just feel like dying. They make sexual comments and say things about parts of my body. They make me very self-conscious, and I get really embarrassed. [560]

I dread having to go buy tampons; I just hate it. It is so embarrassing, but I have no choice. It just seems that every time I go into a store to buy them I meet up with a guy I know. I get so embarrassed standing there talking to a guy with a box of tampons in my hand. [561]

One of the worst things that can happen to a woman is for other people to know she is having her period. I grew up in Vietnam and many women used pieces of cloth to halt the flow of blood. Disposable menstrual pads were too expensive. When you wear cloth or pads you never want to produce a large bulge in your clothes that people can notice. And you don't want to have other people see you wash the blood out of the pieces of cloth. I just hated washing them, and sometimes I would throw them away, but it was expensive to do this. If you don't use cloth, you get blood on your pants. It looks messy and sloppy and others will have no respect for you. I live in Canada now, and I wrap up used menstrual pads and put them in the bathroom wastebasket. But I never want to have anyone outside my family come and use the bathroom unless I empty the wastebasket first. I would just be so embarrassed if they saw the pads there.

I have a recurrent bad dream. I am wearing shorts or a short skirt and walking down the road and it starts to rain. I get soaked, and blood from my period runs down my legs and you can see blood on my skin and in my footprints. Sometimes in my dream I also take a shower. The shower stall encloses most of my body, but not the lower part of my legs, and others can see blood from my period running down my legs. When people see the blood, they stare at me and look surprised. I want to hide the blood, but can't, and feel very ashamed. I have this same bad dream whenever I have my period and feel really tired. The events in the dreams have never happened to me, but I worry that they might. If no one else saw the blood, I still wouldn't like it, because it's dirty and messy. But I wouldn't feel embarrassed. #562

One day at school my girlfriends and I were joking around in the washroom and stuffed tissue in our bras to make us look bigger. When the bell went off for class we rushed to pull the tissue out. As I sat down in my seat in class, I realized I had pulled the tissue out of one side, but not the other. I looked lopsided and all the boys noticed. I was red with embarrassment, and from then on the boys teased me. #563

People are also not happy when others are made aware of their sexual activity.

After I went parking with my boyfriend, I realized I had lost an earring. Normally I would have ignored this, but they were really good earrings that I'd been given as a present. So I phoned my boyfriend and his mother answered. He wasn't at home, and I asked his mother to get him to call me. She wanted to know why, so I had to tell her that I had lost my earring. I was very embarrassed, but she promised to look for it. #564

It's embarrassing when you have to go to the doctor to get a prescription for birth control pills. Often he's known you and your family for years. He frequently asks personal questions and even gives you humiliating lectures. A friend of mine said she felt like running out of his office. #565

Nancy, a friend of mine, told me, "When I go to buy some contraceptives, the clerk has the fucking nerve to stare at me and ask whether or not I'm of age." #566

Guys try to impress each other by talking about their sexual experiences. It's very embarrassing when you learn your boyfriend is telling his friends about you. #567

It's a lot more difficult to masturbate when you share a bedroom with someone, such as a roommate. You have to wait until they are asleep and their head is turned away from you. If they saw you masturbating, it would be enormously embarrassing. #568

People are also embarrassed if they are not engaged in sexual activity, but others think they are.

At the beginning of my biology lab I helped my friend, Wade, with his winter jacket because the zipper was caught. Later, when I was trying to do the experiment, Wade kept squirting me with water. I got mad and finally shouted out, "If you don't leave me alone, Wade, that's the last time I ever help you with your zipper." Well, the whole class stopped still. People stared at me shocked. Then they began to laugh. I knew what I meant, Wade knew what I meant, but everyone else thought I meant something else. I just stood there speechless, because I couldn't believe I'd said something so stupid. #569

18. Being associated with something improper

People are embarrassed if they are associated with something improper.

I used to wear long johns for underwear when I was in junior high. When I went to gym class I would roll my long johns up inside my shorts. One day when we were running in gym class my long johns became unrolled. Everyone looked and laughed. Now that was embarrassing. #570

It's no fun to step in dog shit and have to get it off your shoe. It doesn't make you look very swift either. #571

People can feel embarrassed even if they are not responsible for an incident, and the only association is in the minds of onlookers.

During orientation week, one activity for the freshmen was to blow up rubbers like balloons. I and another girl were sitting in the front row when one of the rubbers flew away from someone and landed in my lap. I was so embarrassed, and didn't know what to do. I tried to hide it, but everyone around stared at me. I could have cried. #572

When I was in high school this dog would come to my yard, smell me, and try to copulate with my leg. I was terribly embarrassed. The dog would wait at our front steps for me to come outside. Once I went to a local store and saw the dog outside waiting for his owner. I sure didn't try to go into the store, because I didn't want the dog all over me. #573

19. Being associated with someone who acts improperly

People are embarrassed when someone they are associated with acts improperly. This may be an acquaintance, colleague, friend, mate, relative, or pet. The individual may act improperly by dressing, behaving, or speaking in a way which is not approved of.

One Sunday our family was late for church and had to split up. I found a seat at the front of the church, but there was an old man already sitting there who was quite dirty. I pushed my young daughter ahead of me into the pew. A few minutes later she screamed, "Mommy, who smells?" I was mortified. Then my daughter insisted on changing places with me, which embarrassed me even more. And to top it off I had to put up with the man's smell, which was almost unbearable. #574

I find it embarrassing when one of my daughters or granddaughters wears an outfit which is too revealing. And I don't like it when my grandchildren dress improperly for church, like they do when they wear patched jeans or a beard. I also get embarrassed when one of them uses bad language or tells a dirty joke. I don't want people to think that members of my family were raised to act this way. #575

My little sister shows off in front of my friends. She likes to get the attention and everyone laughs at her. But I'm embarrassed at some of the things she does. #576

Lots of teenagers are embarrassed to be seen with their parents because their parents don't look and act "cool." #577

I get embarrassed when I take someone home and the house is messy or my wife is sloppily dressed. I feel it reflects badly on myself as well as my wife. #578

My friend and I were out of town. We had a lot to drink and decided to go to a movie. During the film my friend excused himself and was gone for a long time. He suddenly walked back into the theater and just stood there for several minutes looking like he didn't know where he was. Then he called out my name to come and get him. I had to go rescue him, and I felt truly humiliated because every person in the theater laughed and snickered at us. #579

Mom took my sister and me to eat at a pizza parlour. After we ordered, she decided to try a glass of their draft beer. The pizzas arrived, and while we were eating Mom let out a large belch. My sister and I were very embarrassed, and we sank down in our chairs hoping no one would see us. We just wanted to get out of there fast. We asked for a doggy bag for our pizza and took it home to eat. #580

I'm extremely embarrassed when my girlfriend scratches her crotch in public. It is so uncouth, I don't want to be associated with her. #581

One day my mother bought a roast at the grocery store. When she served it to guests that night, she was furious at the amount of fat and bone in it. I thought the roast tasted fine, but the next day she asked me to drive her back to the store so she could complain. Right in the store my mother took this large bone out of a plastic bag and showed it to the butcher. I had to stand there while she flashed this big bone around and chewed out the butcher. To my amazement, the butcher gave her a full refund for a roast we'd already eaten. And as if this wasn't enough, when my mother saw the butcher carrying the bone to the garbage can, she yelled at him to ask if she could have the bone back for our dog. I was about five shades of red by this time, but my mother marched out of the store as proud as a peacock. #582

Sometimes people are embarrassed by a person's presence. This is often someone they do not want to be seen with. They may consider the person to be a member of an undesirable category, such as a low status group as defined by themselves or by their relatives and friends. Examples might include someone who is unemployed, poor, too old, or too young. People can also be embarrassed to be seen with someone who has unattractive attributes, such as someone who is ugly or physically or mentally handicapped.

> I wouldn't want to date someone really fat. I'd be embarrassed to be seen with them. #583

> When I have a friend over, my little brother follows me all around the house and bugs me. It's embarrassing to have a little kid hanging around all the time. #584

People can also be embarrassed when a person they are associated with associates with someone improper. This may be someone who is considered unacceptable because of his or her age, sex, race, ethnic group, religion, occupation, appearance, residence, family reputation, or personal reputation.

> My sister embarrasses me because she's dating a guy from a town that everyone considers backward. #585

> My parents told me they don't want me dating a Catholic boy. They would be embarrassed if their friends found out. #586

People feel embarrassed by the actions of their associates because of the nature of association. People view anything they are associated with as extensions of themselves. Thus everything a person thinks, says, does, and owns is viewed by the person as an extension of himself. A person views negative reactions by others to anything he thinks, says, does, or owns as negative reactions to himself, just as he views positive reactions by others to anything he thinks, says, does, or owns as positive reactions to himself. Also, if others criticize or attack someone that a person is associated with, the person considers this a criticism of or an attack on himself. In the same way, a person views the behavior of those he is associated with as extensions of himself. He views the behavior of those he is associated with as though he is performing the behavior himself. In other words, if person A is associated with person B, when person B does something, person A views this action as though person A is doing it himself.

Each person has many things he does not do because he thinks they are improper or he thinks that others consider them improper. If he accidentally or intentionally does one of these things, and knows that others are aware he has done so, he is embarrassed. When a person is associated with someone who does something the person considers improper, the person is embarrassed. Assume that person A has an association with person B. Perhaps B is a relative or friend of A. Because of this association, A treats B's behavior as though it is A's own behavior. In other words, A views an action by B as though A is doing the action himself. If A considers the action by B to be proper, then A is not embarrassed by it. If A considers the action by B to be improper, then A is embarrassed by it. When there is no association between A and B, A is not embarrassed when B does something that A considers improper. People are embarrassed by the actions of those they are associated with, but not by identical actions by those they are not associated with (see Model 3).

> There was an abortion clinic near my home in Toronto, and occasionally there would be antiabortion demonstrators in front of the clinic. My boyfriend was in favor of abortion, and anytime he saw the demonstrators he would yell, "Get fucked!" at them and make vulgar gestures. When I was with him, I was extremely embarrassed by this. I would tell him to stop, and I'd try to pull his arm down so he couldn't give them the finger. If I had been standing elsewhere and saw a stranger do what my boyfriend did, I'd have thought it rude, but I wouldn't have been embarrassed. #587

Even a minimal association, such as simply sitting or walking with a person who acts improperly, can cause a person to feel embarrassed.

> When I watch an actor in a movie or TV program who does something foolish, I frequently feel embarrassed by it. When he does something particularly foolish, I may find it hard to continue watching. When I was a child and saw a kissing scene in a movie, I would cover my eyes because I found it so embarrassing. I think I must see myself doing the same thing the actor is doing. If I would feel embarrassed to do what the actor is doing, then I actually feel embarrassed. #588

The stronger the association between two people, the more likely each will be embarrassed by the actions of the other. These relationships are

Model 3: Embarrassment by the actions of others

Person A is embarrassed by Person B

1. Person A would be embarrassed to do X.
2. Therefore Person A does not do X.
3. Person A is associated with Person B.
4. Person B does X.
5. Person A is embarrassed by Person B.

Person A is not embarrassed by Person C

1. Person A would be embarrassed to do X.
2. Therefore Person A does not do X.
3. Person A is not associated with Person C.
4. Person C does X.
5. Person A is not embarrassed by Person C.

The stronger the association between two people, the more easily each can embarrass the other.

↑ Association → ↑ Embarrassment

The weaker the association between two people, the less easily each can embarrass the other.

↓ Association → ↓ Embarrassment

outlined in Model 3. Individuals see those they are associated with as extensions of themselves and the actions of those they are associated with as though they are their own actions. Other people make similar associations. They connect a person with his associates and expect the person's behavior to be identical to that of his associates.

Negative reactions are not only directed at individuals. They are also directed at social groups. Social groups include families and various organizations. People associate individuals with the social groups they are members of. Individuals realize that when another member of their social group does something embarrassing, other people are likely to react negatively to their social group and all of its members, including themselves. Individuals are often embarrassed when a member of their social group does something which can cause other people to respond negatively. Individuals are so sensitive to negative reactions, they do not want to have the groups they are associated with and its members do anything which produces negative reactions.

Because they are seen as a group, a family is frequently embarrassed by the actions of one or more of its members. A family may be embarrassed by a member's dress, manners, mannerisms, possessions, occupations, hobbies, choice of music, sexual activity, use of alcohol and drugs, violence, laziness, irresponsibility, failure, divorce, speeding and accidents, stealing, and vandalism. Embarrassment may be caused by something a family member does in the present or did in the past.

My younger sister is sixteen years old. She embarrasses me when she drinks and smokes dope in public. [589]

When I went away to university, I found the students wore beat-up clothes, like cutoff jeans, and sneakers and sweaters with holes in them, and I learned to dress the same way. But when I went home for the summer, my parents were embarrassed by the way I dressed and refused to let me go out of the house unless everything I wore was in good shape. They felt what I wanted to wear reflected badly on themselves. [590]

My mom and dad wear outdated clothes and listen to outdated music. I find it embarrassing to have friends come over and hear that old music playing full blast on the stereo. [591]

My nephew is living with a woman, but they aren't married. Although I love my nephew, I think what he is doing is wrong, and I'm embarrassed by it. #592

My dad frequently embarrasses me. If he's in a store and feels happy, he may start dancing and singing in the aisles. And if he has been waiting in line for a long time to pay for some items, he may just drop the items on the floor and leave. #593

My father embarrasses me when he drinks, because he teases my friends in a gross way. #594

Sometimes I get embarrassed because my father is a bootlegger, and people talk about him a lot. #595

I get embarrassed when my family fights in public. #596

My husband does a few things that embarrass me quite a bit. If we're out or have friends in and we're drinking, he may have a few too many. It really embarrasses me if he gets loud, falls down, or tells crude jokes. #597

My wife and I went to visit another married couple. We were sitting on the couch and my wife decided to rest her feet on top of their coffee table. I was highly embarrassed. It showed a complete disregard for the other couple. #598

It's embarrassing when you are at a church service and your baby won't stop crying. You know it bothers other people and they sometimes turn and look at you. All you can do is take the baby and leave. #599

In order to avoid embarrassment and negative reactions, members of a social group instruct each other as to what kinds of behavior will produce negative reactions from outsiders, and frequently put considerable pressure on their members to get them to change their behavior. They may even disassociate themselves from certain members or dismiss them from the group in order to avoid embarrassment.

A male relative of my sister-in-law got a bad reputation because he jumped over the boards during a recent hockey game and attacked a referee. Not only is this violent, it is also embarrassing. I was at a party, and some people who had read about the incident in the newspaper asked me if the man was my nephew. I told them, "No. Let's get this straight. He has nothing to do with me. I have enough problems in my own family without laying claim to him." #600

Absolutely anything that one disapproves of, or thinks others might disapprove of, is a possible source of embarrassment when it is done by a person one is associated with.

My little brother embarrasses me when he talks like a baby. #601

My parents embarrass me when they try to act young. #602

I'm embarrassed by my mother when she drives slowly, or when she parks in very small parking spaces. #603

My mother embarrasses me when I go shopping with her, because she makes such a fuss when she thinks prices are too high. #604

I don't like to bring my friends home, because my parents ask them a hundred questions about themselves, their family, and what they do. #605

I had a friend over for dinner with my family. I was embarrassed because he sometimes ate with his fingers. #606

My husband embarrasses me, because when my friends call and want to talk to me, he asks them what they want. #607

I find it terribly embarrassing when I'm with my husband's family, because they kiss and hug each other a lot. My own family wasn't like this, and it makes me uncomfortable. #608

I'm embarrassed by my daughter because she stutters when she talks fast. She doesn't have to stutter, because she doesn't do it when she talks slowly. #609

My mother is getting older and she embarrasses me when she repeats the same stories to people she has already told them to. Other people won't appreciate hearing the same story twice, and it makes her look forgetful. #610

20. Receiving negative reactions

People are embarrassed when they receive negative reactions. Thus they feel embarrassed if they are criticized, corrected, argued with, distrusted, rejected, insulted, called names, sworn at, belittled, degraded, punished, or treated as immature. They are even more embarrassed when additional people witness this.

My mom and dad embarrass me when they tell me to go to my room when they have company. [#611]

My parents really embarrass me when they call me an idiot in front of other people. [#612]

My mom corrects my grammar and pronunciation in front of others. I feel stupid and embarrassed. [#613]

I don't like it when my teenage children correct me in public. It's embarrassing, because it makes me look stupid. There's no reason for them to do so, because they usually correct me on unimportant details. [#614]

My daughter started arguing with me at work in front of my customers, and I told her to go home and we'd discuss it later. It's embarrassing and she should know better. [#615]

I get embarrassed when a good-looking guy tries to pick me up and my brother steps in and says, "She's my younger sister, so don't touch her." He thinks I can't look after myself. [#616]

I had a blind date, and when I saw what the girl looked like, I cancelled the date. She wanted to know why, but I wouldn't tell her. She was embarrassed. [#617]

One guy in my neighborhood wasn't attractive, but he had a very nice personality. Once he approached this girl and asked her for a date. She told him he wasn't her type and she didn't want anything to do with him. This shamed him, and he didn't show his face around the neighborhood for weeks. [#618]

I get embarrassed when people point out how weak I am. [#619]

It's embarrassing when a friend tells you you should do something about your bad breath. [#620]

After I say something or tell a joke, if someone says, "That doesn't make sense," or "That's not funny," I feel uncomfortable and kind of embarrassed. [#621]

I don't get embarrassed easily. But I do when I go out for a night with the guys and my wife shows up to check on me. [#622]

My husband waits until the worst possible moment to tell me that I did something wrong or that something I prepared wasn't good enough. He does it when there are a lot of people around. Sometimes he tells me off in front of my friends. He also tells our friends about my faults. I mean, it's not that I'm ashamed or anything, everyone has faults. But he doesn't have to advertise them. It makes him feel superior. But it really embarrasses the hell out of me. [#623]

My previous boyfriend used to drink too much at clubs and then act irrational. One night he went crazy. He pulled me out into the hallway and began throwing me into the walls and hitting me. There were people all around watching and trying to help. But I refused any help, because that would have really set him off. All I wanted was to try to regain my composure. While my friends and others watched, he spit in my face and marched out. I was frozen in place and couldn't speak. Finally a good friend took me home. For a long time I found it hard to face the people who had seen me degraded. It was a horrible experience and one I think I'll never be able to shake. [#624]

Many people recognize that a person feels embarrassed when he is criticized in front of others. Therefore, they usually make sure there are no witnesses present when they deliver criticisms.

21. Being questioned about things that might receive negative reactions

People are frequently embarrassed when others ask them questions about matters which may receive negative reactions. People do not want to draw attention to such matters, and they know if they answer the questions they will give others more information to discuss.

> When I was in school I had a bad problem with acne, so I would put medicated cream on my face when I went to bed. One day a good friend came to see me, and after my mother let him in the house he came in my room and woke me up. My friend asked, "What's that on your face?" I didn't know what to say because I was so embarrassed. So I ran in the bathroom and washed it off. #625

> When I was in secondary school, my brother ran away from home. My parents were quite embarrassed by this and told me not to say anything about it to the kids in school. But when I got to school that day, kids asked me about it and I didn't know what to say. Their questions made me very uncomfortable. The other kids knew about my brother, because there was an announcement on the radio that morning. #626

> My young daughter and I moved into the family residence at the university. Two weeks after we moved in, we were invited to a barbecue for residents. I had hurt my back and couldn't go, but another person volunteered to take my daughter. In the middle of the barbecue my daughter came home crying. She told me people there had asked her if I was an alcoholic and if I had many boyfriends. She didn't know what an alcoholic was and didn't know what to say. They had laughed, and my daughter didn't know what to do. It upset me a great deal because I don't drink and don't have a boyfriend. Even if I did, it's none of their business. #627

22. Recalling or being reminded of embarrassing incidents

People can feel embarrassed when they recall or are reminded about certain incidents.

> When I was twelve years old a friend and I used to steal from department stores. After a while I decided it was wrong, and I quit. Every now and then someone jokingly brings this up. It embarrasses me to think I did stuff like that. #628

People can also feel embarrassed when family skeletons are exposed to light. They would like to forget about embarrassing incidents and would like to think others have forgotten too.

23. Unintentionally causing another person embarrassment

People can also feel embarrassed when they place another person in an embarrassing situation.

> The worst thing that happened when I worked as a waitress was when I served a lady her meal and dropped a bowl of clam chowder in her lap. [629]

> One year my college class attended a conference in Ottawa. While I was there I went to visit an old friend of mine, Linda, and took along a couple of my male friends. Linda lives in an apartment with her roommate, Eileen. Linda and the three of us were all sitting in her living room catching up on the news, when out of the blue this person races into the living room, flings off her towel, and proclaims, "What do you think of this sexy body?" It was Eileen, who'd just finished a shower and had nothing on. The look on her face when she realized there were three strange guys in the room. Eileen tore out of there and locked herself in the bathroom until we left. The poor girl was so embarrassed, but we were pretty uncomfortable too and left a little red-faced. It wasn't funny at the time, but it is one memory of Ottawa that I'll never forget. [630]

People embarrass themselves when they say or do something and learn they have unintentionally insulted someone else. They may make a remark, tell a joke, or relate something that happened which includes a negative reaction. Afterwards they learn or realize that their negative reaction applies to someone present. They may say something negative about a specific person, or about a person's race, culture, religion, political party, family, community, country, or anything else the person is associated with.

> I went to my senior class meeting where convocation ceremonies were being discussed. One girl complained bitterly that they are holding the ceremonies in the hockey rink. She said she wouldn't take her parents to such a disgusting place, and that they should rent the city's per-formance hall instead. After the meeting we all went to the student

lounge. I told my friends that I was annoyed with the snooty attitude of the student who complained, because we can't afford to pay three thousand dollars for a performance hall. I added sarcastically, "Her parents are probably loaded anyway." Then I turned around and saw her standing just three feet away. I was very embarrassed that she might have overheard me. [#631]

My daughter is in university and has a Jewish roommate. Last weekend I visited their room and the three of us got to talking. They told me about a really stingy person, and I stated, "He must be as tight as a Jew." As soon as I said this I realized I'd stuck my foot in my mouth. [#632]

24. Seeing another person embarrassed

People can also feel embarrassed when they see another person in an embarrassing situation.

Sometimes I see a person give a speech, and he stutters and stammers and keeps putting his hands in front of his face. I know how embarrassed he must feel, and I feel embarrassed for him too. [#633]

I was eating in a crowded restaurant, when a waiter carrying a tray of food tripped and spilled the food all over a woman. Everyone there stared at the woman. She looked pitiful. I couldn't help but feel sorry for her. [#634]

I had an appointment to see a medical specialist who shares an office with two other specialists. When I got there there were about twenty-five people sitting and standing in the waiting room. While I was waiting for my appointment a nurse came into the waiting room and interviewed an elderly patient about his medical history. First she told him he did not have an aneurysm, he had a brain tumor. Then she wanted to know about all his previous operations, including a hernia and a vasectomy. She had no hesitation in asking him very personal questions, and in talking loudly so that everyone overheard. I was embarrassed for the man, and I think others were too. I think it was most unprofessional. I considered saying something to the specialist about the nurse's behavior, but didn't because I'm sure she would have found a way to get back at me. [#635]

Feelings which encourage people to avoid embarrassment

People who are embarrassed feel self-conscious, uncomfortable, ashamed, foolish, stupid, ridiculous, belittled, humiliated, mortified, worthless, and/or hurt. They recognize that something has happened which will produce, or is already producing, a negative reaction to them by other people. The negative reaction may consist of staring, laughing, teasing, gossip, and/or loss of respect.

> When I'm embarrassed I have this feeling that everyone can see right through me. I think everyone is looking at me, and if they're not laughing out loud, they're laughing to themselves and trying to hide it. [636]

Embarrassment is a punishing experience, and people want to escape the situation in which it happens, avoid those who know about it, and prevent it from happening again.

> When I'm embarrassed, I want to dig a hole and crawl in it. [637]

Embarrassment is all the more punishing because normally a person is engaged in trying to get positive reactions from others. However, as a result of the embarrassing situation, instead of getting positive reactions, a person receives negative reactions. The enormous effort the person has put into making sure that his appearance and behavior produce positive reactions, and do not produce negative reactions, has come to naught. Often a person blames and criticizes himself for allowing the embarrassing situation to happen.

Signs that one is embarrassed, such as blushing, hiding one's face, making excuses, not knowing what to say, forgetting what one was going to say, crying, fleeing, and refusing to interact with others, intensify the embarrassment. Such actions make clear to onlookers that the person really has done something that calls for negative reactions. They also provide onlookers with additional stimuli to react to and tell others about.

How people try to avoid embarrassment and react when embarrassed

People take various measures to avoid being embarrassed, and respond in various ways when embarrassed. These include the following:

1. Changing one's behavior or appearance
2. Avoiding those who embarrass them
3. Avoiding activities and behaviors which cause one embarrassment
4. Warning others what to expect
5. Preventing others from finding out
6. Checking if anything is wrong
7. Evading responsibility
8. Blushing
9. Hiding one's face
10. Being unable to speak
11. Crying
12. Wanting to disappear
13. Fleeing
14. Not wanting to face those who saw one embarrassed again
15. Pretending one is not affected
16. Laughing
17. Trying to forget about the incident
18. Criticizing oneself
19. Trying to make amends
20. Asking someone to stop embarrassing them
21. Seeking revenge

1. Changing one's behavior or appearance

When people are embarrassed they almost always change what they are doing or the way they look. Normally they do so immediately, because they want to stop embarrassing themselves as fast as possible. Often they try to make sure that they do not repeat the same action in the future.

I came up behind a person I knew, tapped him on the shoulder, and said hello. When he turned to face me, I realized I didn't know him at all. I apologized and made a quick exit. Now I wait until I see a person's face before I make a fool of myself. #638

When I was in the second grade I decided to cheat on a written spelling test. I wrote out the words we had to know on a piece of paper, and then covered them with a second piece of paper I could see through. In the middle of the test the teacher reached down, picked up my papers, and told me not to do it again. I was so embarrassed, I never cheated on a test again. #639

I had a number of pairs of white pants. But when I realized people could see a wet spot on them after I'd used the toilet, I got rid of them. #640

I think twice before I order spaghetti in a restaurant. Why should I torture myself, when it's so hard to appear civilized when I eat it? No matter how well I wind it around my fork, it keeps slipping off. Also, by the time I get it wound around my fork, the meat sauce has fallen off. When I take a mouthful of spaghetti, I always seem to leave a piece hanging out, which I try to slurp into my mouth in an elegant way. #641

It's embarrassing when you are walking your dog, and your dog decides to do a number right in front of another person. I can put up with this, because there is nothing you can do about it, and the person won't stop to watch anyway. But another time I took my dog for a walk, and there was a girl walking a larger dog about a hundred yards away. As I got closer, the leash tightened, because my male dog likes to meet other dogs. The other dog was female and the girl tried to hold her back. It was obvious that the two dogs were about to start what comes naturally. With much embarrassment on both sides, the girl and I managed to get them separated and we hurriedly departed the scene. After that I cut back drastically on walking my dog. #642

When people are embarrassed about their appearance, they may take measures to change it. They may get their teeth straightened, wear a padded bra, get a toupee, have cosmetic surgery, or wear clothes that make them look less fat or less skinny.

2. Avoiding those who embarrass them

People try to avoid those who embarrass them or have embarrassed them in the past. These may be people who ridicule them or reject them, or someone whose appearance or behavior causes them embarrassment.

> There's a kid in my neighborhood that the other kids consider weird. They call him names and treat him bad. So when he sees them at school or in the neighborhood, he goes in the opposite direction and tries to avoid them completely. #643

> In junior high I would have a crush on a guy. If he found out and wasn't interested in me, I felt like crawling under a rock and not coming out. I was so embarrassed, I never wanted to face him again. I thought I'd never get over it, but after several days I did. #644

> I went to an outdoor concert with a friend of mine. While we were there she kept swearing and making crude remarks which people around us overheard. I was very embarrassed, and vowed I'd never go anywhere with her again. #645

> A friend of mine has two children and has been separated from her husband for two years. I used to do things with her before she was separated. But my husband won't let me go to a dance or bar with her anymore. He says it's because people will think she's looking for another husband and they'll see me the same way too. But all she wants is a break from her kids and housework. My husband always liked her before the separation. But now he thinks she'll be out sleeping with everyone, and that if I'm seen with her I'll be called names too. #646

3. Avoiding activities and behaviors which cause one embarrassment

People may avoid activities and behaviors with others which cause them to feel embarrassed. They may be embarrassed by the activity or behavior itself, or by the way those they are associated with behave.

> I don't like to go swimming at the beach, because I'm embarrassed by my physique. #647

I told my boyfriend that I don't like dancing with him in public because he jumps around so much. It embarrasses me. I refuse to dance with him unless he dances like everyone else. #648

4. Warning others what to expect

Individuals let others know in advance what to expect from them in order to avoid embarrassing themselves. Because other people are forewarned, they reduce their expectations and are less likely to be surprised and to ridicule the individual.

You don't want to get too close to me, because I had Caesar salad for lunch and smell like garlic. #649

I smoked a cigarette earlier. You may not want to kiss me. #650

I'm the world's slowest chess player and not any good. So don't expect much of a game. #651

5. Preventing others from finding out

People normally try to prevent others from knowing about situations which could cause them embarrassment. People frequently hide, or cover up, things which could cause them to receive negative reactions or unwanted attention.

My daughter, who is eleven years old, has a winter coat with several big holes worn through the front of it. She wears the coat whenever she goes outside, but she holds the coat together with her hands so that the holes are covered and no one can see them. #652

I like to sing songs I know and make tape recordings of myself singing. But when I play them at home, my brother makes fun of me. Once when some relatives were visiting, my brother played one of my recorded songs while I was in my bedroom. My relatives wondered who was singing. When I heard the song, I rushed out of my bedroom and turned the tape player off. I was quite embarrassed. #653

When I brought a date home, my little sister would get out my baby pictures and show them to him. I thought the pictures were ugly, so

I burned them. That way she couldn't show them to anyone. [#654]

I got my finger stuck in a beer bottle and couldn't get it out. So I had to go to the emergency clinic of the hospital. I kept my hand and the bottle in a paper bag until I saw the doctor, so that people wouldn't see what I'd done. The doctor had to break the bottle. [#655]

Have you ever noticed how people with unattractive teeth cover their mouths when they talk? I'll bet people have made cracks about their teeth in the past, and they don't want it to happen again. One girl I know had medication as a child which permanently discolored all her teeth. She was at a swimming pool the other day and a kid told her if she just brushed her teeth they wouldn't look so dirty. [#656]

Sometimes I have to use the toilet and stink up the washroom at someone else's house. When I flush the toilet, I spray some deodorant in the room. That way no one hears what I'm doing, and the smell of deodorant is natural in a washroom. [#657]

People also try to hide their identity.

I had diarrhea and went to use the public washroom. There was no one else there, but after I sat on the toilet, a couple of girls came in. Do you know how hard it is to hold yourself so the other girls don't hear you? Sounds like farting and shit hitting the water are very obvious to everybody. Believe me, I didn't leave the washroom until everyone was out, so they wouldn't know who did it. [#658]

Sometimes people are able to deal with a situation when it happens so that others do not become aware of it.

When I go to the ballet or a concert I take along a pack of cough drops. Then if I feel I'm going to cough, I put one in my mouth and usually don't cough. That way I don't disturb others and I avoid a lot of unwanted attention. [#659]

I went to the coronation dance at my high school with a fellow I really liked. We were having a great time dancing when my slip started to slide off. I ran to the bathroom as fast as I could, before people could see what was happening. Fifteen minutes later I was able to return to the dance. [#660]

I was organizing discussion groups in class when I noticed a bulge in my pants halfway down my leg. I realized that a facial tissue had fallen through a hole in my pocket. I tried to retrieve it through the hole, but couldn't reach it. I took the remaining tissues out of the pocket to stop this from happening again, and put them in my briefcase. I didn't join the discussion groups until I'd dealt with this, because I didn't want anyone to see what was happening. When I didn't see any more tissues, I sat down in one of the groups. Then I realized I had overlooked another piece which was producing a bulge on my thigh. It was quite noticeable to me, and I looked around the group to see if others were watching me, but no one was. After a while I got up and moved toward another discussion group. Just then a tissue fell out of my pants leg onto the floor. I picked it up, and immediately realized I had done the wrong thing. What I should have done was to take a tissue from my other pocket and pretend to use it, and then reach down and pick up the tissue on the floor, as though I'd dropped it. As the class continued, pieces of tissue continued to move down my leg. By the end of class I'd discovered that the bottom of my pocket was torn completely open and half a dozen tissues were migrating through my pants. They had fallen through the hole before I removed the remaining tissues from my pocket. Then when people were leaving class, another piece fell through to the floor. However, it is quite possible no one else in class realized what was happening. I was concentrating so hard on trying to minimize the damage while conducting the class, that I had no chance to feel embarrassed. I haven't worn that pair of pants since. [#661]

Often a person does not tell others about an embarrassing incident that happened to him, or waits until later when he no longer feels as embarrassed by it.

6. Checking if anything is wrong

When people think others are staring at or laughing at them, they usually try to find out why. They may check their appearance or ask another person if they know of anything wrong.

I was at a party and had had several drinks when I noticed a few people staring at me. I didn't pay much attention to it until I saw more and more people starting to look at me. I decided to check my appearance and went to the bathroom. When I looked in the mirror, I saw that three buttons on my blouse were open, and I don't wear a bra. You could see almost everything. I was so embarrassed that I left the party immediately. Even when someone mentions the incident today, I still get embarrassed. #662

7. Evading responsibility

People may pretend they did not do something that is embarrassing, or they may try to blame others.

Sometimes I'll be in a quiet place and I'm hungry and my stomach growls. It's embarrassing when people stare at me, so I pretend I don't know whose stomach did it. I start looking around too as though someone else is to blame. #663

Someone in class farted out loud, and everyone burst out laughing. They wanted to know who did it, and I knew it was the guy behind me. When I turned to look at him, he blamed it on me, and everyone started razzing me. My face turned redder than my shirt. I denied it, but no one believed me, and this just made me feel more humiliated. #664

8. Blushing

People frequently blush when they are embarrassed. They feel flushed and their checks turn red. They are unable to stop the process.

My husband is really sweet. When we're out he wants to show me off and he brags about me. It embarrasses me a lot, and I must turn about five different shades of red. #665

When I get embarrassed, I turn red. The least little thing makes me blush, even a question from a teacher in class. When I blush, I know others will notice, and this makes me turn redder. I hope and pray others won't notice. But when someone comments, "Oh, my heavens, you're red," I turn even redder. #666

A friend and I were hitchhiking. I had a pie in the top of my knapsack and we stopped at a restaurant to get some ice cream to eat with it. I took off my knapsack and got out the pie while my friend went to get the ice cream. I noticed a woman looking toward me and laughing. I looked behind me to see what she was looking at, but didn't see anything. Then she pointed at my knapsack and mouthed some words and I thought she must be referring to the fact I had had a pie in my knapsack. So I nodded and quit looking at her. When my friend didn't return I decided to see where she was. I stood up and saw my knapsack had tipped over and my underwear was spilled out on the floor for everyone to see. My face felt purple and I was sure it was going to bust. When my friend returned I was stuffing my clothes back in the knapsack and people around me were laughing. I was laughing too, but it was a nervous, embarrassed laugh. [667]

The ability of others to tell that a person is blushing depends on the person's normal skin color.

One advantage of being black is that no one can tell when I blush. When I blush, no one, including my family, notices. On the other hand, I have white friends who turn as red as a tomato, and everyone notices. [668]

9. Hiding one's face

People experience additional embarrassment when they realize they are blushing. They do not want others to know they feel embarrassed, and blushing is proof that they do. Therefore they sometimes try to hide their face. They may cover their face with their hands or turn so others can not see them.

There was a lip-synch contest on campus at which each participant pretended to sing a song that was being played. One of the contestants was well endowed and as she danced around the stage she had to keep adjusting her halter top. In the midst of jumping up and down one of her boobs fell out of her top. She didn't realize this and continued to perform until the end of the song. The crowd went wild with cheers of laughter. When she finished her routine she walked off with her breast still exposed to join her friends at a table. Her friends clued her in and she turned beet red and hid her head in her hands. However, she got over the embarrassment and continued to party. She didn't win the contest, but she never wanted for dates afterwards. [669]

Also, when a person covers her eyes with her hands, she no longer sees other people stare and laugh at her.

10. Being unable to speak

When people feel embarrassed, they are frequently at a loss for words. They do not know what to say. Actually there is little they can say to save the situation.

> One night, Larry, a friend of ours, borrowed a car from his neighbor and gave us a ride. About midnight Larry drove the car back to the neighbor's house. Larry told us to go across the street to Larry's house and sit in his father's car while Larry returned the car keys. We ran over to his father's car and waited quietly in it. All of a sudden Larry's father came roaring out of the house waving a shotgun and ordered us out of his car. I started screaming, which brought Larry running across the street. Larry explained to his father why we were in the car. His father said, "You're lucky I didn't shoot you. I thought you were punks trying to steal my stereo." Larry was so humiliated by his father's actions that he hardly spoke two words to us the rest of the evening. It took months for us to convince Larry that we didn't resent his father or feel his father's actions reflected on Larry. Despite our reassurances, anytime someone mentions the episode to Larry, it strikes a nerve. #670

> On one of my first dates, my date took me to the most popular restaurant for students. I excused myself to go to the washroom. When I returned and sat down I realized lots of students, including my date, were laughing. I asked what the joke was, and my date pointed out that there was a trail of toilet paper all the way from the washroom to my chair and a piece of toilet paper stuck in my pants. I was speechless. I was so humiliated all I could do was ask my date to take me home. #671

11. Crying

When people are embarrassed, they can feel so hurt that they cry or want to cry.

> One of the girls in school is considered unusual because she is quite small. One day the other kids pulled her into the bathroom and dressed her up in dirty old clothes and accessories from the lost and found box. She pleaded for them to stop, but they continued until they had put every item in the box on her. Then they threw her out into the main lobby

where all of the other kids hung out, and locked the bathroom door so she couldn't get back in. She was absolutely mortified. All she could do was sit there and cry. Finally she got up and ran home. It was over a week before she had enough courage to go back to school. [#672]

12. Wanting to disappear

When a person does something embarrassing, and when others react to what the person has done, the person often wants to disappear from sight.

> My girlfriend and I went out to a club and were seated at a table with three males we didn't know. Because I was very shy and insecure, I got out a cigarette for moral support. I also thought I would look cool if I smoked. It was a menthol filter tip cigarette and I lit the wrong end. To make matters worse I didn't realize it and kept puffing away. Everyone around me was laughing, and when I realized why, I wanted the floor to swallow me up. [#673]

> I had a sore throat and went to the doctor's office. The nurse stuck a thermometer in my mouth, but I was too busy looking around the room to notice it. After the nurse left the room I heard her tell another nurse that she couldn't take her patient's temperature, because the patient wouldn't close her mouth. I realized she was talking about me. I felt like crawling under the examination table and hiding for the rest of my life. [#674]

> My husband is overly affectionate in public. I feel like I'm on display or making a scene. It's very embarrassing, and I want to disappear. [#675]

> One day when I was a senior in high school, I was sitting at my desk next to my friend studying for a science exam. The room was completely quiet. Suddenly my friend jumped up, pointed right at me, and yelled, "What do you mean you're gay?" I was so embarrassed I wanted the floor to open up and swallow me. [#676]

13. Fleeing

People often try to or want to get away from those who are staring at them, laughing, or otherwise reacting negatively. They want to escape from the area where the feeling of embarrassment is most intense. This is the area where they are directly exposed to the negative reactions of others.

I was playing the violin in a concert when I suddenly fell off my chair onto the stage. The audience laughed their heads off. All I wanted to do was get the fuck out of the place. [677]

I had my third grade students put on a play for their parents, and the children took turns saying their lines. One boy forgot his lines and just stared at the audience. The audience began to laugh at the expression on his face, and the boy ran off the stage crying. I tried to catch him, but the boy ran outside and locked himself in his father's car. [678]

One day when I was in high school, it was that time of the month and I'd just come from the bathroom. I went to sit down in my chair in class and the students began to laugh. I looked around and there lying at my feet was a tampon. There was a roar of laughter as I ran from the class. I ran all the way home. I told my parents what had happened and that I was never going back to school. But I did go back again the next day. [679]

I was dating a girl from a very strict religious family. One night she and I went to a banquet for my hockey team and we both got pretty drunk. We managed to get back to her house and then drank some more with her brother. The next thing I remember is lying on the living room floor with absolutely nothing on, when someone walked up and put a blanket on top of me. I pretended to be asleep, and peeked to see who it was. It was the girl's mother. I was so embarrassed that I got up early the next morning and made my way home before her mother and father got up. I've seen her mother many times since then, but she hasn't mentioned it yet. [680]

I farted loudly in one of my university classes. I was quite embarrassed, but stayed where I was. Then I did it again, and was so embarrassed I got out of the room. I just left my books at my desk. I went back to the dorm and told some friends what had happened. They laughed, which embarrassed me even more. [681]

One summer day I was painting the outside of my cottage. The cottage is out in the middle of nowhere and there is no one around for miles. Because it was extremely hot, I decided to take off my blouse. Later on

I decided to get something to drink at the local store a few miles up the road. When I was in the store I decided to do some shopping. I ran into a man and his wife I knew and was standing there talking to them when I looked down and realized I was just wearing my bra. I ran out of the store and never returned. I don't think I was ever that embarrassed before, or ever will be again. #682

14. Not wanting to face those who saw one embarrassed again

A person usually does not want to face the people again who witnessed his embarrassment. He frequently tries to avoid eye contact with those who know what happened.

> My mom and I went into the bank. While I was making a withdrawal she went over and carried out a conversation with another customer. When she returned she said, "I was just talking to your psychology professor." "That's not my psychology professor," I told her. "No wonder he looked mystified when I mentioned Skinner, Maslow, and Piaget." Mom kept her eyes averted from the man until we escaped from the bank. #683

After a person is embarrassed he may avoid specific settings or individuals, or he may stop participating in an activity.

> I belong to an organization, and attended a meeting when they were holding elections for offices. The president suggested to me that I run for the position of secretary. So when they asked who'd be willing to do the job, I volunteered. Then the president said in front of everyone, "What? You run? You're the biggest drunk around. You're not organized enough to do it." I was very embarrassed and angry. I left the meeting and haven't been back since. #684

> One night I was out with my friends at a club and had too much to drink. I passed my limit, but that didn't stop me, and I kept ordering drink after drink. Later on I felt sick and threw up on the table where I was sitting. When the bouncers escorted me out, I got sick again, but this time all over the bouncers. The next day I remembered everything that had happened and felt so humiliated. That was three years ago, and I haven't gone back to that club again. #685

I was at football practice, and the coach told us exactly what he wanted us to do in the next drill. When my turn came something unusual happened, and rather than do what the coach said, I took advantage of the situation and made a great play. If I'd done exactly what the coach wanted, I'd have been tackled by a very large offensive player. The coach yelled and screamed at me. One of the team captains tried to talk to the coach about it, but the coach remained quite upset. I was very embarrassed, and quit the team shortly thereafter. [#686]

15. Pretending one is not affected

People are usually caught unprepared when something embarrassing happens. Therefore they do not know how to respond. If they react or flee they are likely to attract even more unwanted attention. As a result they frequently try to ride out the storm and just sit or stand there and take it. They intended to be in that location anyway and have not made plans to be elsewhere.

I was playing a video game in an arcade when a friend came up behind me and pulled down my sweat pants. I was very embarrassed. But I pulled up my pants, pretended it didn't bother me, and continued playing the game. [#687]

A person may also try to cover up his embarrassment by pretending that he intended to act that way, or knew all along what would happen.

I was at a dance and decided to sit down on a chair by the wall. Because it was dark, I didn't realize there was no chair there and fell flat on my ass. I tried to hide my embarrassment by pretending I knew there was no chair there. [#688]

16. Laughing

Sometimes a person who is embarrassed responds by laughing. Often others are laughing at the person, and the person laughs along with them. The person rarely finds the situation funny. Instead, it is a way to try to make the best of a bad situation.

When I was in French class in high school, I farted out loud. The whole class, including the teacher, looked at me and burst out laughing. I laughed along with them, which helped cover up my embarrassment. #689

I went up an escalator and my shoelace got caught in the mechanism. I had to take off the shoe and pull on the shoelace. A crowd of people watched me. I was embarrassed, but I laughed with them. #690

I went to get a burger and milkshake at a fast-food restaurant with my boyfriend. We picked up our order and sat down at a table. I tried to suck my drink through the straw, but it was too thick. So I did what my boyfriend did and took the lid off the container so I could drink from it. But when I tilted the container up, nothing came out. So I tilted it more and more. Suddenly the whole milkshake fell on my face. The restaurant was packed and lots of people saw what happened. The best I could do was laugh at the situation. But my boyfriend was mortified and insisted on leaving the restaurant right away. #691

17. Trying to forget about the incident

After an embarrassing experience one wants to forget about it and wants other people to forget about it too.

The first time I got drunk, my boyfriend dropped me off at my house. It was the one place I did not want to be. So I got mad and started cursing him loudly from our front porch. This woke up my father who discovered I was drunk. This was embarrassing, and the way I got out of trouble was by getting my boyfriend to explain to my parents what had happened. But then my boyfriend went home and told his mother about it, and I was embarrassed all over again. I try to put the whole thing as far back in my mind as possible. #692

18. Criticizing oneself

People frequently criticize themselves after they do something embarrassing. They repeatedly blame themselves for what has happened.

I have a strong, clear voice and was always told by my mother to sing nice and loud in church. So every Sunday I'd go to church and sing my little heart out. In church the congregation sings a few lines, then the priest sings, and this goes back and forth when there's a hymn. Well, one Sunday I was so absorbed in singing nice and loud that I kept on singing during the parts when the priest was supposed to sing. You could hear me through the whole church and people turned around to look at me. I got dirty looks from the older people and laughs from the younger ones. I have never been so embarrassed in my life. I sat there for the rest of the service just shaking my head and saying, "Stupid! Stupid! Stupid! Never again will I sing in church." It's been three years since that happened. I can laugh at it now, but it was not funny then. I'm still self-conscious when I sing in church today and probably always will be. [#693]

19. Trying to make amends

When embarrassed, people often want to make up for what has happened. They hope to straighten things out and leave a better impression in other people's minds.

Tom was in a junior high school basketball tournament. The fans were seated on one side of the gym, and the coaches, timekeeper, and the benches for the players were located on the other side. Tom was one of the best players and guarded a very good player from the opposing team, so considerable attention was focused on both of them. Near the end of the first half, the rear of Tom's shorts ripped. Tom and his coach didn't realize this, but the fans were laughing so hard they had tears in their eyes. The referee stopped the play and told Tom. When Tom reached back he found his shorts were almost torn off. He went to the bench and pulled a pair of shorts on over his own. He was extremely embarrassed. In the second half Tom concentrated so deeply on the game that he hardly noticed the crowd. He had scored six points in the first half. But in the second half he scored twenty-six points to try to regain his self-respect. [#694]

20. Asking someone to stop embarrassing them

When people are embarrassed by the behavior of others, they sometimes ask them to stop what they are doing. They may ask others to quit giving them negative reactions in front of others, or to stop teasing them.

I'm nineteen, and when I'm with my friends and don't have any money, I have to ask my father for some. He tells me I'm a bum. I find it embarrassing and don't like it. When I get a chance to talk to him in private, I tell him I don't like him saying this. #695

I'm embarrassed when my wife treats me like a child or henpecks me in front of others. I always tell her afterwards she's done so, and I tell her how unhappy I am about it. #696

People may also ask someone they are associated with to change her appearance or behavior so they will no longer be embarrassed by it.

I'm separated, and my eight-year-old daughter asked me not to be affectionate with my boyfriend when she brings her friend over to watch TV. #697

21. Seeking revenge

When someone places a person in an embarrassing situation, the person may seek revenge.

I went to the beach with two friends, Linda and Pam. Linda decided to put on a show for all the people around us, and when Pam wasn't paying attention, Linda pulled Pam's bathing suit down. Linda thought this was just a joke and all in fun. Afterwards, we went up to the public washrooms to take a shower. While Linda was in the shower, Pam gathered up Linda's clothes and took off with them. It never occurred to Linda that Pam would take revenge. In order to get her clothes back, Linda had to put a skimpy towel around herself and go outside. This was an unusual sight at the beach, and lots of people stared at her. In the end, Linda was much more embarrassed than Pam. #698

One winter day when we were storm stayed, I was standing at my large picture window watching the snowplow outside when my cousin came up behind me and pulled my pants down. A woman across the street was looking out of her window and saw it happen. I swore I would get revenge on my cousin, and that summer I had my opportunity. I saw my cousin standing on a ladder holding a can of paint while he was painting his porch. So I pulled his sweat pants down around his ankles. He couldn't pull his pants up without dropping the can of paint, and he had to get his wife to come outside and pull his pants up for him. He was facing the main road at the time and lots of cars drove past and saw him standing there. [#699]

Embarrassment and entertainment

People find it entertaining when they see someone in an embarrassing situation. Often the person who is embarrassed has done something inconsistent, incorrect, inappropriate, or unusual. For example, an individual may slip and fall when he is trying to walk, accidentally enter a bathroom designated for the opposite sex, put on an item of clothing incorrectly, mistake one person for another, fall asleep during a lecture or church service, or act startled by something harmless. When a person does something embarrassing, he often does something others have not seen done before, have not seen done in that particular way before, or have not seen the particular person do before. It is quite inconsistent with their previous image of the person. When a person slips on stairs and flies through the air, or says something and puts his foot in his mouth, people witness something unusual and unexpected and are thoroughly entertained. When someone does the very opposite of what he is trying to do and what people expect him to do, it looks so incongruous, ridiculous, and absurd that people are delighted. As long as the person does not seriously injure himself, other people find what happens quite funny.

I watched my husband try to empty the last bit of orange juice from a pitcher into a glass. He wasn't paying attention and the glass overflowed and orange juice spilled out on the table. It looked so foolish, I had to laugh. [#700]

When I saw a cut on my husband's head, I asked him how he got it. He said he had hit his head on the bathroom sink when he was reaching for the toilet paper. I thought that was really funny, and so did my friend when I told her. [#701]

When we were small, my dad came home from work late one night, saw my brother and me lying on the sofa, and told us it was time to go to bed. He repeated himself several times, and because we didn't answer he walked over to the sofa to see if we were asleep. Dad discovered he was talking to two large dolls that belonged to my older sister. She was watching all along and killing herself laughing. [#702]

In this year's summer parade there were two teams of Clydesdale horses. When they passed by the corner where I was standing, one of the horses let loose a load of manure on the street. Subsequently, most of the groups and floats in the parade avoided it. A teenage male next to me watched the scene intently to see what would happen. Then came a large, inflated float which a dozen young men carried by hand. The float prevented them from seeing the street ahead, and one of the men stepped directly in the manure. The teenage male next to me thought it hilarious and let loose howls of laughter. The man who stepped in the manure looked unsure as to what had happened and how to react. [#703]

People also enjoy watching performances in which comedians, hypnotists, and actors present embarrassing situations to entertain their audiences.

Because people find it entertaining when others are in embarrassing situations, people often manufacture the situations. Many practical jokes and initiation rites consist of placing individuals in embarrassing situations.

When I'm in a grocery store with my dad, he likes to accuse me of eating the strawberries or other fruit. From that moment on, the clerk or manager watches me carefully. Dad just wants to embarrass me. [#704]

After I drove my date home, we sat and talked in the car and then I walked her to her door. As I was giving her a good-night kiss, her father opened the door. "Are your intentions honorable, young man?" he asked me. Then he laughed and said, "Get out of here." I was very embarrassed. [#705]

I was studying with two friends in the library when I noticed both of them edging away from me. First one and then the other farted. I was embarrassed being next to them, but what happened next ranks among the most embarrassing moments of my life. Both of them stood up, moved away from the table, and began to yell how gross I was. There were several other people in the area who began to stare at me. I tried to argue, but there were two of them and one of me, so the only thing to do was sit there and endure the embarrassment.

To be honest, I probably deserved this, because I have set one of the friends up on several occasions. Once I told him that a certain girl really liked him and wanted to go out on a date with him. He didn't believe me at first, but after I kept at it, he began to take me seriously. He questioned me constantly about her. I replied nonchalantly that if he was interested it was up to him to ask her out. That weekend we were at a popular lounge where the girl was present. My friend acted real cool and glanced over at the girl every now and then. She seemed puzzled by these glances, and looked back at him. Later he went and asked her to dance. She accepted, but the look on her face showed she wasn't exactly thrilled by the idea. However, my friend seemed happy dancing with her until another guy interrupted them. My friend returned to our table with a very embarrassed and angry look on his face. He was embarrassed because the other guy was her boyfriend. I'd told my friend a big lie, because the girl didn't even know who he was. I bought him a cold beer to ease the tension, and had him laughing in five minutes. [#706]

One summer a bunch of guys at work stuck my head in the window of a car and rolled up the window. Then they pulled my pants down and left me at the side of the road for a half hour. I've gotten over it, but I still find it hard to trust car windows. [#707]

During the speeches after a wedding, relatives and friends frequently tell anecdotes about the bride and groom. Some of these are about previous indiscretions and can be pretty embarrassing to the couple. [#708]

I grew up in Vietnam and we used to play a number of practical jokes at home. If a person leaned forward out of his chair when he reached across a table, I would remove the chair. When he tried to sit back down he fell on the floor. We'd also tie a piece of string to the back of a person's shirttail with a piece of paper on the end of the string. The person would be talking or busy and wouldn't notice what we were doing. The piece of paper had to be big enough so everyone would see it, and it made the person look like he had an animal tail. When everyone laughed, the person would try to find out what was wrong with him. Occasionally we'd play another kind of practical joke when a person was sleeping. We'd take some soot from the side of a cooking pot and draw a beard, mustache, heavy eyebrows, and dark cheeks on the person's face. When the person got up he looked very funny to everyone, and if he washed his face he usually smeared the soot around which also looked funny. My father told us we shouldn't do this because the spirit of a person who is sleeping or dreaming wanders off. When the spirit comes back, if it doesn't recognize the person, it won't reenter the body and the person will never wake up. It was usually the older children and young adult males who played these practical jokes.

I recently watched a practical joke played by adult women in Ho Chi Minh City. My mother, sister, and I were staying with our cousin in her apartment in the city. When we visited a city park, we ran into a family we hadn't seen for many years and invited them to come to our cousin's apartment. They said they would arrive about four o'clock. We then bought some food and took it to the apartment to prepare it. Guests don't arrive on time, so at four o'clock our cousin and two of our friends were in the kitchen, and the rest of us were in the living room. My cousin was seated on a low stool in the middle of the kitchen floor just beginning to clean a fish for dinner for our guests. My mother looked out of the apartment window and announced that the guests had arrived in two cars. Instead of four people there were seven. My mother speculated that the family had invited some friends along. My sister looked out the window too and said they were walking along the street looking for the apartment. My cousin and the two other women in the kitchen panicked, because the apartment hadn't been cleaned and there wasn't enough food for this number of people. They ran around the kitchen grabbing things, while my cousin told them what to get. When I informed my cousin we were just kidding her, she was enormously relieved and laughed. She said, "I can't believe you did that; it was so cruel. It gave me a real scare." The guests arrived at seven thirty. #709

A variation on a practical joke is not to tell a person when he does something that would embarrass him if he knew. Because he can not correct the situation, this ensures that he is not spared any embarrassment.

Occasionally a group of friends will be at a ballgame and one of them will go use the toilet and forget to zip up his pants. His friends won't tell him and will continue to stare and laugh at him. #710

Many party games are designed to handicap participants and contestants so that they can not perform competently and appear foolish. Thus participants may be blindfolded, tied, or forbidden to use their hands or to talk. Examples include blind man's bluff, pin the tail on the donkey, a three-legged race, a race in which an egg is carried in a spoon held in the mouth of each contestant, a pie eating contest, and charades. The audience is much more entertained by the incompetence and failures of the participants than by their successes. Often such contests are made more difficult to ensure the failure of the participants. Thus a piñata may be raised or lowered out of reach of the blindfolded person who is trying to strike it, and the person may be intentionally given false information as to where the piñata is located, such as "It's just over your head," or "It's right behind you." Frequently the contestants do not realize their role is to entertain the audience by failing and appearing foolish.

When people feel embarrassed they usually show signs of it. They may blush, hide their face, flee the area, stammer, criticize themselves, or remain expressionless. People are entertained by an individual's reaction when he is embarrassed. Therefore people also place an individual in embarrassing situations in order to enjoy the individual's reaction.

> I am one of the female assistants at an exercise club. One night my boss told me everyone had gone home so I could go ahead and clean the men's shower room. I walked in and found a man buck naked taking a shower. Luckily he was facing the other direction and didn't see me. My boss is a notorious practical joker, so I overcame my embarrassment, walked out, and pretended I hadn't seen anyone. [711]

> My sister and I went shopping for groceries with our dad. It was that time of the month and I got a box of menstrual pads. When we went through the checkout counter, our luck was bad, because the box of menstrual pads ended up at the top of one of the grocery bags. The grocery boy noticed, and Dad said, "Well girls, this box of thirty should do you both for a month." My sister and I were extremely embarrassed and must have turned forty shades of red. Dad and the boy just laughed. [712]

I was dating a guy named Roger, and we went to a friend's party. They decided to hold a contest at the party to see who had more gall, guys or girls. Roger agreed to enter the contest along with a girl named Angela. Both of them had to get under separate blankets on the floor and take off their clothing, one piece at a time. The winner would be the person who took everything off, and if they both did so, this would prove that one had as much gall as the other. Gradually they got down to their underwear. Then Angela took hers off. Angela had prepared for the contest beforehand and had a bathing suit on under her underwear. Everyone else at the party, except for Roger, was in on the joke. So Roger felt he had to match Angela, and he took off his underwear. Now that he had proved himself, Roger waited to be given his clothes back. However, the blanket was ripped off him and he was left lying on the floor with nothing on in front of everyone. He jumped up and ran into another room to hide himself. I never saw anyone so embarrassed in my life. [#713]

Most people find that when they remember or are reminded of a situation in which they were previously embarrassed, they experience many of the same feelings again.

I went to a club and while I was dancing with a guy he asked me why I was wearing two different shoes. I didn't know what he was talking about. Then I looked at my feet and saw I really did have two different shoes on. I was lost for words. We both laughed, but I was very embarrassed. I don't know how it happened. That was four years ago, and I still get embarrassed when I think about it. [#714]

Embarrassing experiences are a sensitive issue and make a person uncomfortable. Consequently, people frequently mention past embarrassments to tease, or "get a rise" out of, another person.

A female employee where I work was asked out on a date by a customer we all call "the Slimy Little Bugger." We tease her constantly about this because we know it drives her crazy. We say things like "Has the little one been in tonight?" "Guess who was in today asking about you?" and "He told me he wants you to be his valentine." [#715]

The first time my sister got drunk, her friends left her in the car because she didn't feel good. When they finally took her home, she said, "Look at my pants." She had shit herself, but she made her friends promise not to tell anyone. The next week one of her friends let it slip and everyone heard about it. My sister felt really humiliated and claimed she'd never drink again. Other people still tease her about this. #716

People may be teased for days or even years about an embarrassing incident.

One summer day the cows got out of their pasture and ran around our backyard. My mother had just hung out the wash, and one cow got her horns caught in my sister's bra. The poor cow nearly went crazy trying to get it off, and Dad found the bra two days later. That was six years ago, my parents still tease my sister about this, and she still gets embarrassed over it. #717

One night my husband and I were at a party. I went to use the toilet and discovered I'd forgotten to wear underwear. I was highly embarrassed and told a friend what I'd done. She thought it was a great joke and shared it with the others there. That was twenty-five years ago, and they still tease me about it. #718

When person A brings up an instance in which person B felt embarrassed in the past, person A is very likely to produce a reaction in person B. Person B's reaction provides entertainment, or stimulation, for person A. B's reaction also provides entertainment for onlookers. Therefore, A can provide entertainment for onlookers by reminding B of past embarrassments and having onlookers witness B's reaction. The responses of the onlookers provide A with positive reactions. In addition, when A tells others about something embarrassing that B did, A can entertain others and make them laugh. As a consequence, relating accounts of embarrassing behavior is an effective way for A to get positive reactions from others.

My parents like to tell their friends about something I did that they find amusing. Everyone laughs at me, and I feel embarrassed. #719

My husband likes to tell others about something silly I did. I don't like him telling other people. It is personal, and others shouldn't laugh at it. #720

My wife enjoys telling guests about the time I took a hot piece of pie from a pan on top of the stove with a spatula. Instead of putting it directly on the plate which was sitting on the counter next to the stove, I tried to be fancy and balanced it on the spatula as I did a half turn with my back to the stove. I dropped the piece in the middle of the kitchen floor. #721

Laughter is important in both positive reactions and in negative reactions. In the case of positive reactions, a person wants to entertain others, and others laugh at how witty, clever, or much fun a person is. In the case of negative reactions, a person does not want to entertain others, and others laugh at how incompetent a person is or how ridiculous he looks. In both cases people laugh because they find the person highly stimulating. People find embarrassing situations funny because a person is trying to do something or hide something and fails. This is the case when a person goes down a water slide and accidentally loses his bathing suit.

People can relate to others who are in embarrassing situations because people are trying to avoid the same types of embarrassment. People experience the situation as though it is happening to them, and this produces tension, but at the same time they know that it is not happening to them, and this allows them to easily release the tension. Thus they experience tension and release and this gives them pleasure and helps them laugh. The person who is embarrassed, on the other hand, knows he is likely to receive negative reactions from others, and this produces tension. Because he knows the situation really is happening to him, rather than to someone else, he cannot release his tension. Therefore he receives no pleasure in the situation, and feels little desire to laugh.

When a person intentionally, rather than accidentally, does something that people disapprove of, people do not laugh. Instead, they are upset and react with criticism. This is the case when a person deliberately takes off his bathing suit before he goes down a water slide.

Functions of avoiding embarrassment

Embarrassment is a sensitive indicator of the possibility other people will reduce a person's resources. When an individual avoids doing the things which will cause him to feel embarrassed, he avoids doing the things which will cause others to cut off his resources. Most of a person's resources are provided by other people. The person's resources include food and water, positive reactions, sex, and stimulation, and the means to obtain them, such as time, energy, materials, money, jobs, information, and relationships. If a person does things a) which alienate others, and b) which make him look less desirable than his fellow competitors, then others are a) less likely to share their resources with him, and b) less likely to value his resources as worth trading for. Instead others will share their resources with his competitors, and trade their resources for the resources of his competitors. People do not feel embarrassed when no one knows they do something improper. This is because when no one knows, there is no danger that they will lose resources from others.

Embarrassment is an intense, unpleasant experience. Embarrassment occurs when there is the least sign of negative reactions, or when one expects to receive negative reactions. Therefore, embarrassment enables a person to be supersensitive to negative reactions from others. As a result, an individual is made strongly aware that he has done something that others respond negatively to, and he is made strongly aware of just what he has done that causes others to react negatively. As a consequence, a person is much less likely to do the same thing again. Because he is less likely to do the same thing again, he is less likely to alienate others and lose resources. Moreover, embarrassment is so punishing, one makes the effort to learn in advance what behaviors other people are embarrassed by, so that one can avoid the same behaviors and avoid suffering the same embarrassment. As a result, a person is less likely to do the things which will cause him to be embarrassed, is less likely to be viewed negatively, and is more likely to protect his resources.

The feeling of embarrassment is based on our awareness of how we appear to others. In order to feel embarrassment, we must have a sense of how others see us. The stronger this sense and the more accurate it is, the better we can avoid negative reactions and protect our resources.

A person feels embarrassment when others find out he has done something they disapprove of, but the person does not feel embarrassment if he does the same thing and others do not find out about it. Embarrassment drives the lesson poignantly home that one should not let others think that one does the things they disapprove of. Subsequently, one learns to either stop doing such things altogether, or to take greater care to prevent others from finding out one does them.

Because people are so aware of how they appear to others, and are punished by embarrassment as soon as they realize others will view them negatively, people are able to learn by nonphysical means what to avoid in the future so they do not jeopardize their resources. Without this sense of embarrassment, people would have to be physically punished in order to a) know they had upset others, and b) make the association between a specific type of behavior and punishment. When a person causes his own nonphysical pain, he does not have to rely on physical pain from others. Physical pain can produce injury and infection and reduce one's chances of survival. This does not happen with nonphysical pain such as embarrassment.

The individual protects his resources by not doing things which will cause him embarrassment. The better he can sense negative reactions from others, and the more intensely he can experience embarrassment, the better he can protect his resources. Embarrassment occurs as soon as there are signs that others are reacting negatively to a person, or as soon as a person realizes he has presented others with a reason to do so. The immediate occurrence of embarrassment also allows one to stop one's behavior sooner and thereby protect one's resources faster. Also, the immediate occurrence of embarrassment allows one to make a mental association between a specific behavior and receiving punishment, and one is less likely to repeat that behavior again.

As a consequence of embarrassment, individuals conform to group expectations, perform acceptably, and gain the cooperation of others. Those who embarrass themselves appear stupid, foolish, immoral, and/or inept to others, and are not likely to gain their cooperation. Those who do not embarrass themselves, on the other hand, do not appear stupid, foolish, immoral, and/or inept, and are therefore more likely to gain the cooperation of others. Those who gain the cooperation of others are given more opportunities to participate in cooperative endeavors and obtain more resources.

Excess behavior

Excess behavior is behavior in response to feelings which results in one acting contrary to the purposes the feelings are designed for. As a consequence, one loses resources rather than gains resources or protects them. For example, the feeling of embarrassment encourages people to avoid ridicule, and by avoiding ridicule they normally avoid losing resources from other people. However, there are situations in which people seek to avoid ridicule but actually lose resources.

Because of a fear of embarrassment, individuals are on their best behavior whenever they are in a public setting. However, in many public settings, the public that are present have little or no control over the individual's resources. If the individual does something embarrassing, there is no loss of resources. Therefore the effort made by an individual to act and appear proper in these settings is largely wasted time and energy.

In addition, one can be so concerned about the possibility of embarrassment that one does not do things that are in one's interest to do. As a result one may fail to obtain information, goods, or services which will enable one to deal with health, sexual, and other needs.

> Many people are too embarrassed to buy certain things they need at a store. My sister won't buy menstrual pads because so many guys hang out at the store and tease her. She sends someone else to buy them for her. Others don't want to buy contraceptives because this is a small place and everyone will hear what they're doing. [#722]

> I don't want to go into the library and check out books on certain topics, because the library staff know me and will probably talk about me. Other people must feel the same way, because library books on topics like sexual difficulties, venereal disease, alcoholism, and divorce are frequently stolen. I'm even quite circumspect when I look for articles in reference books on personal topics and photocopy them, because I don't want others to know I'm concerned about these topics. [#723]

> It's embarrassing when you need to go to your doctor with a venereal disease or unwanted pregnancy. I'm sure his estimation of you goes down. I think that's why many people put off seeing the doctor as long as they can. [#724]

Also, a person can be so apprehensive over the possibility of being ridiculed that he does not dare take chances or risks. He is scared to do something that others are not doing, and he will not obtain resources that may be available. The gain in resources might far outweigh the possible loss of resources through ridicule. Also, many of the things he might try would not be ridiculed by others, but his fear of possible ridicule prevents him from attempting them. In contrast, an individual may learn too well what he will be ridiculed for. As a result of previous ridicule, he may stop doing the things which he should do to get resources. For example, if he is teased about the appearance of his date or about his dancing, he may stop dating anyone whose appearance does not satisfy his friends, or he may refuse to dance from then on. When a person ceases to try an activity, he never learns to perform it well. Often things that a person has been teased about by other children, he would not be teased about by other adults, but he refuses to do them from childhood on, sometimes for the remainder of his life. One suspects that if a person continues to deal with the same people who once ridiculed him for a particular behavior, they are likely to do so again if he repeats the behavior in the future. However, if the person deals with a different group of people, perhaps in a different locale, he might not be ridiculed for that particular behavior and his avoidance of it becomes unnecessary.

A person is often a member of several different groups in society, and each group has its own ideas of proper and improper behavior. It is difficult for an individual to satisfy all of these groups at the same time and to avoid ridicule by all of them. As a result there can be numerous conflicts when a person who is a member of one group participates in another group. Thus behavior that is desirable and not ridiculed by one's peer group, may be undesirable and ridiculed by one's relatives, and vice versa. Such conflicts consume a great deal of time and energy.

> My parents embarrass me because they are so old-fashioned. It's real embarrassing when Mom picks out her kind of clothes for me when my friends are around. #725

An enormous amount of effort is expended by each individual in society trying to guarantee that he does not do anything which can be ridiculed. In order to avoid embarrassment an individual not only has to reach a high level of performance, he also has to maintain it. It is not enough to make sure that one is perfectly shaven, clean, dressed, and made-up; one also has to check during the day to ensure that one does not have dirt on one's clothes, or food on one's face or between one's teeth, or that one's makeup does not need retouching. Similarly one has to carefully monitor and govern what one says and does to make sure others will have no grounds for negative reactions. One has to remain above reproach, and the level of perfection which is sought is obsessive. Also, when one decides to engage in behavior which others would ridicule, one has to devote effort to keeping the behavior concealed from others. A sizable portion of human behavior is dedicated to expending time and energy in these ways, and one wonders whether this effort could be put to different uses which would obtain more resources.

Society and avoiding embarrassment

Organizations and its members are subject to embarrassment in the same way that individuals are embarrassed. Society provides the means to subject individuals and organizations to considerable public embarrassment. At the same time, society provides individuals and organizations with facilities and instruction for avoiding embarrassment and maintaining privacy.

Organizations and the individuals associated with them are subject to embarrassment. They are embarrassed when it becomes publicly known that they have done something incompetent, neglectful, inconsistent, stupid, wrong, or immoral, or that they have failed. As a result organizations and their members can be ridiculed and lose resources. When they do something embarrassing, other individuals and organizations become less willing to share resources with them or exchange resources for their resources. Consequently, organizations seek to keep anything which could generate negative reactions from public view. Organizations attempt to protect themselves from embarrassment by making sure information about the organization which is released to the public warrants positive rather than negative reactions. When unfavorable information is made public, organizations try to protect themselves through denials, remaining silent, pretending nothing happened, preventing others from finding out, passing the buck, conducting their own investigation, playing down the situation, criticizing themselves, punishing whistle-blowers, blaming and removing specific employees, and changing their behavior.

Society employs considerable means for embarrassing individuals and organizations. Through newspapers, magazines, books, television, film, and radio, individuals and organizations are identified by name and shown to deserve negative reactions. Journalists, police, and government representatives conduct investigations and ask questions to expose embarrassing information. Selected information, photographs, editorials, cartoons, letters, plays, and jokes are used to ridicule individuals and organizations before the public. Information on private lives and criminal activities is publicized. The public is interviewed and their negative reactions toward specific individuals and organizations are made public. Even when a situation is manufactured or misunderstood and individuals and organizations have done nothing to feel embarrassed about, they still feel embarrassed because of the likelihood of negative reactions. Public ridicule and criticism of real and supposed situations make very clear to those who are not involved what they must avoid doing if they want to avoid being embarrassed themselves. Also, public knowledge about individuals and organizations is used to select participants in cooperative endeavors. Reputations, letters of reference, credit reports, criminal records, and other forms of information are used to accept or reject individuals for employment, loans, business partnerships, social clubs, and marriages. Reputations of organizations determine whether or not people join, patronize, accept employment with, or invest in the organizations.

At the same time, numerous facilities and practices within a society are used to help individuals and organizations avoid embarrassment and maintain privacy. People frequently live in private homes and apartments, sleep and engage in sex in private bedrooms, and work in private offices. They use doors and window curtains and blinds to prevent others from seeing what they are doing. They use private telephone lines when they can get them. They receive private mail, use computer passwords to protect privacy, and have private medical files, tax returns, grade transcripts, salaries, and bank account and loan statements. There are norms and laws against trespass, listening to other people's telephone calls, opening other people's mail, and looking into their windows. There are also protections against the violation of privacy by government representatives. Locks are used on doors, cabinets, desks, diaries, and file cabinets to help to maintain privacy. An individual's biological privacy is protected through private bathrooms, toilet stalls, and dressing rooms, and boxes of menstrual pads are placed in brown bags and birth control pills in unidentifiable covers. In addition, there are products to help people remove and mask odors and keep their clothes clean. Facial and bodily features which are likely to be ridiculed by others can be temporarily hidden by cosmetics, and permanently altered and removed by cosmetic surgery. Mirrors are placed in public areas to enable individuals to check on and improve their appearance. Instruction is provided to help people avoid embarrassment in various ways. Courses and books teach people how to speak in public; remember names; dance socially; and sing, dance, act, and play an instrument in front of an audience. Instruction in good manners often includes rules to follow which reduce the likelihood of embarrassing others.

One can view society as composed of two worlds. One is the public world in which people work hard to obtain positive reactions and to avoid negative reactions. Wherever one looks in the public world, one sees people presenting their best appearance and behavior. The second world is the private world. Here people do and say the things that would receive negative reactions if they were done and said in the public world. An embarrassing event occurs when someone unintentionally introduces a behavior from the private world into the public world. The public world is so cleansed of private behavior that the sudden appearance of a private act surprises or shocks those who see it. People put so much effort into making sure that they act appropriately in the public world, that when someone slips up and does something inappropriate, it is the last thing people expect to see and they find it funny.

AVOIDING CRITICISM

Brief contents

Detailed contents

Introduction

People are very much concerned with avoiding criticism. People do not want others to react negatively to them, and criticism is evidence that they do. Criticism hurts, and because of this hurt people hate to be criticized. This is true whether the criticism is directed at their appearance, mannerisms, actions, morals, attitudes, relationships, family, associates, education, possessions, or their productivity. Criticism of a person is an indication that the person's resources are likely to be reduced. When people are criticized, they feel hurt, and they change their behavior so they do not receive further criticism. People also try to escape hurt by not doing the things that they see and hear others criticized for. When people avoid criticism in order to escape hurt, they reduce the chances that their resources will be decreased. People feel hurt as soon as they are criticized. This provides them with a maximum amount of time to change their behavior and prevent the loss of resources. Criticism produces tension. Criticism is a negative reaction and is inconsistent with the image a person wants to have of himself and wants others to have of him.

Criticism of others

One of the most common things people do is criticize others. Criticism is an unfavorable reaction to what others do.

> In our community people don't like each other and always criticize one another. The Gestapo would have a field day here, because everybody would sell everyone else down the river. #726

Criticism is the primary tool that people use in their attempts to get others to change their behavior so that people can establish consistency with their models. (See the chapter on Establishing Consistency in a later volume.) In other words, criticism is the means people use to get others to act consistent with what they want.

After a couple of my customers complained, I realized I'd have to tell one of my salesmen he had BO (body odor). I was reluctant, because I didn't know how he would react. So I was surprised when he accepted it calmly. He took care of the problem and there's never been another complaint. #727

Well the dinner wasn't bad, considering the roast beef was overcooked, the potatoes were cold, and the gravy was lumpy. #728

People use criticism for many reasons, including getting others to change, removing inconveniences, improving things, indicating disappointment, expressing upset, showing disagreement, helping the person they criticize, helping a third party, having something to say, getting a reaction, winning attention, expressing envy, gaining support from others, explaining their own actions, and getting revenge. People commonly criticize those who cause difficulties for them, differ from other people, and do not do what they think they should.

People frequently criticize others for causing them difficulties. They respond negatively to people who inconvenience them, disturb them, hurt them, or do something that might hurt them. They also criticize those who criticize them and reject them, as well as those who do not understand them, cooperate with them, or treat them with respect.

I don't appreciate it when the kids leave the top off the toothpaste and don't replace an empty roll of toilet paper. I always mention it to them. My philosophy is "Don't make work for other people," but it's not theirs. #729

I was baby-sitting for two four-year olds, when an argument broke out between them over possession of a book. Margaret refused to give the book to Diane, so Diane told Margaret she was ugly and that I hated her. #730

One of my clerks charged a customer ten dollars less than she should have. The price was correctly stated on the item, but she read it off wrong. I was quite upset and made sure the clerk knew why. #731

When you work for the police department, you have to take a lot of verbal abuse from the public. No one likes to get a ticket for parking in a no-parking zone, running a red light, or speeding. When you give them a ticket, some people say, "Is this all you guys have to do? Pull over innocent people?" and "You're just making money for the city by picking on the little guys. Police are the slackest bunch of people I've ever seen." People do not like to have the police interfere with what they want to do. One guy got upset when I was rerouting traffic around a parade. He called me a "Fuck Ass!" and squealed his tires. Another guy had to be taken to jail for being drunk in a public place. He kept saying, "Why do you always pick on me? You guys are real assholes. Don't you have anything better to do?" Once we answered a call from a man whose barn had been spray painted by vandals. He was very upset with us, and claimed it wouldn't have happened if we'd been doing our job. Another time there was a report of vandalism at an elementary school. When we got there there was no one around, but I could hear kids yelling from the neighboring woods, "Go away, you assholes," "You pigs can't catch us," and "Fuck off, fruits!" Then there was the time workers at a local plant were on strike, and were angry at us for trying to protect people who were driving delivery trucks. They shouted, "Look at the scabs help the other scabs," and "Police are fucking traitors." Even some of my own friends say that police drink all the liquor they confiscate, and just look for a place to hide and sleep during the midnight shift. [#732]

People also criticize others because they look or act different.

He's covered with tattoos. I can see why he never takes his shirt off. [#733]

I never heard anyone sneeze so loudly. You can hear him from one end of the mall to the other. I was in the supermarket the other day, heard him sneeze, and knew just where to find him. I've told him he should try to sneeze like other people. [#734]

My friends and I like to stand around the student center and make remarks about other students. I'll ask, "Why would someone want to look like that?" about a guy who shaved a design in his hair and dyed it. A friend will reply, "Maybe he had a traumatic experience during toilet training." And each of us will try to outdo the other with a clever comment. [735]

I know how much remarks hurt when you're overweight. My relatives say, "You always were fat," "It's too bad someone in this family had to be fat," and "Move over, the cow is coming through." [736]

In addition, people criticize others for failing to do what they think they should do, not doing what they would do themselves, showing poor judgment, and acting unacceptably.

My son went to a martial arts competition in another province. He rode with older members of the club, and was impressed that they drove as fast as they could and didn't wear seat belts. I told him they don't have any common sense. I'm not going to let him go with them again. [737]

I took my teenage children to visit a family friend who is seriously ill. The children wanted to leave as soon as possible so they could go do things with their friends, and kept telling me it was time to go. They were so rude. When we got home I gave them a half hour lecture. [738]

Lots of the skateboarders spend their time practicing tricks and doing drugs. To get money, they shoplift and sell what they've stolen. What a useless life. [739]

My husband pays more attention to the family dog than he does to our son. [740]

My daughter is always complaining about my smoking. This makes me feel guilty, and occasionally I stop. But I'm not going to let her bully me into quitting something I want to do. [741]

For the last three months, all my parents have said is, "Tara, why can't you get a job?" "Tara, why are you so lazy?" and "Tara, can't you do anything useful?" They know there's a recession on, but because it hasn't hit them, they think it hasn't hit me. They've always thought I'm lazy. But really I'm not. I just do things differently than they do. It doesn't make me lazy just because I haven't gotten a job offer. They should be showing support, not criticizing me. [742]

How people criticize

People express criticism in many ways, which include the following:

1. Indicating disapproval
2. Bringing up a subject
3. Correcting what the other has done
4. Making critical statements
5. Pointing out consequences
6. Using sarcasm or ridicule
7. Threatening loss of resources
8. Removing resources

1. Indicating disapproval

People indicate disapproval in several ways. These include giving the person a questioning look or disapproving stare; acting annoyed or upset; not speaking or showing affect; refusing to cooperate; using a gesture of disapproval, such as shaking one's head or covering one's face with one's hands; yelling or swearing; and hitting, kicking, or pulling the other person.

> When someone nearly causes me to have a traffic accident, I honk loudly. I don't have to yell, "Stupid idiot!" They know exactly what I mean. #743

> My daughter is taking a French immersion course. I'd like to learn French and I ask her how to pronounce different words. When I try them, she rolls up her eyes and tells me, "You'll never be able to do it, Mom." #744

> My father gave me a hard time for almost everything. Once he was waiting up for me when I got back from a date. He wanted to know where I was and why I hadn't done the dishes. I told him I was at the show and had forgotten about the dishes, but I'd do them right away. He wouldn't accept this and started calling me names. One thing led to another and he hit me and broke my arm. #745

2. Bringing up a subject

Another way people criticize is by bringing up the subject they want to criticize. They may mention the subject, ask what happened, ask what the other person thinks, offer a suggestion, or nag.

> I told the taxi driver, "I can't get the seat belt to work." He said he'd have to get it fixed. #746

> I asked the secretary if she had had a chance to get more printer paper. She said she would do it today. #747

> When the boss doesn't get around to ordering something we need in the store, I don't keep reminding him. I wait until the next time a customer asks for it. Then I tell the boss someone wants it and ask if we have any in the store or on order. #748

3. Correcting what the other has done

People frequently imply criticism when they correct what another person has done. There are numerous ways in which people attempt to correct the other person's behavior.

> When my wife fixes my coffee or soup and it's not hot enough, I take it to the microwave and heat it some more. I'm sure she gets the idea that she didn't get it right. #749

> Last night I fixed spaghetti. I don't rinse the starch off the noodles, because the noodles lose all of their flavor. My husband, on the other hand, doesn't like the taste of starch on his noodles. So when I served the noodles, he took his portion and rinsed them in hot water. #750

> When my friend came to dinner, we served her stew and she started pouring salt on it before she'd even tasted it. It annoyed me, because the stew was spicy to start with. You'd think she'd make sure it needed salt before she added it. #751

> It bothers me when my wife changes something I've done. When we're at the grocery store, I look through the plums or mushrooms

or something else and pick out the best ones. But then she goes through the same tray, picks out some I didn't like, and puts back some of the ones I did. It's like she's criticizing my judgment. If I'd known she was going to do this, I wouldn't have bothered in the first place. #752

4. Making critical statements

People also make critical statements and tell others what they do not like about their actions. They may complain, state their opinion, or give a lecture.

My wife has a lump in her breast and needs to get it checked out by a doctor. But she hasn't gotten around to it, and continues to treat other things as more important. I told her today, "You should make this top priority." #753

Jennifer, why is it you never want to do anything for anyone else? When we ask you to do something, you immediately disappear, claim you are busy doing something else, or tell your brother he's supposed to do it. #754

Your problem is related to the kind of business you run. You don't get your paperwork done because things are so hectic on the sales floor. Because you don't get the paperwork done, your stress level is sky-high. This has been going on for some time and you haven't straightened it out. So you, not the business, are the problem. What you should do is hire someone to work on the sales floor one morning a week, and spend that time getting your paperwork done. #755

5. Pointing out consequences

In addition, people criticize by pointing out the possible consequences of the other person's behavior.

You should write off for your university applications as soon as possible. You won't have time once your twelfth-grade classes begin. #756

If you push your chair back from the table, instead of lift it, you'll scrape and mark the hardwood floor. [#757]

Emily, you could cause a fire. You wrap the shower curtain around the pipe in the bathroom to get it out of the way. The curtain is plastic and the pipe gets very hot. [#758]

I think that's the worst idea you've had. You'd cut your sales in half within a year. [#759]

Sometimes people report consequences they have experienced themselves, seen on television, or read about.

Did you check under the car for the cat? Cars are the number one killer of cats, and I've had three killed by them. Once my father ran over the family cat when he drove out our driveway. [#760]

Don't run and jump in the house. Most accidents occur at home. [#761]

6. Using sarcasm or ridicule

People also use sarcasm or ridicule to criticize what they do not like.

When my fifteen-year-old daughter lets out a loud belch, I look at her and announce, "A paragon of charm." [#762]

We're going to send you to a specialist. When you think we're talking about you, your hearing is exceptional. But when we call you to do something, you can't hear a thing. It's obvious. You're chore deaf. [#763]

My family frequently make negative comments about each other at the dinner table. The other day Dad wore a new sweater, and Mom said, "Where did you buy that? The Salvation Army thrift store?" My brother remarked, "It looks better when you walk backwards." Another time they criticized a project my brother had made for his sewing course. Mom said, "It's terrible. Your seams are crooked and don't look right." My sister added, "Gee, that's a dumb course. It'll get you nowhere." My brother told my sister, "Shut up, dink weed!" Another time, they criticized what Mom had cooked. One said, "My God, the color of that," and another, "This is what dead people eat." Mom told them in the future they could make supper themselves. [764]

7. Threatening loss of resources

People also criticize another person's actions by threatening to remove resources.

> If you want to use the car today, you'll have to get your dishes washed, change the kitty litter, and vacuum the hall. You said you'd do them yesterday, but didn't. [765]

> If you want to keep this job, you'll have to be on time from now on. [766]

> If you don't put on your seat belt, we'll just sit here. I'm not going to drive you. [767]

8. Removing resources

People also remove resources from others. They frequently do so in order to punish others, get them to change, or make it difficult for them to engage in undesirable behavior. Such actions serve as criticisms of what others are doing.

> I give my children ten dollars a week each for allowance, and dock them two dollars for each day they don't do their chores. When they are really bad about getting them done, I won't let them watch TV. [768]

> My son just totaled the family car, and we've decided not to get another one. He's eighteen, but it's clear he isn't mature enough to drive, and we don't want him killing himself and others. We told him that this is why we're not getting another car. We can manage without one until he leaves for college. If we got one, he'd put constant pressure on us to use it because he "learned a lesson from the accident" and "it will never happen again." [769]

Direct and indirect criticism

In certain situations, people express their criticism directly to the party they feel deserves it. They are likely to do this when they have much more control over the other party's resources, than the other party has over theirs. This is the case when parents correct children, teachers evaluate student work, and bosses and supervisors criticize employees.

> I doubt if a day goes by that my wife and I don't correct our teenage children. It's usually a task they have "forgotten" to do, or something they are doing in an inconsiderate or sloppy way. #770

> My newest worker has turned out well. Initially, she had problems handling credit card sales. She put Visa Card sales on Master Card forms, and vice versa. I felt bad having to explain it so many times, because there were lots of new and confusing things for her to learn. If I see the staff do poor work, I bring it to their attention right away. It's not because I want them to feel bad. It's because I want them to do things right. I think they understand my point of view. #771

In situations where there is no such disparity in the control of resources, the party being criticized has little to lose by reacting and attacking back, and there is greater chance of conflict. People experience considerable anxiety and stress in expectation of and during confrontations, and seek to avoid them. Confrontations consist of negative reactions, and people hate negative reactions. When people do not want to confront a person directly, they may initiate a rule which includes everyone, or they may diplomatically share the blame by making a statement such as, "We'll have to be more careful in the future, so it doesn't happen again." They may also seek to avoid a face-to-face confrontation by going to the mass media or a government representative. For example, they may write a letter to the newspaper or contact an official to try to get a zoning law enforced.

People commonly avoid confrontations by voicing their criticisms to someone other than the person they are criticizing. Frequently people express their criticism to third parties who are likely to agree with them.

Sometimes I find myself in a group where everyone is talking about other people, or just plain gossiping, and I get involved too. When you talk about who's pregnant now or who's fooling around with whom, you don't consider anything wrong with what you're saying. It doesn't mean you dislike the people you talk about or feel they are terrible. #772

Criticism to third parties is seldom limited to a comment or two. Instead there is usually a thorough discussion, which may cover what happened, the offending party, his past behavior, the behavior of his associates and family, what he may do in the future, what his behavior means, and what one should do about it. Often this conversation is repeated to additional people and elaborated on. It is frequently enriched with humorous comments at the expense of the person being criticized. Thus criticism often generates additional criticism. Such criticism hurts the reputation of the party being criticized and frequently damages his ability to obtain resources from others. People are well aware of the nature of these criticism sessions, because they participate in them when others are criticized. They certainly do not want people to hold such sessions at their expense.

When people talk about me, I feel they dislike me. I don't think it makes anyone feel good to be disliked. It leaves me with a terrible feeling knowing people are talking about me. I'd rather have them talk to my face than behind my back. #773

Criticism is a primary means of social control. People have been hurt by criticism in the past and do not want to be hurt again. Most criticism of a person is made when the person is absent. However, people are sometimes told by their friends what others are saying about them. In addition, people frequently hear what others are being criticized for, and realize if they behave in the same way they can expect to be criticized too. Also, criticism is frequently backed up by a reduction in the person's resources. This is done by the party who criticizes the person and by others who hear the criticism.

Feelings associated with criticism

When people are criticized they immediately feel hurt. Because they feel hurt, they may cry.

> In the fifth grade, I couldn't hold my pen properly. The teacher started criticizing me, which made me cry in front of my classmates. [#774]

When people feel hurt, they become upset, and subsequently feel unhappy, depressed, and/or demoralized. They may feel rejected, disliked, hated, put down, or made to look small. They may conclude that the person who criticizes them does not respect them or care about them, and that their relationship with the person is in jeopardy. Sometimes they feel attacked and react with anger. When people know that others are aware that they have been criticized, they frequently feel embarrassed or humiliated.

> When people make little critical comments to me, I get paranoid. I feel hurt, but keep my feelings bottled up, and they build up until I have a good long laugh or cry. Sometimes I talk to my best friend about it, or take a long, vigorous walk to try to clear my mind. [#775]

> When my family criticizes me, it gets on my nerves and I really take offense. I deny what they say and push it aside until I can think about it later. [#776]

> When I'm criticized, I dwell on what was said, even if I pretend to brush it off. If it's my parents who criticize me, it really hurts because I always try to please them. When friends criticize me I try not to let it bother me. If I'm in a good mood, criticism doesn't affect me as much. If I'm down or depressed, criticism eats away, and I withdraw from everyone else and really analyze what was said. [#777]

> When I'm criticized, my first feeling is anger. What gives that person the right to tear me apart and knock me down? Then what they said starts to sink in and I feel hurt. I'll sit down and think about it. Then I try to pick myself up and keep my mind occupied. Maybe I'll read a book, watch TV, or take a bike ride. [#778]

299

My boyfriend sometimes complains about my performance in bed. He pretends he's just joking, but I know he's serious. It gets me so crazy. It's a pretty personal subject and I just can't believe he complains. Every time he complains, I feel like crying. Actually, I usually do when he's not around. #779

I coach high school kids, and frequently have to tell them what they're doing wrong. Some take it calmly, but others get upset, tell me off, and even walk out of practice. One kid left in tears. The next practice his father showed up, started shoving me around, and would have beaten me up if others hadn't stopped him. #780

People normally try to hide how they feel when criticized. Often they do not want to risk additional criticism that they are "too sensitive" or "took it personally."

I try to hide the hurt I feel. I wear a fake smile, and everyone is fooled, except for my best friend who knows me too well. #781

Often the amount of hurt people feel from criticism is related to a) who voices the criticism, b) what the criticism is, c) the situation in which the criticism occurs, and d) how often the criticism is expressed. The more one wants resources from a person or depends on a person for resources, the more the person's criticism hurts. Therefore children are likely to be hurt by criticisms from parents, adults by criticisms from their mate, and individuals by criticisms from their friends.

My brother told me, "You're twenty-four years old and still live with Mommy and Daddy. When are you going to grow up and move out?" That really hurt. What he said didn't matter, because I pay rent to them and am going to school. What bothered me was the fact my brother said it. #782

Like everyone else, I don't like to be talked about behind my back. But it makes a difference who is doing the talking. If a friend or someone I like stabs me in the back, I feel hurt and betrayed. When it's some-one I like and trust, I value their opinion. I feel really awful inside, and because I'm so hurt I want to get back at them. But if the person talk-ing about me is a real idiot or someone I couldn't care less about, it doesn't bother me much. Still, I don't like being talked about, because the people I do care about may hear these things, and I don't want to get a bad reputation. #783

I bought a pair of large, outrageous earrings and wore them to work recently. A lot of people made comments about them, but the comments didn't bother me because I liked my earrings and was comfortable with them. Then my best friend saw them and questioned my decision to wear them to work. I felt she was attacking my personal judgment. Her opinion really matters to me and I was very hurt. #784

It makes a big difference whether the person criticizing you is your current wife or your previous one. Your current wife you take very seriously. The previous one is so irrelevant she's hardly a nuisance. #785

Criticisms carry less impact when they come from people that one does not need resources from or want them from.

One of the girls I work with said she liked my hair better before I had it permed. I wasn't really hurt because she always says things like that. We just ignore her remarks at work. #786

What is criticized is also important. There are certain subjects one is sensitive to. Often this is because of previous criticisms from others or because one thinks the criticisms may be true. Criticism of these subjects, even if it comes from strangers, can cause considerable hurt.

I haven't been doing well in school. So it really bothers me when people tell me, "That's a stupid idea," or say something sarcastic, like "That's intelligent now, isn't it?" #787

An acquaintance asked me, "Have you put on weight lately?" I was really hurt. I figured I must be huge for someone I hardly know to make such a remark. #788

I'm sensitive when my parents compare me to my older brother. He started university at an early age, earned two professional degrees, and landed a great job. I do well in school too, but my degree is in liberal arts. My parents constantly make negative comparisons between us. #789

The situation in which the criticism occurs also has an influence on its impact.

When my husband and I fight, we both say things we don't mean, like "I hate you" or "I wish I'd never married you." But one time we were sitting at the table eating breakfast and he said he was bored with our marriage. Let me tell you, that hurt. If he'd said the same thing during a fight, it wouldn't have mattered. #790

In ballet class you are very dependent on criticisms, or "corrections," from the teacher. Without them you keep making the same mistakes and don't improve. Often the favorite students get the most corrections. If you don't get any, you may feel the teacher doesn't care about you or think you are worth correcting. On the other hand, a correction occurs because you are doing something wrong, and everyone else in class watches the teacher correct you. So you feel self-conscious about it. Occasionally a student rejects the criticism. One student I know, who thinks she's a better dancer than the teacher, replied quite brusquely, "OK, I can do it. I can do it." #791

When people are criticized in front of others, they have the added discomfort of feeling embarrassed or humiliated.

Don't expect me to take it kindly when you criticize me in front of a room full of strangers. And don't expect me to talk to you for some time afterwards. #792

It really pisses me off when my girlfriend starts nagging me in front of the guys about something I did. The next time I see them they all tease me about being henpecked, and that I do not like. #793

People sometimes purposely criticize others in front of other people in order to increase the impact of what they are saying.

Right now our office is split by a war. Our side wants to be left alone. The other side wants to force us to do things their way. Our best weapon is to make public all the stupid things the other side has done, and that's what we're doing. Once they've been embarrassed enough, they'll be willing to call off the fight and leave us alone. #794

People also purposely avoid criticizing a person in front of others in order not to embarrass him.

Another factor is how often a criticism is expressed and how often one is criticized. For example, if one is criticized too frequently, the criticism can lose its impact.

> My roommate constantly puts me down. She thinks everything I wear is just awful and frequently remarks, "Oh, you aren't wearing that to work are you?" It used to really bother me, but now I understand her better. She criticizes others to make up for her own insecurities. [795]

People sometimes recognize that others feel hurt by criticism. As a result they may avoid being critical, or try to temper critical comments with positive ones.

> When I want to use constructive criticism, I try to say some positive things in conjunction with the negative ones. Otherwise the person I criticize may overreact. [796]

> When I grade student papers I point out all the weaknesses in the paper. In addition, I usually try to find something positive to write on the top of each paper too, like "well organized," "thorough treatment," or "nice use of examples." If I don't, I feel they may get discouraged because of all of the criticisms. [797]

How people respond to criticism

People normally consider everything they are associated with as an extension of themselves. Therefore if anything they are associated with is criticized, they take it personally and consider it a criticism of themselves. This can be anything they do, think, say, own, or belong to, or anyone they are related to or otherwise associated with.

> My wife used three ice trays to prepare several plastic bags full of ice cubes for a party. I noticed that after she emptied each ice tray and

refilled it with water, she wiped the bottom of the tray with a dishrag and then stacked the three trays on top of each other. When I saw her do this, I pointed out that a dishrag is one of the dirtiest things in the house because it collects particles of food which feed large quantities of bacteria. Therefore the bacteria were being wiped onto the bottom of each ice tray with the dishrag and then placed in contact with the water in the ice tray beneath them. My wife became upset and blurted, "Stop picking on me!" Later she added, "The dishrag wouldn't be dirty if you washed it properly after you do the dishes." #798

People are very sensitive to negative reactions from others. They constantly seek to determine what lies behind other people's comments and actions, and are quick to identify instances of criticism. For example, the comment, "We're out of bread," may imply "You forgot to get bread today," or the remark, "There's a jar in the pantry," may imply "You shouldn't have bought another jar. We already had one. Be more careful next time." People listen for negative implications in anything that is said to them or about them.

Sometimes I can't stand living with Melina. If I'm in the apartment, just thinking about something, or being quiet for no reason, she'll ask what's wrong or what's bothering me. She always thinks she's done something to annoy me. And she's forever telling me that it's better to talk about these things than let them get worse, because we'll end up fighting. If she only knew. Most of the time the only thing bothering me is her asking what's bothering me. #799

A man from our church injured his back and wasn't able to take his children to church. A woman mentioned this to a friend of mine, and my friend suggested that the children go with my husband and me. However, the woman replied, "Oh, don't ask them. They always come at the very last minute." It didn't matter to the woman that we sing in the choir or that I teach Sunday school. All that mattered was that we always arrive at the last minute. And I find that's true of our other neighbors. Anytime we do something they think is wrong, they feel they can criticize us. #800

People frequently worry that others may be talking about them in a negative way. When they are insecure about their appearance or behavior, they fear others will react unfavorably to them. When they or their relatives do something that others disapprove of, they worry they are being gossiped about. When others are not friendly, people frequently think it is because of something bad others have heard about them.

People are also sensitive to being teased about their appearance, behavior, and possessions. This is true even when the person teasing them is simply seeking positive reactions, or trying to produce an entertaining response, and intends nothing critical.

> When people ask me, "Have you had your ears lowered?" I feel very uncomfortable and don't know what to say. They're trying to be cute, but I feel they're mocking me. I wish they'd simply ask if I've had my hair cut. [#801]

> A neighbor's boy who is nine was visiting our house, and we started teasing him because his two front baby teeth have fallen out. We called him "Toothless Joe" and asked him who he had his latest fight with. The boy's response shocked us. He threw a tantrum and started raving and screaming. [#802]

People do not want to appear foolish or ridiculous in the eyes of others, and certainly do not want to be the butt of negative comments, even if the comments are made behind their backs. Therefore they are quite sensitive to attention which is other than favorable.

> I went out to a club Friday night with a group of friends. One of the girls with us got drunk and made a fool of herself. We were none too pleased with her actions. The next day we continually teased her. We asked, "How's your head today?" and said, "Your feet must be awful tired from dancing up such a storm last night." She was terribly embarrassed. [#803]

People respond to criticism in a number of ways. The primary way is attempting to avoid criticism, and people use a variety of tactics to do so. They may also ignore or reject criticism, or they may attack the other person and seek revenge. In addition, people normally try to re-assure themselves that the criticism is unjustified.

The tactics that people use include the following:

1. Not doing what they hear others criticized for
2. Avoiding situations in which they might be criticized
3. Not associating with those who are criticized
4. Ceasing to do what they themselves are criticized for
5. Hiding their behavior from others
6. Evading responsibility for their actions
7. Avoiding people who criticize them
8. Avoiding situations in which they are criticized
9. Avoiding activities in which they are criticized
10. Ignoring criticism
11. Rejecting criticism
12. Attacking the person who criticizes them
13. Seeking revenge
14. Reassuring themselves that the criticism is unjustified
15. Obtaining resources from people who do not criticize them

1. Not doing what they hear others criticized for

People avoid doing the things they hear others criticized for. When peo-ple hear criticism directed at others, they learn what kinds of behavior are likely to get them criticized too. To prevent this from happening, they alter their own behavior in advance. Thus people will not wear clothing they hear others ridiculed for wearing, or say or do things others are criticized for.

> When I moved to the local community it never occurred to me you weren't supposed to do the wash on Sundays. I thought you just hung your wash out when you did it. Then I heard a local woman say she didn't like to see people putting out wash on Sundays. I thought, "Boy, listen to her. Well, it won't stop me." I assumed she was the only one who felt that way. Then I heard others mention it too. I realized this bothered people, and I became very sensitive to it and didn't do it. In fact, I became paranoid, because I didn't want to be gossiped

about. Then one day I was hanging out my second load when I realized, "Oh, my God, it's Sunday!" I almost took the load back in. But I'd already dried one load, so the damage was done, and I went ahead and finished. No one said anything about it, but I thought they were probably all talking about me. After that day I never hung my wash out on Sunday again. #804

My daughter and her friend, Joanne, are in the sixth grade. Joanne has a number of warts on her hands and fingers. The other kids in school say, "Oh, yucky! You've got warts," yell "Wartmonger!" at her, and tell other kids about her warts and laugh and giggle at her. Joanne is really sensitive about this and only wears shirts with sleeves long enough to cover her hands. She wears gloves through the winter and into the spring until the gloves start to attract attention. During the summer she wears an oversized jean jacket and closes her hands so her fingers don't stick out. Now my daughter also has a wart on her finger and another on her wrist. My daughter's warts are hardly noticeable, and no one mentions them, but she's become quite self-conscious about them. She has started wearing long-sleeved shirts which go as far as her fingers. She wants the warts removed, and I've made an appointment with the doctor to have this done. #805

I work very hard on the novels I write. I want them to be as perfect as possible, so they are harder for others to criticize. #806

Many people who are complimented on an accomplishment try to play it down. I think it's because they don't know what to say. They don't want to say how much they wanted to achieve this, or how hard they worked for it, or how pleased they are at their success. They know they'll be criticized for boasting. #807

Because people attempt to avoid what others are criticized for, there is considerable conformity in dress and behavior, and considerable resistance to acting independently of others.

It's hard to believe how concerned school kids are with clothes. They all wear the same pants, shirts, jackets, and caps, and look like carbon copies of each other. I'm sure they hear kids ridiculed for wearing the wrong thing. It doesn't matter how much something costs or how nice it is, if it isn't what other kids are wearing, they don't want it. And there's absolutely no way you can force them to wear it either. Kids today are obsessed with having the right designer labels on their clothes. Certain labels are acceptable and others aren't. I bought some nice shirts for my son in a trendy store in Toronto. But because he wasn't familiar with the label, he didn't want them. After his friend told him it was a desirable label, he wore the shirts all the time. [#808]

There are lots of things I would do except for the fact others are highly critical of them. You don't have to do more than one or two things that people disapprove of before you get quite a bad reputation. [#809]

People also try to avoid criticism of themselves by trying to keep their own family members from doing things that others disapprove of. Other people react negatively to alcoholism, drug use, reckless driving, causing an automobile accident, having a baby out of wedlock, child neglect, physical and sexual abuse, stealing, vandalism, fighting, adultery, and getting a divorce. People try to control their family members through criticism. Normally when a family member does something others do not approve of, a primary concern of the other family members is the unfavorable things people will say about the whole family.

I no longer live in the same community as my parents, so I don't care about keeping my house really clean. It's because I just don't have the time. But when my parents' neighbors from home come by to visit me, I do a thorough cleaning job. I wouldn't want them to return home and talk badly about our family. I know how hurt Mom and Dad would be. [#810]

2. Avoiding situations in which they might be criticized

People avoid situations in which they might be criticized. They do not want to put themselves in a position in which others may criticize them.

My dance teacher asked if I would like to be in the yearly dance performance, and I said no. If I were a good dancer, I wouldn't mind. But I don't like to have people see me do things in an amateurish way. [#811]

My nine-year-old daughter was sick and threw up at night. The next morning she felt fine, but didn't want to go to school. She was afraid she would throw up again and the other kids would make fun of her. They say things like "Oh, gross!" and "What a stink!" So I let her stay home. #812

I'm taking an introductory psychology course this year, and all of the students have to do certain projects. The current project involves three violations of norms. For the first violation you locate two people who are sitting at a table together in a restaurant or coffee shop and then sit down with them and observe their reactions to you. These are people you don't know. For the second violation you enter a restaurant, sit at a vacated table which has not been cleared, and eat some of the food left on the table. The food has been left there by a confederate. A different confederate watches and records the reactions of other people in the restaurant. For the third violation you eat a banana by holding it horizontally like a slice of watermelon and notice the reactions of other people. Most of the students I talked to are too embarrassed to do the project and are faking their data. #813

When people do not put themselves in situations in which they can be criticized, they avoid negative reactions from others.

3. Not associating with those who are criticized

People also try to avoid associating with individuals and groups who are criticized by others. Often they assume the criticisms are true. They also realize that if they associate with those who are criticized, they are likely to be criticized themselves. People are particularly likely to avoid those who are criticized when they want positive reactions and other resources from those making the criticisms.

I think the primary reason teenage kids don't want to be seen in public with their parents is that parents are criticized by their friends. Kids are much more insecure about being accepted by their friends than they are about being accepted by their parents. #814

I work in a business office with other employees, and the staff have always been very friendly to me. Then I started dating the boss's son. The boy's father, my boss, found out and disapproved. The very next day the staff in the office wouldn't even answer when I said hello. #815

4. Ceasing to do what they themselves are criticized for

When people are actually criticized, they frequently change their behavior to avoid further criticism.

> Anytime I make the slightest negative comment to my roommate about her clothes, makeup, or hair, she changes them. If I suggest her red sweater would look better than her yellow one, she switches to the red one. If I ask why she's braided her hair, she unties it right away. [#816]

> I don't like family reunions, but my family criticizes me until I go. They call me antisocial and make me feel guilty. I end up going and have a very unpleasant time. [#817]

> We try to be friendly with customers at work, and I said, "Hello!" whenever customers entered the store. But then the boss said all my hellos sounded phony. I really didn't know how to change them, so I switched to "Hi!" [#818]

> One of my buddies told me I drank too much. I thought about it and realized he was right. Now I try to control it. [#819]

> I was concerned about women's issues. I felt I could make a useful contribution in the area and I began to publish books on the subject. Then I delivered a paper at a regional conference, and women who were present criticized me. They felt because I was a man, I had nothing to contribute. I immediately quit working in the area and will never go near it again. [#820]

People may continue to respond to a criticism for a long period of time.

> Years ago someone told a friend of mine she talked too loudly. Today she still speaks in a monotone and so softly that I have trouble hearing her. I have to keep asking her to talk louder. [#821]

> Several years ago I told my mother she smelled and should use a deodorant. It must have upset her, because she keeps bringing it up. [#822]

I won't dance in public. We had to dance in grade school, and I was taller than all the boys, and others commented on this. Today, I won't go anyplace where people are dancing unless my husband promises he won't try to get me to dance. If there's a wedding dinner and dance, I make sure we leave before the dancing starts. The only place I dance is at home when there's music I like. [#823]

5. Hiding their behavior from others

A common response to criticism is to hide behavior that people criticize. Normally when a person is aware that others disapprove of a particular kind of behavior, the person attempts to keep them from learning of his own involvement in it. Often this tactic is successful.

Lots of people don't tell others that they believe in ghosts and certain superstitions. They know others will consider them foolish, and they don't want to be laughed at or ridiculed. [#824]

I like X-rated magazines and going to strip shows. But I sure don't mention this at work. It would be a choice piece of gossip and would not help my advancement. [#825]

People usually pursue activities that others disapprove of out of sight, such as in the privacy of their home or out of town. Sometimes they prepare and rehearse an excuse in advance to use in case others find out. When people are discovered to be engaging in undesirable behavior, rather than give it up, they often attempt a new means of hiding it.

Regular cat food makes our cat sick, so we have to buy an expensive kind from the vet. There's a stray cat that comes around our kitchen door to beg for food, and I feed him the same kind we use for our cat. If I used a cheaper kind, our cat would eat it too when he goes outside and it would make him sick. My wife doesn't like me giving this food to the stray because it is expensive. So I always wait until she's out of the kitchen and upstairs before I put the food outside for the stray. [#826]

My wife found out I was having an affair when she listened in on a phone call I made from home. I promised to end the affair, but didn't. After that I only called from my office or a pay phone. [#827]

6. Evading responsibility for their actions

People also seek to avoid criticism by evading responsibility for their actions. Thus they use excuses, fail to admit involvement, deny involvement, and blame others.

No, I didn't get the salad ready for dinner. I had to study. I have a test tomorrow. [#828]

The reason I got home so late is that Daniel, who was driving, took Jason home first, and Jason lives thirty miles out of town. [#829]

It's not entirely my fault I wrecked the family car. It was night and I was driving down the highway with several of my teenage friends. I don't know how fast I was going because the light on the dash was broken. When I entered the village I didn't slow down because I didn't see the sign with the lower speed limit. Then in the middle of the village I went to pass another car full of teenagers, and while I was alongside, they sped up. When I finally got around them there was another car just ahead waiting to turn left at the intersection. I tried to cut to the right because I thought the car was going to turn. But the car didn't turn in time and I hit it square in the rear. If I'd known it wasn't going to turn, I'd have stayed in the left lane, passed the car, and there wouldn't have been an accident. [#830]

7. Avoiding people who criticize them

People seek to avoid those who are critical of them. Often they distance themselves from them, or wish that they could. People frequently feel injured by or upset with those who criticize them, and they want nothing more to do with them.

When my wife criticizes me, I get out of the house. I go to the gym and work out. [#831]

He and I used to talk about lots of things. But when I heard what he said about me, I didn't want anything more to do with him. Today I'm civil and say hello, but that's it. [#832]

When my boss doesn't like the way I do things, I get upset. I just want to say, "To hell with it!" and quit. #833

When I'm criticized at work, I feel stupid, incompetent, and like a worthless piece of shit. I can't quit because I have to earn a living. I reassure myself that I must be doing my job well or else I wouldn't have a job. #834

I asked the owner of a booth in the farmer's market how much a bunch of spring onions costs. She replied, "Why would it matter, when all you're getting is a few onions?" But I think I have a right to know when I'm buying them. She was critical of my question, and I decided she isn't a nice person. That was two or three years ago, and ever since then I don't buy things at her booth, even when she has items I want. #835

I'm in favor of family life courses in the schools which teach sex education, but my friend and her husband are really opposed to them. Every time I visit their place, her husband really goes at me and attacks what I think. He says everything in front of their four children, and when I'm there the children stare at me and I feel really uncomfortable. I used to visit much more often, but now I only go every three months or so. They ask, "What's the matter? It's been such a long time since you visited us last." Each time I go things are worse, so I don't want to go anymore. #836

My grandmother lives on the West Coast. She is almost an invalid and quite old, and her next-door neighbor helps her a great deal. The neighbor lets me know how my grandmother is doing. I like the neighbor and she invites me for dinner when I visit my grandmother. It's not easy finding birthday and Christmas presents for someone as old as my grandmother. But this neighbor is very critical of my selections and tells me so over the phone. Because of her criticism, I feel like avoiding the neighbor, and don't want to talk to her on the phone anymore. #837

My mother hired a cleaning woman to help her around the house, and it was the woman's first day at work. The woman used a stronger cleaning agent on the bathroom floor than my mother uses, and the substance got on the bathroom rug. My mother was just furious. She yelled at the woman, fired her, and would not pay her the money she'd already earned that day. Then she called the employment agency and told them the woman was a terrible worker, in order to make sure she wouldn't get work again. This was so unfair it really bothered me. At lunch, my mother wanted to know what I thought about the matter, and I told her the woman didn't deserve this treatment. My mother got up from her unfinished meal, drove off in her car, and was gone all afternoon. She'd never done anything like that before. That evening my father said she wanted to talk to me in their bedroom. She was crying and said it was foolish for us to fight over a mere cleaning woman. She missed the whole point. [#838]

8. Avoiding situations in which they are criticized

People also seek to avoid situations in which they are criticized.

Students don't want the other students to think they are a teacher's pet or a brown-noser. When a teacher gives a student too much favorable attention, the student may decide to do worse in class. [#839]

My boss keeps telling me I'm doing things wrong. Often she tells me to do things one way, and later when I do it her way, she has changed her mind and tells me again I'm doing it wrong. Well, I've learned. I'm going to quit taking the initiative and no longer going to look for things to do at work. Instead, I'm not going to do anything unless she tells me to. That way I won't do anything wrong. [#840]

My mother was not happy about my skinny physique and told me so. After that I noticed every comment about my build made by others. I went to church camp one summer, and the most popular priest there was as skinny as I was. But he used to call me Mahatma Gandhi. Today I never go to the beach because I'm so self-conscious about taking my shirt off. [#841]

I find police work has many negative features. Not only do you work with damaged personalities, but you have to take a great deal of abuse from the public when you do your job. The public do not like to get traffic or speeding tickets and often tell you so. I think many police officers try to escape dealing with the public by getting an administrative job. That's why I'm trying to get one. There's a traditional saying among the police. The first ten years of your career, there are three kinds of people: the police, citizens, and assholes. The next ten years of your career, there are only two kinds: the police and assholes. And the last ten years, there's just you versus all the assholes. #842

9. Avoiding activities in which they are criticized

People also avoid activities in which others do not think well of their performance.

> When I was in elementary school, there was a lot of competition to be the best at each sport. Kids who couldn't keep up were teased. After a while the kid who was being teased would no longer join in the sport that his friends were competing in. When a school day was set aside for sports, some of these kids would stay home and not come to school. #843

> When I took a language class, the teacher decided to have us sing folk songs so we could pick up the rhythm of the language. The first time we did so, he stopped the song, addressed me by name, and told me not to sing with them. I guess I was so off-key, he felt I was ruining the song for everyone else. Before that I'd always joined in group singing. But I haven't once since then. I've even quit singing hymns in church and carols at Christmastime. #844

Many people shy away from math and science courses because they have done poorly in them in the past.

Sometimes people continue to engage in a behavior that others disapprove of, but do not give others the opportunity to criticize them.

> Students do not like to have to do a lot of work in a course. If you require difficult assignments, many students give you a negative evaluation at the end of the course. When I give students easy assignments, I get much better evaluations. If I get negative evaluations I feel discouraged and wish I could leave teaching. So I quit giving students evaluation forms to fill out, and I find I enjoy teaching a lot more. #845

10. Ignoring criticism

In some instances people ignore criticism. They may consider the criticism irrelevant or unfounded or the person too insignificant to matter. In some cases they find the criticism so ridiculous it is laughable.

> We pick up our daughter when she finishes her karate and music lessons, or else we give her cab fare to get home. We told her we don't want her to ask her teachers or the other students for a ride home. She says our problem is we are "too polite-y." [#846]

> Mom, listen to what you're saying. This isn't you. Don't you have a brain of your own? You only say what Dad tells you to say. You wouldn't want us to do any of this if he didn't tell you so. [#847]

11. Rejecting criticism

People also reject criticism.

> My wife always criticizes me for going out with the guys on the weekend. I used to argue back, but now I let her say whatever she wants and just leave. [#848]

12. Attacking the person who criticizes them

People also respond to criticism by attacking back and criticizing the person who criticizes them.

> My friend is heavier than me, and had the nerve to tell me I should lose weight. I couldn't believe it. She has no right to say anything about my weight when she has a very obvious problem herself. [#849]

> This guy has the gall to criticize the marks I make at university. Where does he get off criticizing me? It took him an extra year to finish high school, and he doesn't even go to university. It really pisses me off. [#850]

> I was in a liquor store and this guy berated a clerk because the store did not carry more Canadian wines. Then he insisted on speaking to the manager, and repeated his criticism. I bought a couple of bottles,

and because I was walking some distance and felt one bag wouldn't be strong enough, I asked for a second bag to put the bottles in. The guy then turned on me and claimed it was people like me who caused all the pollution and environmental problems in the world. I told him he was psychotic. #851

I went golfing with two friends. Jim is a better golfer than Andrew, but was playing very badly. Andrew, on the other hand, had a good round, and when we'd finished he told Jim, "I know exactly what your problem is." Jim stopped him with the statement, "I don't want to hear your goddamn advice, because you're not half as good as I am, and you don't know what you're talking about." #852

Last week one of my co-workers was displeased with my work. He said I was careless and messy and that a ten year old could do a better job. I can take criticism, but I don't need to be called down in front of everyone, and he pushed me to the limit. Well, my temper started to boil, and I told him what I thought of him. I also pointed out that everyone at the office considers him a loser. What I said must have hurt him a lot. The guy provoked me, and he got what he deserved. If someone hurts me, I make a deliberate attempt to hurt them back. #853

One-third of the students have switched out of one of my high school classes, and yesterday the teacher brought this up. He asked students why others had dropped out, but no one said anything. The teacher stated maybe the class was too elementary for some students and too demanding for others, but he was trying to find a middle ground. He continued to ask students about the course, and no one volunteered anything. Then one girl spoke up and said according to students she knew who had dropped the course, maybe the problem was the teacher. The teacher asked her to explain, and she told him she had heard others say that the teacher was obnoxious, immature, boring, and couldn't teach. She said they didn't like some of his mannerisms, like banging his books on the desk to make a point. The rest of us sat there stunned while she said these things. Most of us agree completely with her and we say the same things about him, but not to his face. The girl added, "This isn't what I say, it's what I hear from other people." The teacher looked at her and said, "I don't know about that. Well, I don't think that's the only reason people would quit the class." But the girl insisted, "I know some who have quit, and that's what they told me." The teacher then decided he'd give us a poem to read. Before he presented the poem, he went through a silly dance step he often does, and then stated, "Some people might say that's a pretty stupid thing for a teacher to do." The poem he had us read dealt with a frog named Warty who thought the whole world centered around him. Warty believed he was so wonderful that the universe was created just for him. He thought God made the toadstool for Warty to sit on. After giving us the poem, the teacher looked around the class and said, "I think we have some Wartys in this class." Then he added, "I've been teaching for more than twenty-five years, and I've never been so insulted in my life." After class the girl went up to the teacher and told him she wasn't voicing her own opinions, and didn't mean to insult him. The teacher told the girl he was going to call her Warty for the remainder of the term. My parents went to a parent-teacher interview the next evening, and this teacher told them there were some students in the class who didn't belong there. #854

13. Seeking revenge

People often try to get back at the person who criticizes them, or wish that they could do so.

I knew that two girls were always talking about me on the school bus, because while they talked to each other they would look over at me and laugh. It made me feel very bad inside and hurt, especially because one of the girls used to be a friend of mine. I didn't understand why they were talking about me, because I didn't do anything. I wanted to know what they were saying, because I might have been able to straighten it out. Often things that are said are not true, and you don't want false rumors about you going around that can cause you to lose your friends. I never found out what they were saying, so I tried to ignore the girls and grew to dislike them. I was hurt and mad, and I wanted to get back at them and talk about them. #855

When my mother got mad at me, I did things to make her madder. She was always after me to do my homework. Once I forgot to study for a test and made a sixty-five. When she saw the test, she got angry and said I'd have to quit playing hockey until I got my grades up. She made me study the subject every night until the next test. But when I was given the test, I just signed my name on it and handed it back. When my mother saw my blank test, she flipped out. She didn't know I was allowed to drop my three worst marks. #856

14. Reassuring themselves that the criticism is unjustified

People normally try to reassure themselves that criticism of them is unjustified. Often they conclude that the person criticizing them has overreacted, is unreasonable, or misunderstands them or the situation. People frequently talk to someone close and seek reassurance that they acted in a reasonable way and the criticism is unjustified. Sometimes they go to the person who criticized them or someone in contact with the person to explain their behavior and try to set the record straight.

15. Obtaining resources from people who do not criticize them

People also turn to those who do not criticize them in order to get resources.

> I spend my time with friends I can trust. I avoid the so-called friends who stab you in the back. They pretend to be friends but dump on you when you aren't there. #857

> When I need something or have a problem, I go to an administrator I get along with. If there's some asshole administrator who's given me problems in the past, I try to go around him. #858

Functions of avoiding criticism

The hurt that people feel when they are criticized serves an important function. It brings the message distinctly home that others disapprove of what they are doing and are likely to reduce their resources. Normally others make very clear exactly what the behavior is that they disapprove of. Because most of a person's resources are provided by other people, it is very much in each person's interest to know when he is doing things which are likely to cause people to cut off these resources or to limit his access to resources in the future. Such resources include food and water, positive reactions, sex, and stimulation, and the means to obtain them, such as time, energy, materials, money, jobs, information, and relationships.

319

When people think badly of another person, they are less willing to allocate resources to that person.

> My eighteen-year-old son has decided to spend the summer having fun with his friends. We don't approve and we've tried to get him to do something more constructive, like get a summer job, but he refuses. We don't want to make it easy for him, so we leave very little gas in the car. Maybe he'll develop more appreciation of money when he can't go anywhere. [859]

> I was psyched up for my driver's test, and cleaned the car and ironed my learner's permit. The test was going great, until we were in the middle of downtown and the examiner said it was pointless to continue. This stupid man told me I followed other cars too closely; didn't make my left turns quickly enough; and didn't have the right of way, but I know I did. It was the most awful thing that could happen. The whole situation made me feel so mad and defeated. [860]

Also, when people disapprove of a person, the resources that person has to offer are no longer considered as desirable, and others are less willing to exchange their own resources for them. In other words, the person being criticized becomes handicapped relative to others in the competition for resources.

> I went to a club with a friend of mine from university. A male student asked her to dance and she accepted readily. Afterwards she asked others about him and was told he was on the university basketball team. When he approached again, she turned her back on him. I wanted to know why, and she said, "I don't want anything to do with him. Members of the team are only after one thing. Lord knows what I'd catch." [861]

> A friend of mine wants me to go with her to the Harley Club. She's been several times and says, "Most are businessmen who ride Harley-Davidson motorcycles as a hobby. They're just normal guys dressed a little different. They are really polite and fun to party with." But my reaction is fear. I'm afraid to go. We've all heard horror stories of what happens to women in their clubhouse. I've heard them since childhood and can't shake them. It doesn't matter how sweet the individual is. People, including me, think anyone who dresses like that is bad. [862]

My sister went out on several dates with a premed student and he became quite enamored of her. Then his family found out my sister had had an abortion, and they put pressure on him to break up with her. I can't understand how they found out. She had the abortion in Toronto and none of our family members told other people about it. Maybe someone in the local hospital talked when my sister had a test to see how many weeks she was pregnant. #863

The resources of family members and friends of the person being criticized also become less desirable to other people because the family members and friends are associated with the person being criticized. Therefore, a person and those he is associated with may suffer a considerable loss if the person acts in ways which result in his being criticized.

The parents of a family in my neighborhood have been into drugs and everything. Their kid isn't invited to birthday parties in the neighborhood, and people don't want their own kids playing with this kid either. #864

The sharp negative feelings that one experiences when criticized act as an alarm that one's resources are threatened. These feelings occur at the first sign that others disapprove of one's behavior. If one does not change one's behavior, one's resources are likely to be curtailed by those making the criticisms. Often people do not wait to be criticized. Because they have been hurt by criticism in the past, they are normally quite attentive to learning what people criticize others for. They do not want to go through the experience of being criticized again, and are usually willing to restrict and alter their behavior beforehand to prevent this. Actually this is more advantageous to the person than waiting until criticism actually occurs. When people criticize another person, they already feel negative enough about him to restrict the resources they give him. Often by the time a person hears criticisms of his behavior it is too late to fully protect his resources, because others are already cutting them off or making plans to do so.

One of my workers is often late, and I told her I need her to be on time. She was very apologetic. If it continues, I know I'll have to fire her. #865

My employee does everything very slowly. There's so much that needs to be done at work, it really bothers me watching him poke along. I can't afford to hire an extra worker, so I may have to replace him. The other day I suggested he do something quickly and he got quite defensive. I know I'll have to do something soon. #866

Last night I wanted to talk to my teenage daughter and went to her room. As I tried to talk, she kept asking, "Are you finished?" She told me not to repeat myself, and even tried to push me out of the room, because she didn't want to waste any of her time talking to me. I told her she was rude and spoiled. Afterwards I talked it over with my husband. We work so hard to make money for her ballet and voice lessons and to get her teeth fixed. But she won't treat us with respect. We decided we're going to quit paying for all these things for the next four months. If her behavior improves enough, we'll start paying again. #867

My son is required to wash the dishes, but never does so until I get angry or tell him he can't use the car until he does them. It is really frustrating trying to cook with a countertop covered with dirty dishes and a sink full of them. Also, there are no clean plates to eat on. Last night he went out with his friends and promised to do the dishes when he returned. But this morning when I woke up he still hadn't done them. He's so lazy. All this summer, he's spent his evenings and nights with his friends and then slept all morning. It's been three days now since he's done the dishes. So I went in his bedroom and told him that he didn't live up to his promise and I wasn't going to give him his allowance this week. He argued he hadn't been warned in advance that I'd cut off his allowance. I also told him he'd no longer be allowed to have his friends over when there are dirty dishes in the sink. I told him I wanted him to start washing them in the next five minutes, and that I wasn't leaving for work until he'd finished them. I didn't want him going back to bed as soon as I left the house. But when I left his room he pushed his chest of drawers against the door and returned to bed. I insisted he open his door and he did so and got back in bed. I went and got a container full of cold water and told him I'd pour it on him if he didn't get up. I pointed out since he wouldn't act like an adult, I was forced to treat him like a child. He got up and went in the bathroom and locked the door. I told him I wanted him out of there, but he didn't reply. So I left for work and took his compact disk player and his disks. I'm not giving them back until he does his chores on a regular basis. #868

Even if a person is wrongly accused, and did not do what he is criticized for, he still feels hurt and his resources are still threatened.

When one's resources are threatened, the sooner one acts to protect them, the better. Normally criticism is the earliest indicator of a possible loss of resources. Because punishing feelings occur immediately after criticism, one has more time to change one's behavior. The hurt associated with criticism causes one to react, and by altering one's behavior in order to avoid the hurt, one prevents additional criticism and minimizes the damage. If one does not change one's behavior until one actually loses resources, the loss of resources is often greater.

Because people respond to hurt from criticism, they do not have to be attacked physically to get them to change their behavior. The more hurt that people feel when criticized and the more they try to avoid this hurt, the better they protect their physical well-being. Conversely, the less force one has to use to get others to change their behavior, the less likely one is to be injured in the process. Therefore it is to one's advantage to be able to use criticism, rather than physical force, to change another person's behavior.

People do not experience hurt when they criticize others. Therefore they feel little constraint about criticizing others, and frequently do so. Normally it does not occur to people that their criticisms will cause the other person to feel hurt. As a result they are often surprised when the other person acts hurt or angry. Nevertheless, people have learned that there are some individuals who "do not take criticism well," "are too sensitive to criticism," "take it personally," and "overreact." Therefore, people often hesitate to criticize others to their face because they are uncertain what the reaction will be. They do not want to have to deal with tears, arguments, anger, violence, or being criticized themselves. However, people experience little anxiety when they criticize a) others behind their backs, b) those in positions where they are unlikely to strike back, such as subordinates and dependent relatives, and c) those they have criticized before who did not react.

In order to avoid criticism and the associated hurt, people do what others want them to do. As a consequence they comply and coordinate their behavior with others. The more people cooperate and the more predictable they are, the more likely it is that group endeavors will be successful, and that resources will be obtained and conserved. The more resources that are obtained and conserved, the more resources there are to allocate to the individual participants.

> When the workers in my store do what I want them to do, we restock the shelves faster and make more sales. The more sales I make, the more hours I can hire each worker each week, and the more likely the store will survive. If the store survives, the workers and I will have future employment. [#869]

Excess behavior

Excess behavior is behavior in response to feelings which results in one acting contrary to the purposes the feelings are designed for. As a result, one loses resources rather than gains or protects them. For example, the feeling of hurt encourages people to avoid criticism, and by avoiding criticism they normally avoid the loss of resources. However, there are situations in which people seek to avoid criticism but actually lose resources.

People engage in a number of types of excess behavior. These include a) detecting criticism when no criticism is intended, b) seeking to avoid criticism when there is no danger of resources being reduced, c) avoiding criticism but failing to prevent the loss of resources, and d) trying to avoid criticism to such an extent that people prevent themselves from obtaining resources. Such instances waste time and energy and interfere with the optimum acquisition of resources.

People are so concerned with detecting criticism in order to avoid it, that they sometimes identify instances of it when it is not really there.

> I thought you asked where I got this dress because you didn't like it, not because you just wanted to know. [#870]

> I was daydreaming at my desk and facing in the direction of one of my clerks, who was helping a customer. When the customer left, the clerk insisted, "What? What did I do wrong? I saw you watching me. Go ahead, tell me." But I wasn't even aware of the clerk or what he had been doing. [#871]

People also attempt to avoid criticism when there is no need to do so, because there is no danger of their resources being reduced. Many people in secure positions are scared to undertake actions that would get them noticed.

> He's a coward. He's got tenure, he's well thought of, and he wants to get better working conditions just as much as we do. There's no danger of his losing anything, but he won't speak out. [#872]

Others are scared to do things they would like to do when they are outside of the settings where others control their resources, such as when they travel. Thus they do not change their behavior when they are no longer in the vicinity of their employers and neighbors. In other words, they play it too safe.

People also act to avoid criticism, but fail to gain access to resources or to prevent the loss of resources. Thus many people behave in socially desirable ways but fail to get the jobs and mates they want or fail to keep the jobs and mates they have. There are numerous factors responsible which are not influenced by the behavior and reputation of a specific individual. Such factors include economic competition, technological change, population growth or decline, prejudice and discrimination, accidents, wars, floods, droughts, storms, disease, depressions, regional disparities, resource allocation, and proximity to educational facilities.

People also try to avoid criticism to such an extent that they prevent themselves from obtaining resources.

> When you teach, you learn that many students do not want to get up in front of others to give a report or make a presentation. Some students avoid courses where this is required. Others try to convince the teacher to let them turn in a written report instead. They will try all kinds of excuses to get out of doing an oral presentation. Sometimes two or three students in a course will take a zero on the assignment and lose twenty percent or more of their total grade rather than face the class. I reassure them that most people are nervous and tell them the more times they give oral presentations, the easier it will be to give one. I also ask them if they would refuse to give an oral presentation in their future job, and risk being fired. Some state they are going to find work where they won't have to make any oral presentations. Rarely do the things I say do any good. Even if I give them a second chance and tell them

they can sit at their desk and just read their notes out loud, they won't come to class that day. It's because they know how much criticism hurts, and are so worried that the other students might think or say something negative about their presentation. #873

My friend used to tell me, "I know how people at home gossip about anyone who's been seen in a lounge or club in town. So I refuse to go to them. I'm not going to let them gossip about me." As a consequence she didn't meet any eligible males in clubs and didn't go on dates. Eventually she became involved with a married man who decided to leave his wife. The outcome was far more gossip than if she'd gone to clubs. #874

Even though I'm middle-aged, I've never been in a serious relationship. I don't want to take a chance on getting pregnant, because my parents would be so upset. I grew up in a community where lots of girls get pregnant and I know what people say. #875

Society and avoiding criticism

Individuals, groups, organizations, businesses, political parties, governments, and societies are involved in criticizing each other and trying to avoid criticism. Individuals, groups, and organizations are criticized for prejudice, discrimination, automobile accidents, traffic violations, drug use, irresponsibility, child abuse, sexual harassment, theft, embezzlement, violence, murder, extremism, deception, immorality, fraud, and tax evasion. Businesses are criticized for defective and dangerous products, false advertising, poor service, overcharging, excessive profits, exploitation of workers, discrimination, unfair competition, patent infringement, pollution, avoiding responsibility, and fraud. Political party members and government officials are criticized for patronage, use of public funds for private purposes, influence peddling, wasting public funds, making poor decisions, failing to solve problems, discrimination, breaking laws, dishonesty, buying votes, falsifying election returns, sexual immorality, sexual harassment, and hiding damaging information. Populations of countries are criticized for backwardness, inefficiency, laziness, graft, crime, poverty, unsanitary practices, overpopulation, starvation, bizarre foods, disease, immorality, prostitution, sexism, child abuse, abortion, infanticide, rape, economic disparities, unfair trade practices, inflation, religious intolerance, persecution, police brutality, torture, propaganda, secrecy, brainwashing, lack of personal freedoms, extremism, ruthlessness, barbarism, aggression, terrorism, and subversion.

All segments of society try to avoid criticism. They hide information that could be criticized, try to avoid negative publicity, select representatives who are unlikely to be criticized, defend their actions, attempt to control investigations by conducting them internally, remove those who are criticized, expel whistle-blowers, counterattack their critics, and educate others about their praiseworthy accomplishments.

The mass media, including television, the radio, newspapers, magazines, books, and the Internet, are a primary vehicle for airing criticisms. Problems, questionable behavior, contentious issues, and criminal activities are frequent topics of media attention, and those criticized are usually identified by name. Criticism of a specific target normally results in additional criticism in the various media. The mass media in turn is criticized for sensationalism, oversimplification, distortion, fabrication, inadequate investigation, bias in favor of owners and advertisers, and dependence on government communiqués.

Criticism is often tied to cutting off resources. Thus individuals, groups, and organizations which are criticized are avoided, investigated, restrained by laws, forced to change their practices, punished, attacked, and outlawed. Businesses which are criticized lose customers and are forced to disclose information, comply with restrictions, recall and alter products, change policies, pay fines, and control pollution. Political party members and government officials who are criticized lose privileges, support, positions, and elections, and are investigated, charged, and forced to resign. Countries which are criticized lose tourists, aid, loans, and investment; are subjected to trade tariffs and quotas; and are blockaded, invaded, and conquered.

People feel hurt when criticisms are directed at their group, organization, political party, government, or country. They frequently experience these criticisms as criticisms of themselves. Often others associate them with the segment of society being criticized. Criticism enables people to learn what they should not do if they want to avoid future criticism. The hurt that is associated with criticism grabs their attention and notifies them that behavior must be changed quickly in order to avoid further hurt. The faster they change their behavior, the less resources are lost by the segment of society they are associated with. The less resources their segment of society loses, the less resources they are likely to lose themselves.

A great deal of consistency and conformity within relationships, families, organizations, communities, and cultures can be attributed to attempts to avoid criticism and the hurt that accompanies it. People go to considerable effort to avoid being criticized. They find it much less painful to comply with the wishes of others than to weather criticism.

AVOIDING THOSE WHO REJECT YOU

Brief contents

Detailed contents

Detailed contents

Introduction

Rejection is the process of indicating to others that one is not willing to expend one's resources on them. People have limited resources, such as time, energy, money, and materials, which they expend in their efforts to satisfy their feelings. In order to have their resources available to use with certain individuals, they can not exhaust their resources on everyone else. Therefore they use various means of rejection to inform others that they do not want to expend resources on them.

People approach other people in an attempt to satisfy their feelings. Their approaches cost them resources. When they are rejected by another person, they feel hurt, and this hurt drives home the message that they will be unable to satisfy certain feelings or any of their feelings through the other person. In order to avoid feeling hurt by rejection, people avoid those who reject them, and stop trying to satisfy their feelings through them. Therefore they do not waste more of their resources by continuing to approach uncooperative people. Instead they turn to other people who do not reject them to satisfy their feelings. People feel hurt immediately after being rejected. This encourages them to immediately stop wasting their resources on individuals who are unlikely to provide them with the resources they want, and this allows them to immediately redirect their resources toward other individuals who are more likely to provide them with the resources they seek.

What each person needs and tries to obtain from other individuals is in a state of flux. People's circumstances change, and they receive information about the changing circumstances of others. People frequently reevaluate what they need and recalculate what others could provide them. As a result, people make numerous approaches to others in their efforts to determine whether others are willing and able to satisfy their feelings. In response, those who are approached indicate the types of resources they will and will not provide, and this changes over time. They use rejection when they are not willing to provide what others want.

Why people reject others

People have limited resources and employ them with the people they want to satisfy their feelings. As a result they do not have resources available for others. However, others frequently approach them in an attempt to satisfy their own feelings. When people reject others they are informing them that they are unwilling to dedicate their resources or certain of their resources to them.

There are several winos who hang out on one of the streets downtown. When I walk past them, I'm careful not to look at them. I don't want them to hassle me for money, and I don't plan to give them any. [#876]

I constantly run into a woman I know, who wants to get together for coffee or dinner. She's lonely and looking for a friend. I tell her I'm sorry I don't have time. I need all my time for my family and work, and have none to spare for her. [#877]

My sister applied for a job as a waitress and the owner told her the position was already filled. But we knew it wasn't. Later a relative of the owner told me the real reason my sister wasn't hired. She isn't pretty enough. The owner wanted someone who would attract all the boys to eat there. [#878]

People also reject others they consider unsuitable for their friends and relatives.

Jane's parents are upset she is dating a boy from a family with no ambition. The boy's father and mother work as laborers at a fish plant during the summer, and draw unemployment benefits during the winter. The boy already has a part-time job at the plant and will probably follow in their footsteps. Jane's parents totally reject the boy and do everything they can to discourage her from seeing him. [#879]

There are a number of reasons why people reject others. Normally they have already committed their time, energy, and materials to other people and endeavors. In addition, the person making the request may be unacceptable because people do not like his appearance, approach, personality, attitudes, beliefs, ideas, health, sex, age, race, ethnic group, behavior, reputation, family, friends, products, services, or employer. Also, people may hope to find someone else who is more acceptable. People tend to welcome requests from those they want resources from, and to reject requests from those they do not want resources from. People also reject requests which produce unacceptable risks for themselves. When they are approached by someone they have no interest in, people frequently feel annoyed.

Nevertheless, needs and relationships are often in a state of flux. Therefore, over time one's willingness to commit resources to a specific person may change.

> I was quite interested in a girl who was already engaged. After her marriage broke up several years later, she asked me if I was still available. But in the meantime I'd met someone else and gotten married. #880

How people reject others

There are a variety of ways in which people indicate to another person that they are not interested in expending resources, expending certain resources, or expending certain resources at that particular time on the person. People convey these messages through the following means:

1. Lack of interest
2. Lack of response
3. Failure to reciprocate
4. Lack of concern
5. Avoidance
6. Lack of respect
7. Failure to meet commitments
8. Outright rejection

Often people show they want less contact with a person when they reduce the amount of resources they expend on him.

1. Lack of interest

People reject others by showing a lack of interest in them and in certain types of interaction with them. People do this when they do *not* look at others, greet them, smile at them, initiate interaction, ask them about themselves, go over to speak to them or join them, offer them food or drink, include them in conversations or activities, ask them to dance, ask them out on a date, patronize their business, attend their performance, mention them to others, or ask others about them. People also indicate a lack of interest when they monopolize a conversation, cut conversations short, and show a greater interest in other things and other people. When others approach, people who are not interested in them may continue what they are doing, look elsewhere, watch or listen to other people, leave, or join someone else. If people wore permanent smiles, everybody could interpret this as a willingness to provide them with positive reactions and other resources. Because people control who they smile at, they can indicate who they are willing to allocate their limited resources to.

2. Lack of response

People also reject others by not responding to them. They do not return looks from them, listen to what they say, act interested in what they say or do, buy what they are selling, discuss or display their work, read what they have written, listen to their music, eat what they have cooked, answer their questions, smile or laugh at their jokes, do what they ask, find time to get together, adopt their ideas, follow their suggestions or advice, or acknowledge the things others do for them. People may also respond minimally or fall asleep while the other person is talking.

A guy asked this girl to dance at a club. She stared at the guy for a second, then turned to her friends and continued her conversation. [881]

My sister was a very popular baby sitter, and children were delighted with her. When the children grew older they were no longer excited to see her, and she felt hurt. [882]

I recorded some great instructional programs that made learning French easy and fun. I wanted my young girls to watch them and offered them so much money an hour to do so. But they didn't show any interest in the idea at all. They wanted to play, read, and watch cartoons on TV. I felt rejected. [#883]

When I moved here I attended meetings of the committee for community development. My friend was secretary of the committee and received a token salary. Then my friend decided he didn't want to be secretary anymore. He told me I should volunteer for the job because no one else wanted it, and at the next meeting I announced I'd be willing to take it. I thought I was doing them a favor. But the others just ignored me as though I'd never spoken. Then they asked, "Is there anybody here who'd like it?" as though I wasn't even there. Finally when no one else volunteered, they decided to advertise the position, which they'd never done before. They ran a notice in the paper and gave it to someone else in the community. [#884]

3. Failure to reciprocate

People reject others by failing to reciprocate. They do not return the other person's greeting or smile, shake their outstretched hand, return their invitation to a dinner or party, call or write back, or give them a card or present in return for one they are given.

My girlfriend keeps telling me she loves me. I know what she wants. She wants me to tell her I love her too. But I don't want to rush things. [#885]

4. Lack of concern

Another way people reject others is by showing a lack of concern about them. They do not do things for them, phone or drop by to see how they are, remember their birthday, give them messages from others, help or support them when they are having problems, visit them when they are sick, or show an interest in the things that matter to them, such as their graduation, promotion, wedding, or public performance.

My mom was so unhappy with her relationship with my dad, she took an overdose of sleeping pills. Dad cared so little he wouldn't drive her to the hospital, and when she was recovering at the hospital, he didn't visit her once. [#886]

5. Avoidance

People also reject others by avoiding them. They cut contacts with them short, refuse to look in their direction, claim they have to go somewhere or do something else, avoid places where they might meet, fail to contact them or include them when they have the opportunity, avoid their friends and relatives, take their business elsewhere, and use various barriers to minimize contact.

I had my first boyfriend in high school. We got along really well, and I was quite happy. After we had gone together a month, he stopped calling me and wouldn't say much to me at school. He even started sitting on the other side of the classroom. I began picking myself apart and wondering what was wrong with me. I finally confronted him and asked why he'd become so cool. He said he was interested in another girl. #887

I asked a woman working at the library out for dinner. She was quite attractive and nice. But she had such a different outlook on life, I didn't want to pursue things. After that, I stayed away from the library. It would have been awkward to run into her again. #888

The only way I can get any work done at the office is to shut the door. My colleagues leave their doors wide open and spend most of the day visiting each other and talking. #889

I've seen girls use all kinds of excuses to reject guys in bars and lounges. They'll say they don't feel like dancing, they're tired, they just sat down, they are leaving in a few minutes, they are about to dance with their friends, or their boyfriend doesn't want them dancing with other guys. One girl was approached by a drunk, and grabbed the nearest guy and pretended he was her boyfriend. The drunk began hitting the guy and the bouncers had to intervene. Sometimes when a guy goes over to talk, the girl will get up and go to the bathroom or join a friend at another table. One girl told me, "Half the time I walk away; the other half I say, 'No.' Now if he's cute, that's another story." #890

6. Lack of respect

People also reject others when they show a lack of respect for them. They are curt, interrupt them, do not take them seriously, do not introduce them to others, do not acknowledge their contribution, disregard their interests, fail to convey their messages to others, show favoritism to their peers and siblings, say negative things about them, criticize or humiliate them, insult them, yell at them, swear at them, and do not treat their work, possessions, friends, relatives, or pets with respect.

> My little brother is short and really fat. The other kids call him "Blimp" and won't play with him. Sometimes he comes home from school crying. #891

> When I was in junior high, I wasn't much to look at and didn't have many friends. The most popular guys hung around the washrooms, and every time I walked by they would yell rude things at me. I felt like a sideshow freak. I wanted to get back at them, but never had the courage. #892

> A so-called friend told everyone that my girlfriend is so nice he can't see what she sees in me. I was not amused. #893

> Some guys are very rude when they turn down girls who ask them to dance. One told me, "This chick came up and asked me to dance and all I could do was laugh in her face. I told her she had to be kidding. I mean the look of the bitch." Another said his favorite line is "Go bark up someone else's leg, ya dog." #894

7. Failure to meet commitments

People reject others by not meeting their commitments to them. They break appointments or dates, are late, do not show up, and fail to deliver on promises.

> I loaned my roommate two hundred dollars so he could move back home. I never heard from him again. #895

8. Outright rejection

People also reject others outright. They say no to a request; turn down an invitation for a dance, drink, date, or sex; reject others' help; refuse to participate in their activities or adopt their beliefs; push them away; strike them; argue with them; refuse to see or talk to them; tell them to "Shut up!"; refuse them entrance; tell them to leave or "Get lost!"; fail to consider them for a position or task they would be interested in or qualified for; reject their application for membership, promotion, a job, a course, or a program; do not elect them; drop them from a task; give them a poor grade; fail them; fire them; expel them; break up with them; divorce them; close the door in their face; lock them out; hang up the phone on them; refuse to answer the phone or door; fail to respond to messages from them; return mail from them unopened; and reject people and things associated with them, such as their friends, relatives, pets, work, possessions, and gifts.

A close friend of mine lives in California and I hadn't seen her for several years. So one morning I called her long-distance. Instead of being glad to hear from me, she said her mornings were for writing and she was not willing to talk to me. It was a real slap in the face. #896

I'm middle-aged and was turned down for an office job because I once had a drug problem. I had gone through a rehabilitation program and hadn't touched drugs for five years. Even though I'm highly qualified for the job, the business decided that they didn't want to take a chance. #897

My fifteen-year-old brother wouldn't go along with the other guys in his peer group and smoke, drink, and chase girls. They'd tell him, "Come on, take a little drink," or "Why don't you take her out? She looks easy." One day he told them he wasn't going to start smoking, hated the taste of beer, and would ask a girl out when he felt like it and not a minute before. After that they decided he was queer and ignored and avoided him. #898

There is a woman who has repeatedly been in the mental ward who hangs out downtown. She seems desperate for attention, but her techniques for getting it really turn people off. Initially when she approached me, I was friendly and listened to her, but she got to be such a pest that now, like everyone else, I try to avoid her. When she sees me across the street she starts yelling loudly. I ignore her and just keep on walking. But often she succeeds in catching up with me. Then she'll ask if I've seen someone I've never heard of, or she'll launch into accounts of how much trouble she's causing her relatives who are out to get her. She goes to the police and courts to file complaints. The one message that comes across is that this woman is going to make trouble for everyone she deals with. I try to be civil, but she keeps grabbing my arm and striking my shoulder. Once I told her, "Don't touch me." I'm astounded I said that to another human, because it's such a strong form of rejection, but I want her to stop grabbing me. I've also told her if she hits me again I'll hit her back. Now when I pass by I don't look at her, and when she speaks to me I ignore her. #899

People also prevent others from having access to possessions, economic opportunities, and information. When others are present people may whisper, break off a conversation, move away, or go behind a closed door to talk. Rejection can also occur in the form of negative publicity, persecution, fines, imprisonment, and execution.

Preventing others from feeling rejected or hurt

People know that certain things they do may cause another person to think he is being rejected. Each person tends to be very sensitive to rejection, and is quick to believe he is being rejected, even in instances when no rejection is intended. Therefore, when people do not want to alienate another, they try to make clear no rejection was intended. Often they do so by explaining in detail why they acted as they did or by suggesting an alternative time to do something together.

I apologize for closing my door while you were waiting to see me. I was talking to my husband on the phone. He has just resigned his job, and we had to talk about what he's going to do next. #900

It's too late for a walk, and I'm kind of tired. Why don't we go tomorrow? #901

I'm quite nearsighted, but I don't like to wear my glasses when I'm out in public. So I frequently fail to recognize people I know. I have to tell my friends this, so they won't get upset if I don't speak to them. [#902]

When you buy and sell used books you have to constantly reject books that people want to sell you. You reject the books that no one else is interested in buying and the ones that are in poor shape. However, it is almost impossible to reject a person's books without making the person feel rejected too. So you try to explain that you already have boxes of similar books no one will buy, and that most people are looking for the latest paperbacks that they haven't read yet by their favorite authors. Sometimes people understand; sometimes they don't. [#903]

People frequently recognize that rejection will cause others to feel hurt. Therefore they may try to take the sting out of rejection with an excuse or a compliment. Thus instead of saying, "I don't want to go out with you," a person may say, "I've already made other plans for the weekend." And instead of explaining, "We hired someone who is more suitable than you," an employer may respond, "We had many fine applicants for the job, and regret we are not able to hire all of them."

Feelings which encourage people to avoid those who reject them

Rejection is a painful and punishing experience. People are very sensitive to rejection, and react to it immediately. Normally people feel hurt and wounded. They take it very personally. Sometimes they react to the hurt with shock and anger. Often they feel discouraged, depressed, unhappy, embarrassed, and humiliated. Frequently they feel sorry for themselves, worthless, unloved and unlovable, that no one cares, and that life is not worth living. Often they want to cry and get away. However, they usually try to hide these feelings from others.

My nephew, Eddie, is seven years old and painfully shy. His father pays very little attention to him, but everything Eddie does is "for Daddy." Once when his parents were away, Eddie spent most of the evening drawing a picture for his father. When his parents returned, his mother praised the picture, but his father ignored it. Eddie raised the picture to show it to him, but his father pushed it away and sat down. Eddie began to cry and ran out of the room clutching the picture. His mother told me later her husband never wanted children and doesn't like them. [#904]

My first boyfriend became more interested in my sister and started dating her. My parents liked the idea because it meant my sister would have a date for the senior prom. No one saw my point of view. I decided my sister must be more attractive and have a better personality than me, and I felt ugly and awkward. My confidence and self-esteem hit rock bottom. I was depressed for months and considered suicide. [#905]

When I'm rejected I lose my self-confidence and feel inadequate. I hunch my shoulders, stare at the ground, and don't know where to put my eyes. [#906]

If I audition for a theater part and don't get it, I begin to doubt my abilities. I rationalize theater is not important to me after all. These doubts continue for a few weeks. [#907]

If you leave a job interview feeling really positive, it's a real letdown when they tell you later you didn't get the job. I feel awful, like I'm not good enough for them. It's also embarrassing when you've told a lot of people that you're applying for the job. I get really depressed and convince myself I didn't want the job anyway. [#908]

A new broker has joined the brokerage office where I have my account. She moved from another firm and tried to bring all of her former accounts with her. Today she looked like she was about to cry. She is very upset that her previous firm is winning back some of her accounts. [#909]

I made a lunch date with a friend of mine a week and a half in advance and we agreed to meet at a restaurant. I got there first and told the waitress I would wait and order after my friend arrived. My friend is very reliable and normally punctual so I was surprised as time passed and she didn't arrive. The restaurant has two rooms and a passageway between them which makes it impossible to see who is in the other room. I was at a table in the back room and at one point thought I heard my friend's voice in the front room. I got up and went to see in case she didn't know I was in back, but the person speaking wasn't her. I started to feel hurt that my friend hadn't shown up. The waitress asked if I wanted to go ahead and order, but I told her I would wait a while longer. The waitress is an acquaintance of mine, and I was embarrassed having her know the other person didn't come. I considered using the phone in the front room to call my friend and see if something had happened. But when I'd looked in the front room earlier, I'd noticed a woman I knew eating there. I didn't want her to learn I was stood up. I sat at the table and felt like crying. Finally I went ahead and ordered, because I would have felt foolish leaving the restaurant without eating. It would have made the fact my friend didn't come appear all the more significant to the waitress. After I left the restaurant I called my friend to find out what had happened. It turned out she had forgotten all about it and was very upset and apologetic. We made another lunch date. But this time I went to her office and we walked over to the restaurant from there. I was not going to take the chance of waiting in a restaurant again and having her not show up. [#910]

I feel very hurt when I'm stood up on a first date, which has happened several times. Usually I feel really pleased with myself for getting up the gumption to ask the girl out. And I feel high because this attractive girl accepts. Then after she has accepted, I usually think a lot about her and what might develop between us. So when she doesn't show I really don't want to believe it. I always wait much longer than I should in the hope something prevented her from making it on time. I've waited an hour and a half at times still hoping she'll show. Then I get to feeling really down and have an almost impossible time trying not to look glum. Usually I try to contact her to see if something happened because I'm still hoping we'll get together. Sometimes she has someone cover up for her and say she has gone out of town. I feel really unhappy and depressed, and I call up a really close friend and go have a coffee and tell her about the whole thing. A day or so later I'm OK, but still bruised by the experience. When I run into the girl later on, I'm friendly, because I want her to think it didn't really matter to me. However, I'm only superficially friendly. I don't want to start having a good conversation with her and do something stupid like ask her out all over and get stood up again. Sometimes I wonder whether the girl accepted the date because she can't say no, if she had second thoughts about going out with me, or if someone else asked her out that she's more interested in. [#911]

343

It's the most depressing thing in the world to think nobody wants you enough to have you as their special date on New Year's Eve. I can remember one New Year's Eve when I got together with three friends. One of the girls was really souky and unhappy she didn't have a date. She kept moaning about this guy who hadn't called to ask her out, and she went home around ten o'clock. That left three of us. We were drinking to have fun, got pie-eyed, and were laughing to kill ourselves. However, I was also upset that night because back in November this guy had asked me out for New Year's Eve. I was supposed to go out with him, but the stupid bastard never called to tell me what the plans were. So of course I wasn't going to call him and ask. Then on New Year's Day he called to say hello. I was pissed off as hell, because I'd been expecting him to take me out the night before. #912

When you get older, you know you might die soon. But none of your relatives want to spend any time with you. You feel you've outworn your welcome. #913

One often feels hurt when one is rejected, even when one knows that the other person still cares and one's relationship with the person is not threatened.

Sometimes when I try to phone a close friend, she's not there and I leave a message to call me back. If she doesn't bother, I start feeling hurt and unhappy. #914

When I got home, my younger daughter was standing in the hall crying. Her sister had locked her out of our apartment. #915

Instances of rejection frequently leave a lasting impression, and one may remember them for years. Painful feelings can reoccur whenever one thinks of the person one was rejected by or has subsequent contact with him or her. Often the more resources one receives from a person, the more their rejection hurts.

The worst year of my life took place after my girlfriend broke up with me. I was quite serious about her and we'd made plans for the future. When we broke up I felt like I'd been kicked in the gut. I was miserable. And every time I thought about her I felt as awful as before. The only way I could avoid thinking about her was by staying busy. My self-confidence was so low I went and talked to a plastic surgeon about improving my appearance. Half a year later I moved to another community. I needed change and a fresh start. #916

I felt most rejected when my boyfriend broke up with me. I was so in love with him, I was devastated. I felt so worthless because this perfect guy had rejected me. I thought it must be something I'd done. I felt life was the shits, was really depressed, and wouldn't go out. Eventually, with the help of my two best friends, I got my act together. I never could have made it without them and it took about a year. #917

When anything associated with a person is rejected, the person feels that he himself is being rejected. It does not seem to make much difference whether what is being rejected is the person's appearance, behavior, work, beliefs, ideas, experience, race, culture, possessions, family, pets, or organizations. A person can even feel rejected when there is little reason for him to think that others would share their resources with him in the first place.

I feel kind of hurt when people around me plan a party or get-together and don't invite me. They may even be strangers that I've never met before. No matter who they are, I feel excluded. #918

How people respond to rejection

Because people rely on others to satisfy their feelings, it is extremely important for them to recognize to what extent they can satisfy their feelings through specific people, and to identify how their relationships with others are changing. It is necessary for them to know precisely what they can and can not currently expect from specific people. Through instances of rejection they learn just what the limits of their relationships are. A relationship can be viewed as the attempt by two people to satisfy certain feelings through each other. Acts of rejection cause people to reevaluate their relationship with the person who rejects them. Often they conclude that their relationship is less than they had supposed, and they may conclude that they are not valued or even liked.

Responses to rejection

People respond to instances of rejection in various ways. These include the following:

1. Thinking about their rejection
2. Continuing to try to satisfy their feelings through those who reject them
3. Ceasing to approach others in the way which caused them to be rejected
4. Deciding to avoid, reject, or reduce involvement with those who reject them
5. Attacking those who reject them
6. Seeking alternative people and means to satisfy their feelings

1. Thinking about their rejection

When people are rejected, they normally think about it a great deal. When rejected, they frequently want to be by themselves, talk about it to someone close, or do something to pamper themselves.

> When I'm rejected, I don't have the energy to make polite conversation with other people. I just want to be alone. I feel emotionally exhausted and usually go to bed. Later I feel like seeing my best friend and telling her what I've been through. #919

> When I've been rejected, I take long walks or go outside and feed the birds. #920

> When my parents or friends reject me, I go off to the barn and talk to my pony. My pony's my friend. #921

> I usually go shopping to take my mind off what happened. Then if I still don't feel better, I treat myself to an expensive dinner at a nice restaurant. #922

Frequently people conclude that they have been treated unfairly and do not deserve rejection.

It's like I feel used. When my friends want smokes or something, they come to me. But when I need a friend or someone to talk to, they are always busy. #923

I put up with my children and grandchildren when they wet the floor, broke my favorite teacup, and woke up crying and screaming at all hours of the night. But now that Grampy and I are getting older, they can't put up with us. #924

In order to avoid taking rejection personally, people often attribute their rejection to their politics, sex, age, race, nationality, or some other factor.

There's no reason I should have thought I'd get a job with the government. They know my family never supported the Liberal Party. #925

2. Continuing to try to satisfy their feelings through those who reject them

People frequently continue to try to satisfy a specific feeling through those who reject them. Often people do not want to accept the limits that others establish for them. However, when they persist in trying to satisfy a specific feeling through the same people, they usually encounter additional rejection.

It bothers you when your teenage kids don't want to be seen with you in public. Often they don't want to go to a movie or shopping with you. If you go somewhere together, they try to walk or sit some distance away from you. They don't want their friends to see them with their parents. If you bring it up, it certainly doesn't change their behavior. #926

Arnold started dating Lisa, and wanted to spend more time with Lisa than she was willing. Lisa told him she needed a week for herself that she could devote to her work and studies. She also wanted to see some friends she hadn't seen for a time. But Arnold started calling her at work and wanted to discuss their relationship. She tried to reassure him that everything was all right between them, and she was just busy. But he kept calling. Lisa became quite annoyed and told him that being apart for one week would not be enough. So Arnold called her more often and sent her flowers. As a result Lisa told him it was all over. Arnold continued to call, and started dropping in at work and at her home to try to get back together with her. Lisa became increasingly annoyed and was very glad when he finally left her alone. #927

There's a restaurant in town which doubles as a coffee shop. A lot of people like to spend an hour or so there every day. One problem is an elderly poet, named Hilton, who hangs out there and is often quite obnoxious. He looks really disreputable, like he has been sleeping in the gutter, and he is quite argumentative and not interested in what others have to say. People try to ignore him, but it doesn't do much good. I was sitting at a table eating dinner with three other people the other evening when Hilton walked in the door. Every one of us lowered our heads and stared at our food. No one would dare look up in case he caught our eye and used it as an invitation to join us. But he came over anyway and stood right next to us. No one would look at him, and he continued to stand there. Finally he said, "Tell me if you'd rather I went away." Of course no one would say so, because no one wanted to deliberately hurt his feelings, and I asked how he was. After he talked to us for a minute he wandered off. I was actually surprised, because normally no matter what cues you give him, he joins you anyway. Then we spent the next ten minutes talking about how unpleasant Hilton is. Two people at the table said what bothered them was that he always spit on their food as he talked. I said it's clear he has a real need for others because he keeps approaching the people he knows, no matter how hard they try to ignore him. I think he feels as a poet he has a right to be disreputable and obnoxious. However, none of the rest of us could get away with this kind of behavior, because we'd lose all our friends if we tried. #928

There's a popular idea that persistence will get you what you want in the end. Because of this idea, people sometimes keep approaching the person or employer who rejected them. My experience has been that it's wasted effort, and one should accept the rejection and soldier on. I suspect when people persist, it's usually because they have a difficult time accepting rejection. #929

Repeated encounters with rejection, and repeated experiences with hurt, make it easier for people to stop trying to satisfy certain feelings through a particular person or organization.

Frequently people are so committed to a relationship, job, or training program that they feel locked in and can not easily leave when they experience rejection.

> I don't have a choice. I know I do badly in math courses, and I failed statistics the first time I took it. But I have to pass statistics to get my degree. So I'm taking the course again this year. [#930]

> It's hard to deal with failing a test after you've spent long hours studying for it. When I fail one, you'll hear me saying, "Fuck!" and "Bastard!" I spend my hard-earned money trying to get an education so I can get a decent job. I don't intend to arse around. [#931]

> I spent all that time working on the damn project and then had some twit tear it to shreds in five minutes. I had to change my proposal to fit his ideas. This has happened before, and it makes me wonder if I'm just wasting my time. Some days it pays to stay in bed. [#932]

People who are rejected frequently try to straighten out what happened. They may confront the other person and tell him how they felt when they were rejected. Often they want to find out if there is an acceptable reason why it occurred.

> When someone rejects me, I try to talk to them. It usually turns out the person was in a rush, had a bad day, or was not in the mood for company. [#933]

Often a good explanation and apology from the other person allow one to continue a relationship. Sometimes people attempt to remove a factor which they believe caused them to be rejected. For example, they may try to change their appearance or performance to minimize the chance of further rejection.

> When I did badly on my paper, I went to see the teacher. I hoped he would let me rewrite the paper. [#934]

> When I was in ballet school, my teachers kept criticizing the way I held my arms. I worked really hard and now my arms are one of my best features. [#935]

I know a girl who is twelve, overweight, and not athletic. When her classmates pick teams to play ball, she's the last one chosen. Frequently the supervising teacher forces one of the teams to take her. She is often close to tears and once refused to play at all. When she plays she tries to get an unimportant position and is very nervous about making an error. #936

People do not forget rejection. They expect less from those who have rejected them, and they expect less success from themselves in the future.

3. Ceasing to approach others in the way which caused them to be rejected

When people are rejected, they commonly stop approaching others in the way which caused them to be rejected.

A good job came up I wanted to apply for, and I contacted a teacher who has written letters of recommendation for me before. But he said he was only recommending his best students for this job, and in my case he wouldn't write one. It was an unpleasant surprise, and I'll never ask him for a letter again. #937

My friend applied for promotion several times and was rejected every time. He's quit trying, and I don't think he'll apply again. #938

I've watched girls who don't get asked to dance at clubs. At first they show they're interested in dancing. They stand near the dance floor, move in time to the music, and glance around casually. After a while, when they haven't been asked, their movements slow down, then cease, and the girls stare at the dancers. Then they go to the washroom to check their makeup. Finally they go sit down at a table. #939

I'm always hearing girls complain that guys just sit around the clubs and don't ask them to dance. What they are forgetting is most guys have been turned down repeatedly. When it happens, the guys feel hurt, and they feel embarrassed having the other people witness their failures. They don't want to take the initiative anymore unless they feel fairly certain they'll be accepted. I think a lot of guys hope a girl will indicate she's interested first so they won't have to go through another rejection. #940

My wife is so uninterested in sex, I feel I'm really imposing when I make physical advances. We do have sex about once a month and I suspect it's because she feels it's her duty. When we have sex, I try hard to please her and she almost always reaches orgasm. But she thinks I'm oversexed and says reading a book is more entertaining. I've become really reticent about making advances, and usually masturbate instead. #941

4. Deciding to avoid, reject, or reduce involvement with those who reject them

Another response of people is avoiding, rejecting, or reducing involvement with those who reject them.

Well they didn't invite me to their party. I'll never invite them to one of mine again. #942

About once a week I go into the local coffee shop to get a soup and sandwich. But the last time I went in, I sat there for twenty minutes and wasn't even noticed by the waitress. The place was not very busy, and she served others seated near me. I felt very self-conscious and embarrassed, because other people must have seen I wasn't being served. I finally walked out and told myself it would be a long time before I went back. That was several months ago, and I haven't been back. I always tip well, and I don't make problems for the waitress. I think she just didn't notice me. #943

One evening my girlfriend went to a banquet, and another evening she went drinking with a mixed group of friends. Both events were planned in advance, and she didn't invite me either time. I realized I was more involved with her than she was with me, so I backed off and quit calling her. #944

Math is a huge problem for me and I always do badly. I freeze up when I have to solve a problem on a test. If there's anyone with math block, it's me. I'm not taking another math course, if there's any way to avoid it. #945

I have done tons of things for a friend of mine. I've often bought her coffee and meals and paid her way to movies because she doesn't have any money. I've also spent many hours helping her with applications. A couple of times she's been in a position to do something for me, but she neglected to do so. Occasionally she travels with friends to Halifax and it never occurs to her to ask me if I'd like a ride there too. Recently she went over to Moncton to a Dolly Parton concert and had an extra ticket she didn't use, but she never thought of asking if I'd like to go along. I got upset by that, because I really would have liked to go. What it says is she doesn't really care about me. I decided, that's it; I'm not going to do things for her anymore. And I haven't. #946

I spend a lot of time with my girlfriend and her two girls, aged nine and eleven. Last time we went to dinner the younger girl ordered meatballs and we all asked for a taste. She gave her mother and sister one but said she didn't have enough to let me have a taste too. I felt rejected and hurt. Then she gave her sister a second taste. Later I ordered a milkshake and everyone wanted a taste of that. I gave a taste to my girlfriend and her older daughter, but told the younger girl she couldn't have one. She looked hurt and I told her it was because she wouldn't let me have a taste of her meatballs. I said I'd be happy to share with her if she'd share with me. #947

I went to pick up my VCR (video cassette recorder) at the shopping mall, where it had been repaired. There was a snowstorm that day, and I certainly didn't want to try to walk home carrying my VCR because it might be ruined. I spent fifteen minutes calling and recalling the four taxi companies in town, but they were so busy that they left their phones off the hook, and I couldn't get through. I was scared I'd be at the shopping mall for hours trying to get a cab. Then I ran into a girl I'd known for years. She was currently teaching some jazz dance classes I was interested in taking and we talked about them. I brought up the fact I really needed a ride five blocks away to my home because I couldn't get a taxi. I rarely ask a favor of anyone, so asking a favor of her was out of character. She said she was sorry, but she just wanted to get on the highway and go home. Then I saw her go in the grocery store to buy groceries. Afterwards I thought a lot about what had happened, and felt I was not asking all that much from her. I decided I wouldn't take her dance classes if she was the last teacher on earth, and I certainly wouldn't go out of my way to be friendly to her again. I just don't want any future contact with her. It makes you realize you can't expect help from anyone that you don't constantly do things for. #948

Often people separate themselves from the agent of rejection in order to get away from the hurt they feel.

> I was quite interested in a girl I was working with at a summer resort, but she wasn't interested in me. At the end of the summer she asked if I'd write her. I told her, "No, definitely not." The hurt was too strong. I didn't want any more contact with her. [949]

> I've known a number of people who have moved to another part of Canada to distance themselves from a person they broke up with. They have too many painful memories and feelings associated with breaking up with the person and don't want to experience them anymore. [950]

People may also decide they do not like those who reject them.

> I just hate unfriendly people. You've met them and talked to them. But when you see them the next time, you speak and they don't reply. Or else you want to say hello to them, but they don't look at you and you don't get the chance. I feel they are really rude, and I tell myself, "Don't bother trying to speak to them again." [951]

5. Attacking those who reject them

Occasionally people attack those who reject them.

> Elizabeth, a four year old, spends the day with a baby sitter because both her parents work. In the evenings and on weekends she has to compete with her brother and younger sister for her parents' attention. Her father focuses on her brother and takes him practically everywhere with him. Her mother spends most of her time with Elizabeth's baby sister, who is so cute and cuddly everyone wants to spend time with her. Therefore, Elizabeth gets much less attention than the other two children. Elizabeth is very jealous and responds from time to time by hitting her baby sister and taking her toys. On occasion she has told her mother and father she hates them, which gets her a beating. [952]

> Richard asked his older brother to play a game of ball with him. His brother said no, but Richard ignored this and continued nagging him. Finally his brother exploded and told Richard to go away and leave him alone. Richard shoved him angrily and went to his own room, where he

threw his ball repeatedly against the door. His brother ignored the loud noise, and eventually Richard stopped. #953

When Angus was nine years old, his friend Jim told him that his parents decided they didn't want him spending time with Angus. Angus returned home, got his father's hammer from the shed, and went to Jim's house and smashed in the headlights of their car. #954

Some males who are turned down when they ask a female to dance react by insulting the female. They say, "I didn't want to dance with you anyway, slut. The guys dared me," or "Well I guess a fuck is out of the question," or "That's OK. I was just going for a shit anyway." People also say negative things to others about the person who rejected them, such as "She's a prude," "She's a snob," "She's green (inexperienced)," or "She's been with every guy in town. I might catch something." One guy who was turned down for a dance stood up on a chair in the lounge and announced, "This girl is too damn good for any of us guys. Make sure you stay away from the bitch." #955

When this guy rejected me, I made up stories about him so everyone else would give him a hard time. It worked, because people can't wait to hear terrible stories about others. #956

Tammy was a very good basketball player, and felt sure she'd make the school team. But at practice she kept showing off instead of doing what the coach said. At the final cut Tammy was dropped. She threw a fit, and announced, "I didn't want to play on this shitty team anyway. You guys suck." #957

6. Seeking alternative people and means to satisfy their feelings

People commonly turn to alternative people and means when they encounter rejection. For example, after they are rejected, they may ask someone else for a date, enter a different school or training program, or apply for another job.

The head of the business school at the university told me I would have to leave the business program and find a different major because I had a bad grade in a math course. I was very upset. I left university and enrolled in a computer school downtown. [#958]

I watched a man at the club. Everyone he asked to dance turned him down. So he danced by himself. [#959]

When my girlfriend broke up with me, I felt nothing in life mattered. So I went out with my buddies and drank away my summer's earnings. It was all I could do at the time. Alcohol was an escape, but my feelings were still there when I woke up in the morning. [#960]

Charlene was a waitress at a popular bar. When she was fired she felt devastated and humiliated. She never wanted to set foot in the bar again. Afterwards, when people wanted her to meet them at the bar, she gave an excuse and suggested another place where she felt more comfortable. [#961]

I had had a cast on my foot for six weeks and was supposed to get it off on Saturday. But when I went to the local hospital, the doctor there told me that they don't do X-rays or remove casts on weekends. I didn't think this was true, and I got really mad and told him what I thought of him. He's a doctor and should take care of a patient whenever the patient needs help. I was very ticked off and stayed that way for two hours. Then I went to a hospital in another community and had the cast removed. [#962]

When I was in college I fell in love with a girl, but she wasn't interested. Then the same thing happened with another girl. I was so hurt both times that I knew I didn't want to go through this again. So I dated and married a girl I wasn't in love with. [#963]

Preparing for rejection

People can not obtain resources from others without approaching them. Often they have to approach many individuals and experience many rejections in their efforts to get the resources they want, such as an acceptable job or mate. Therefore, they frequently try to prepare for rejection by psyching themselves up beforehand.

I always have to bite the bullet the first time I ask someone out. I tell myself if I don't go ahead and take the chance, I'll never forgive myself, and as long as I'm going to do it, the sooner I get it over with, the less anxiety I'll go through. #964

I like to go out, meet guys, dance, and have a ball. Sometimes I ask guys to dance. I feel much more confident if I have a few bottles of courage juice inside me. When you're buzzing, it's a lot easier to laugh off rejection. When I'm sober, I don't go around asking guys to dance. I'd probably die of humiliation if some guy rejected me when I was in my right frame of mind. #965

Functions of avoiding those who reject you

Rejection notifies people that they can not expect to obtain what they want from those who reject them. The feelings that people experience when they are rejected make this message painfully clear. As a result, the message is less likely to be missed and less likely to be forgotten. Because of the intensity of the psychological hurt, people do not have to be taught by physical means to stop making these demands on specific individuals. Physical means are more costly than psychological means. They consume more energy and they can cause bodily injury to either party. Because of psychological hurt, people are less likely to continue to try to get the same thing from the person who rejected them. If they do try, they are likely to waste more resources (time, energy, money, and materials) by continuing to expend them unproductively. After rejection, people are more likely to turn to different individuals to satisfy their feelings. Therefore the hurt they experience redirects them to put their resources to more productive use. When people are rejected they immediately feel hurt. Thus they are immediately instructed to stop wasting their resources. This allows them to retain the maximum amount of resources to use with other people, and to have the maximum amount of time in which to do so.

The hurt others feel when rejected is also advantageous to the people who reject them. Because of this hurt, others who are rejected are less likely to approach people in the same way again. With fewer individuals making demands on their limited time, energy, and materials, people can more easily direct their resources toward the few others they want to give them to.

When people reject others, they do not experience the hurt that those who are rejected feel. Therefore people are free to reject others whenever they choose. Nevertheless, people are aware that they cause others hurt when they reject them, and are often sorry to do so. They do not want to feel guilty afterwards for hurting others. This places them in the dilemma of wanting to reject others, but not wanting to cause them the hurt of rejection. They have two alternatives. They can reject others, keep their resources free for their own purposes, and live with the knowledge they have caused others hurt. Or else they can choose not to reject others, assign them the resources they would rather commit elsewhere, and know they have not caused them the hurt of rejection. Although people commonly decide to reject others, at times they try to avoid doing so.

For some reason taxi drivers always want to talk to me. I could care less about them and what they say, and I'd rather sit quietly and think about things. But I try to be polite and make the effort to respond. I don't want to be rude and hurt their feelings. [#966]

Things were not working out between my girlfriend and me because of personality differences. I wanted to break up, but I knew she'd be really hurt. She'd told me she wouldn't want to live without me. I felt so guilty about the hurt I'd cause her, that I couldn't end things, and the relationship continued for a year or two longer than it should have. During this time I felt like a caged animal. Finally I went to a counselor, who said I shouldn't try to protect her from personal growth, which she'd experience with the separation. I broke up that weekend. I still feel guilty. I just hope she finds someone more suitable. [#967]

Rejection and criticism

There are both similarities and differences between rejection and criticism. First, there are important similarities. People reject and criticize others because the presence or behavior of others is not consistent with the

357

models people currently hold and execute (see the chapter on Establishing Consistency in a later volume in this series). People both reject and criticize others, what others do, and how they do it. Both rejection and criticism constitute negative reactions. When people are rejected or criticized, they feel hurt. In order to be effective, both rejection and criticism depend on people feeling hurt. Many people become angry when they are hurt, and this is true for both rejection and criticism. There are also similarities in the ways people respond to both rejection and criticism. People frequently cease to do what it is that caused them to be rejected or criticized, avoid those who reject or criticize them, attack those who reject or criticize them, and/or approach alternative people to satisfy their feelings.

At the same time, there are significant differences between criticism and rejection. When people criticize others, they usually want to change their behavior. People express criticism by a) indicating disapproval, b) bringing up a subject they wish to criticize, c) correcting what the other has done, d) making critical statements, e) pointing out consequences, f) using sarcasm or ridicule, g) threatening loss of resources, and h) removing resources. When people want someone to change his behavior, they usually want him to do things their way. If people succeed in getting another person to change, he may act more consistently with their models, and people will experience less tension. Greater consistency frequently provides more cooperation and more resources. Normally people are interested in continuing to cooperate with those they criticize.

In contrast, when people reject others, they are usually interested in avoiding or getting rid of others. By removing them, people are free to allocate their limited resources to those they want to allocate them to. People do not only reject specific others. They also reject specific behaviors which they want others to stop. Rejection of specific behaviors enables people to limit their involvement with others. Criticism is one of the tactics used to reject others, in order to either drive others away or to get them to stop specific behaviors. Rejection is indicated through a) lack of interest, b) lack of response, c) failure to reciprocate, d) lack of concern, e) avoidance, f) lack of respect, g) failure to meet commitments, and h) outright rejection. Roughly speaking, rejection is applied to get rid of a group, an individual, or a specific behavior, and criticism is applied to add, remove, or alter a specific behavior.

Excess behavior

Excess behavior is behavior in response to feelings which results in one acting contrary to the purposes the feelings are designed for. As a result, one loses resources rather than gains or protects them. For example, the feeling of hurt causes people to avoid others who reject them. As a result people do not throw their resources away in unproductive directions. However, there are situations in which people avoid others who would provide them with resources, because people are afraid they will be rejected and feel hurt.

Because of previous rejection, many people respond in ways which prevent them from obtaining resources they might be able to get. They may a) stop trying to get a specific resource from a person who rejected them, but who would be willing to give them that same resource in the future or on an occasional basis, b) stop approaching a specific person who rejected them, but who would be willing to give them other kinds of resources, c) quit approaching everyone in regard to satisfying certain feelings, or d) avoid situations in which they fear they might encounter rejection.

Following rejection, people may avoid seeking a specific resource from a specific person who would be willing to give them that same resource in the future or on an occasional basis.

My birthday was the coming Thursday, and I called up my closest friend and made a date to take her out to dinner that night. Then I made a reservation at one of the best restaurants in town. I couldn't afford it, but I wanted to do something special. I knew I'd have an enjoyable evening talking to my friend. But on Wednesday afternoon I ran into my friend and she told me she had something else to do Thursday evening. I explained I hadn't told her it was my birthday, because I didn't want her to feel she had to get me a present. She apologized but said she still wouldn't be able to make it. I felt sorry for myself and like crying, and I went home. I didn't want to spend my birthday alone. I sat there feeling that no one really cared about me. I decided I wasn't going to make any effort in the future to get together with this friend, and I wasn't going to invite her over again to watch her favorite program on cable TV. #968

Following rejection, people may stop approaching a specific person or organization that would be willing to give them different resources than those they requested. People treat rejection of anything associated with them as rejection of themselves. Therefore they often act as though they have been totally, rather than partially, rejected.

> This girl at university usually spoke to me. One night at a bar she asked me to dance and I told her I didn't feel like it. From then on she pretended she didn't know me, and wouldn't even look at me. #969

> After we were married, my wife and I applied for a bank loan and were turned down. Everyone in the community knew we'd been refused, and we were quite embarrassed. We went and got a loan from another bank, and we swear we'll never do business with the first bank again. #970

> When I got involved in a legal case, I asked a friend of mine to write a letter of support for me. He didn't want to do it because he was scared he'd get involved. I learned I couldn't count on him. If I need any help in the future, I'll go to someone else. #971

Because of their previous experiences with rejection and hurt, people may stop or become hesitant about approaching everyone in regard to satisfying certain feelings.

> If I don't know a girl, I'll never speak first. I'm scared she'll reject me. #972

> I usually don't get rejected when I ask a girl out. It's because I try to make damn good and sure how she feels before I take the plunge. I'm so slow in moving, I've lost the interest of many females. I just can't handle rejection at all, and this is a good way to avoid it. #973

> Lots of the guys who get turned down for a dance don't ask anyone else all evening. Many laugh about it with their friends, but I think they're just hiding how they feel. #974

> I know a number of women in their thirties and forties who have given up actively looking for a partner. Going out to clubs and dances

has been unproductive for them, so they no longer try. They stay home or they do things with their girlfriends. [#975]

I'm not going to waste my time filling out more applications for jobs. I can't even get in to get an interview. [#976]

Because they fear rejection, some people avoid situations in which they might be rejected.

I've written a lot of short stories about my experiences growing up. I must have thirty stories finished now, and I keep them in a box. I sent an outline of one of them to someone I know who works for a magazine, and he was very encouraging. But I've never tried to publish them, because I don't want to deal with rejection. Anyway, writing them is good therapy. [#977]

I have a tremendous fear of rejection. I'm always anxious others will reject me, and I work very hard to be acceptable to others. I avoid any kind of conflict, and don't challenge others, even when they're wrong. I keep my feelings to myself and people ask me, "Don't you ever get angry?" When I'm around others, I say, "Hello," "Goodbye," "Thank you," and "Sorry," far too much. I smile so often that people ask, "Do you go to sleep smiling?" and "Do you take happy pills every morning?" I am very nervous with others, and my whole demeanor is apologetic. I am acutely aware of what I say, how I say it, and what my facial expressions are while I say it. After I deal with someone, I examine how I've behaved, worry I did the wrong thing, and decide what I should change in the future. For example, I may decide that my response wasn't enthusiastic enough when they were excited about something. All this is so draining I'm often exhausted. I try to be alone as much as possible just so I can relax. I often eat in my apartment instead of in a public place in order to avoid others. Before venturing outside my apartment, I usually listen at the door to make sure no one is in the hall. I do all this to protect myself from rejection. [#978]

One response to rejection, suicide, completely stops the psychological hurt, but also ends one's access to resources.

Society and rejection

Many of the resources that people want are available only from groups and organizations. These provide services in the areas of health, education, welfare, information, communication, transportation, economic development, protection, safety, stimulation, and recognition. Such services are normally too expensive and too difficult for individuals to provide for themselves. People make numerous requests for these services, and a high percentage of requests are rejected. They are rejected because the resources of groups and organizations are limited, certain endeavors are considered more important than others, and needs and priorities are always changing. Just as individuals often feel little hesitation in rejecting others, members of groups and organizations usually feel little hesitation too.

Rejection by groups and organizations is similar to rejection by individuals. People feel the same hurt when they are rejected by a social club, sporting team, school, scholarship committee, employer, professional association, promotion board, loan committee, funding agency, publisher, licensing board, awards committee, court of law, zoning board, compensation committee, human rights commission, or immigration authority that they do when they are rejected by an individual. As a result of this hurt, they are less likely to apply to the same party in the future, and are more likely to direct their own resources into alternative channels, which may prove to be more productive.

A friend of mine studies dance and helps teach ballet to children in a ballet school. She decided at the last minute to take an intermediate-level ballet examination. This is a formal examination conducted by a visiting examiner from Ontario. When my friend learned she failed the examination, she was so upset she cried for four hours. She started crying again when she told me about this over the phone. She was devastated. She decided she was not going to dance anymore, not going to teach dance in the future, and not going to take the exam again. My friend is the last person I would think who would respond this way. She isn't moody or high-strung. Instead, she is easygoing, strong, mature, stable, and in control of her emotions. [#979]

NOT HURTING OTHERS

Brief contents

Detailed contents

Detailed contents

Introduction

People are very much concerned with not hurting others. They consider the impact their actions are likely to have on others, and try to avoid doing things which would hurt them. They do not want to cause others pain, injure them, fail to take care of them, make them feel bad, upset them, cause them to lose resources, neglect them, embarrass them, be rude to them, cause them inconvenience, let them down, fail to meet promises to them, fail to help them, disappoint them, do things they disapprove of, or do things which would cause them to feel hurt if they learned about them. The feeling that encourages people to not hurt others is feeling bad as a result of self-criticism. Self-criticism is a negative reaction, and people hate negative reactions. When people hurt others they often hold themselves responsible. They blame themselves and feel disappointed, upset, or angry with themselves, and they feel guilty. These are punishing feelings and people try to avoid experiencing them in the future. Therefore, people try to follow courses of action which will not cause others to feel hurt, and when they do hurt others they frequently seek to make amends.

When people hurt others, they damage them physically, cause them to lose resources, or otherwise upset them. When others are hurt, they are less viable and less able to provide people with resources, and they are alienated. Those who are alienated are less willing to provide those who have hurt them with resources. When people do not hurt others, they do not damage or alienate others and cause others to be unable or unwilling to provide them with resources. The more successful a person is in feeling bad as a result of self-criticism, the less likely he is to hurt others, the more likely he is to make amends when he does so, and the less likely he is to lose resources.

Signs that a person feels hurt, such as crying, crying out, and showing he is upset through his facial expressions, notify others that he is being hurt. The more successful a person is in showing signs of being hurt, the better he can indicate his hurt to the other person who is hurting him, and the more likely he will be to make the other person feel guilty and stop hurting him. Therefore the better a person is at showing signs of being hurt, the better he protects himself from further hurt and loss of resources.

366

People feel hurt and tend to show signs of this immediately when others do things which hurt them. As a result others are likely to stop hurting them sooner. Therefore, showing immediate signs of being hurt provides immediate protection for oneself and one's resources. At the same time, self-criticism, or guilt, frequently occurs as soon as one thinks one has hurt others. This gives one time to stop causing further hurt and to try to rectify the situation.

People receive most of their resources from very few other people. It is an expensive process to try to find replacements for these people in order to get the same resources one is already getting. Therefore it is in one's interest not to damage or alienate them. Guilt encourages people to take good care of their present and future human resources so that they do not lose them.

The phrase, hurting others, is used in this chapter to include a) causing others physical or psychological hurt, b) causing others to lose resources, and c) failing to help others.

Activator

Crying

People notify others that they are hurting them by showing signs of being hurt. They show signs of being hurt by crying and crying out. Crying and crying out are automatic responses to feeling hurt. When a person is hurt he normally cries or cries out, or feels like doing so.

> Nicholas, my sister's one year old, cries when he's hungry, tired, or sick. He also cries when he's ignored. He will cry and cry until he's picked up and played with. [#980]

> In Vietnam it is common for parents and family friends to tease a child by pretending to reject it. This is done to children between three months old and three or four years of age. Adults do this to entertain themselves and others by producing a strong reaction in the child. The adult will yell things such as "Be rid of you," "Go away," "Nobody loves you," "I don't love you," "You don't belong here," and

"You look ugly." Sometimes the adult pretends to hit the child too. The child will cry and cry and cry, or sob, and frequently sticks out its bottom lip. This form of teasing is known as giết hại (English pronunciation: yit hi). This is because the adult frequently says, "Giết hại đi," to the child (English pronunciation: yit hi dee). The word, "giết" means kill or murder, but the expression, "giết hại đi," means "be rid of you." Thus a person may ask why a baby is crying loudly and be told, "I giết hại the baby," and the person may say, "Don't giết hại the baby." After someone has teased the child this way, the person who teased the child or another adult will comfort the child and tell it that it is loved and the child will stop crying. Not everyone teases a child this way, but an adult may do so several times a week. #981

My boyfriend told me at the last minute he had arranged for us to go meet some friends. I tried to get nicely dressed, but he insisted there was no time left for me to put on my makeup, and he rushed me out of the apartment. When we were in the car, I complained he hadn't given me enough time to get ready. He got angry and yelled at me. He was so unfair I cried for fifteen minutes. My face was red and swollen, which made it look all the worse. #982

When my parents do something unfair to me, I start crying uncontrollably. I may cry for a half hour or more. I try to tell them how unfair they are, but they never agree. If someone else is unfair to me, I get mad but I don't start crying. Even if I'm out with other people, when my parents do something unfair to me, I can't control myself and I cry. It's very embarrassing. I certainly don't want to, but no matter what I tell myself, I cry anyway. #983

When a person cries or cries out he informs the person who is responsible for hurting him or taking care of him that he is hurting. As a result, the person responsible is more likely to feel guilty and to stop hurting the person or to try to help him. Also, crying and crying out interrupt another person's focus, or mental concentration, and cause him to refocus on identifying who is making the noise and why. If he can get the other person to stop crying, he will be able to focus again on what he would rather concentrate on.

When I hear my baby cry, I have to go see what the matter is. Maybe she's hungry, or wet, or wants to be held. If one thing doesn't work, I'll try another until I figure out what the problem is. When you do the right thing, your baby stops crying. I can't imagine not doing this. If I didn't, I'd feel I was a very bad mother. Once I had to go to the store to get some food and left my baby sleeping. I was gone for half an hour, but when I got back she was crying very hard and must have been crying for quite a while. I remember this vividly and feel really bad I was not there when she needed me. I felt so guilty, I didn't do this again. When I'm out of the house and hear someone else's baby cry, I look to see what's happening. If the baby's mother isn't trying to do something, I'll wonder why. Sometimes I even suggest a solution to the mother. #984

Crying helps when people ask others to take responsibility for helping them.

It is common in Vietnam for someone in need to come to you, explain their situation, cry, and obtain your help. For example, a woman in your town, who is not a close neighbor, may come and tell you, "My children are hungry, I have no money or job, and I have no rice to cook tonight. Can I borrow some rice?" Because she cries, you help her and loan or give her enough rice for a meal or two. If she just came by and asked for help, you probably wouldn't help her. No one has very much, you can't help everyone, and you have to look after your own family. Or someone may come and tell you, "My husband is sick and I have no money to take him to a nearby town for treatment. When we get some money we will pay you back." Even though you know they'll never have the money to repay you, because they cry, you usually give it to them. They have to cry for other people to have lots of sympathy for them and give them what they need. This is true whether the person asking for help is a relative or not. My sister-in-law was in love with a distant relative, but the two families did not approve of the relationship. So one day she collected her clothes and took off with the man and married him. Her family disowned her and said she was no longer their daughter. A year or so later she sneaked back and told her mother how hard their life was. Because they were having such a hard time and because she cried, the family sympathized with her. They gradually accepted the couple and acknowledged their marriage. It is common in Vietnam for people to cry and get something they want. It happens a lot. More women than men do it, but men cry too.

There is a Vietnamese expression, "Nước mắt chảy lòng," or "Tears melt your resolve." No matter how hard and firm a person's resolve, tears can soften it. For example, let us say that I go to you to collect the rice or money you still owe me. I am adamant and give you a lecture. I point out that it is overdue and I must have it, and I insist you return it now. You apologize, explain why you haven't been able to return it, and are upset and cry. So I soften and ask, "When will you have it?" And once again I postpone collecting it. [#985]

Unless a person shows appropriate signs, others do not realize the person is experiencing hurt.

I bought a replica of one of the ninja weapons for hand-to-hand combat. The traditional weapon consists of two short wooden sticks joined by a short chain. But instead of wood this one was constructed of soft rubber. I was at a friend's house, and his little brother put on his football uniform with all the padding so I could try out the weapon on him. Everything was going fine, because the padding prevented him from being hurt. But then I hit him on the back where there wasn't any padding, and he began to cry. I felt really bad, and the big reason I felt bad was that I had made him cry. When he stopped crying, I felt better. But I let him play with the weapon to make up for hurting him. [#986]

Sometimes I take my two kids along when I go out to a restaurant with friends. My girl is seven and my boy ten, and they can get really unmanageable. They talk loudly, play at the table, and run around the restaurant. When we get home I spank them. I make them lie down and I hit them on their bums with a stick or ruler. They cry, and if they don't cry, I hit them harder and more often until I can see they're hurting. [#987]

Young children cry whenever they feel hurt or strong tension. Thus they cry when they are hungry, wet, sick, or tired; are in pain; want to be held; feel lonely, ignored, rejected, or deserted; are anxious or frightened; are unable to get something they want; or are criticized or receive other negative reactions. Older children and adults often feel like crying in the same situations. However, if they do so they are likely to receive negative reactions from other people, and to be criticized and embarrassed. They learn not to cry in most situations, because if they do others will think they are unable to control their emotions and are "crybabies."

People also cheat, or pretend to cry, in order to get others to stop hurting them or to help them.

I was visiting my girlfriend when her nine-year-old daughter slipped and fell on her bedroom floor. She cried and complained loudly that she had hurt herself. I went in to comfort her, but she wasn't interested in attention from me and refused to get off the floor. She lay there calling repeatedly for her mother and her sobs became more and more contrived. Finally, after fifteen minutes of this, her mother went in to comfort her and she got up off the floor. #988

Jane, my ten-year-old daughter, came to tell me her older sister had drunk half her chocolate milk and wouldn't apologize. I told her I didn't want to get involved. Jane then ran in her room, slammed the door, and had a long, loud fake cry. Later, when the three of us watched TV in the living room, Jane held a blanket around her which covered everything except her eyes. She continued to complain strongly about what her sister had done, and said, "It's the principle of the thing." When I asked which principle was involved, it was clear she didn't know what principle meant. I told her sister to apologize and she did so in a laughing manner. "So do meaningfully!" cried Jane. Her sister responded, "I'm so sorry I drank your chocolate milk," in a most contrite way, but it was clear she didn't mean it. #989

There are also cheats in Vietnam. These are people who use fake tears to convince others to give them something. Such people do not have a genuine problem, but make up one and pretend to cry. This is fairly common. If someone comes and asks for money or rice, someone else may warn you, "Don't trust her. Those are her fake tears." There is a popular play in Vietnam, Đắc Kỷ Trụ Vương (rough English pronunciation: dack-keeh tru youn), in which a concubine uses fake tears and a fake illness to get the king to carry out her revenge. #990

Additional means of notifying others one is being hurt

People use means other than crying and crying out to indicate they are being hurt. These include a) facial expressions which express upset or distress, b) acting hurt, and c) telling others they are hurting or that others are hurting them.

One moment my girlfriend is sugar sweet, the next she's really bitchy. I may make a harmless comment, like "Red just isn't your color," and she turns into a little monster. She sulks, her comments drip sarcasm, and I feel guilty as hell. The storm passes after half an hour, and she's back to her old self again. [#991]

People act hurt when they avoid a person, ignore him, respond minimally, and appear injured. Often when people believe a person is avoiding them or responding minimally, they ask themselves if they have done something to hurt the person.

My mother doesn't like my boyfriend. So when she learns I'm going against her wishes and seeing him, she quits speaking to me. If there's a special occasion which is very important to me, such as Christmas, she'll say she doesn't want to exchange gifts. She does this to make it clear I've hurt her and to make me feel guilty I've done so. [#992]

Once, when my baby was six months old, I placed him on his stomach in the middle of a table. He was still too young to turn himself over or sit up, and because he was on his stomach he could only move a few inches. I was in the same room about seven feet away, and kept looking over at him as I fixed my face in the mirror. Then I heard a sudden noise and a short cry. I turned and saw he had fallen from the table to the concrete floor on his stomach. He fell so hard he couldn't cry for a minute. It was all my fault, and I felt so bad. I didn't think it was possible for him to get to the edge of the table. A week and a half later he vomited blood. The doctor couldn't find anything wrong, but I think it was internal bleeding. That was eighteen years ago, and I still feel very guilty. [#993]

In addition, people tell others that they are hurting them or have hurt them in the past.

I think at some time in their life every teenager avoids their parents in public places so their friends won't associate them together. This is why I often walked well ahead of my parents when we went to the shopping mall. Then when we got home my parents would make me feel extremely guilty by asking, "Why do you always walk so far ahead of us when we go somewhere? Are you ashamed of us?" [#994]

My parents always made me feel guilty when I stayed out too late at night. The second I walked in the door my father would come up to me with a mad look on his face and say, "Where the hell have you been? Your mother has been up all night waiting for you, worried sick something might have happened. Don't you consider anyone's feelings except your own?" #995

What people criticize themselves for

People criticize themselves for things they do.

Wayne has been divorced for four years. His two children live with their mother and both have been having problems at home and at school. Wayne says, "I always blame their behavior on the divorce. I know they were hurt and resented my leaving. I think this is their way of getting even. We hurt them, so they are hurting us in return. Maybe if we had worked harder at our marriage, we could have made it work. Then my kids would have a normal life and be happy, rather than be living in a broken home full of sadness and problems." #996

People also criticize themselves for things they fail to do.

Carla is my friend. She is engaged to Ted and very much in love with him. I know Ted is not very faithful, but I said nothing about it because I didn't want to hurt Carla. Then one night Carla found Ted in bed with another girl. Naturally she nearly went nuts over it. I could have prevented this if I had spoken up. I let my friend be hurt just because I didn't have the guts to say something. #997

There is considerable variation between individuals as to what specific actions cause them to criticize themselves. Different individuals can criticize themselves for opposite actions.

I kept my baby, and I wonder if I did the right thing. Maybe she would have had a better life if she'd been adopted. I mean at least then she would have had a normal life. You know, with two parents. #998

I gave my baby up for adoption and feel so guilty about it. I have a child walking around somewhere who is going to think I didn't want him. He hates me; I just know he does. I mean if someone rejected me like that, I would hate them. The only way I can live with it is by believing he has a good family now and is happy. #999

Each person has some things they feel guilty about, and other things they do not feel guilty about.

There are things I feel guilty about. But I didn't feel any guilt when I wrecked my parents' car. I ran into another car, but nothing bad happened. The other driver had whiplash, but it was only temporary. I found it inconvenient that I didn't have use of a car afterwards. #1000

Often a person appears to be very inconsistent.

I don't feel guilty when I don't do my chores at home. When I haven't done dishes for several days, Mom gets upset because the kitchen is all messy and she doesn't want to use it. That doesn't bother me. But I feel guilty when Mom says she'll wash the dishes. It's my job and it's wrong for me to make her do them. #1001

It wasn't me. I didn't say that about you. I don't know where you heard that I said it, but I didn't. I heard it from Tricia. So blame her. Don't blame me. I just repeated what she told me. I didn't know that it wasn't true. I don't feel guilty, but Tricia should because she started it. #1002

I have never once shoplifted in a store. I've always felt that if I'm not going to pay for something, then I shouldn't have it. I would feel both furious and mortified if someone accused me of shoplifting. On the other hand, sometimes a store makes an error and puts the wrong price on an item. Maybe they'll put the price of the smaller size on the bigger size, or they'll just attach the wrong price and the item will cost a fraction what it regularly does. When this happens with an item I regularly buy, I'll buy as many as I think I can get away with without bringing their attention to their mistake. I never feel the least bit of guilt when I do this. I don't know why I would feel guilty about shoplifting, but not about paying too little for the items which are priced incorrectly. In both instances I hurt the store. I could easily point out the pricing error to the cashier, but instead I'm really pleased to take advantage of the situation. #1003

The things that a person feels guilty about can change with time, as the person's knowledge and situation change.

When I was growing up we never even thought about pollution, environmental impact, and recycling. But today I often try to use less plastic, and I get items repaired rather than replace them. I feel guilty when I'm wasteful. It's not much, but every little bit helps. [#1004]

Frequently people criticize themselves after they have had time to think about what they did and realize they did something they consider wrong.

What I do is go through a sequence. I do something, think about it, realize what I did was wrong, feel bad, and then try not to do it again. For example, I told a friend what I wanted for a birthday gift. Then I realized I had put him in the position of having to get it for me. I shouldn't have done that and I felt bad I had asked for something. It can be a while later before I realize I shouldn't have done something. When I was twelve and lived in Toronto, there was a boy who used to hang around my best friend. The other guys hated this boy and called him names. I would tell my best friend he shouldn't let this boy hang around him. Some time later I realized I was wrong to say this to my best friend. I have no right to tell someone who he should be friends with. [#1005]

During the summer I spent a month in New York City. One day I got on the subway and sat down. Seated directly across from me was a man dressed only in a T-shirt, pants, and sneakers with the laces missing. There were rivulets of dried blood on his face and neck. He looked like someone had beaten him up and all he had were a few clothes to get home in. There were other people in the subway car, and the man stared back at anyone who looked at him. I just sat there like everyone else. Ever since, I've always felt I should have gone over and asked if I could help him in some way. I was wrong not to ask. Maybe he could have used a couple of dollars to help him get where he was going. I think when something unfamiliar happens, you don't know what to do, because you need time to mull it over. Probably the best you can do is decide what you should do if it happens again. [#1006]

Sometimes events occur too quickly for people to determine what they should or should not do at the time. Other times people let another person convince them to act in a particular way. Afterwards they think about the situation and blame themselves for not doing the right thing at the time. A person may even realize that something he did or did not do in the past hurt others, and begin to feel guilty years afterwards.

There are certain factors which are related to a person's being more likely or less likely to feel guilty. People are more likely to feel guilty when a) they are personally responsible for hurting another person, b) they could have done something to prevent the person from being hurt, c) they have face-to-face contact with the person, d) the person is a major source of their positive reactions, e) what they did is considered wrong by other people, f) the person experienced a great deal of hurt, g) they see the person express hurt, h) the hurt is lasting or permanent, i) the final outcome is bad, j) people see the consequences of their actions, k) they think about what they did, l) they define what they did as bad, m) they are repeatedly reminded of what they did, n) others know about and blame them for what they did, o) the person they hurt had never hurt them, p) they are unable to apologize or make it up to the person, q) they are not forgiven by the person, r) they have poorer relations with the person afterwards, s) they have witnessed a person being hurt in this way before, t) they themselves have been hurt in this way before, and/or u) they already feel guilty for doing the identical thing on a previous occasion. People are less likely to feel guilty when a) someone else is responsible for hurting the person, b) there is nothing they could have done to prevent the person from being hurt, c) they have no face-to-face contact with the person, d) the person does not provide them with positive reactions, e) what was done to the person is not considered wrong by other people, f) the person is only slightly hurt or not hurt at all, g) they do not see the person express hurt, h) the hurt is very temporary, i) the final outcome is good, as in the sense, "All's well that ends well," j) people do not see the consequences of their actions, k) they do not think about what they did, l) they do not define what they did as bad, m) they are not reminded of what they did, n) others do not know about or blame them for what happened, o) the person they hurt had previously hurt them and may have done the identical thing to them, p) they apologize or otherwise make it up to the person, q) they are forgiven by the person, r) they have very good relations with the person afterwards, s) they have never seen a person hurt in this way before, t) they themselves have never been hurt in this way before, and/or u) they have never done anything like this before.

The sense that one is personally responsible for the hurt of another person is a key factor behind self-criticism and guilt. There are many different kinds of situations in which one may hold oneself responsible. One may consider that one's action causes the other to be hurt, or that one's lack of action causes the other to be hurt. One may criticize oneself when one believes one has done something wrong to another person and the person is not hurt. One may be the only person that someone who is experiencing hurt has to help him, as in the case of a mother and her crying child. One may be the only person present who is aware of the situation or who would be willing to do something about the situation, as in the case of the parent who wants to develop a child's talents. One may be the only person available with the knowledge or resources to deal with the situation. One may think that there is something one could have done that would have produced a better outcome. One may blame oneself for failing to realize what should be done in the situation. In the case of an unavoidable accident, one may think that if one were not present the accident would not have happened.

> I was driving home one night and hit and killed this drunk man who was walking along the side of the road. I know everyone says it was an accident and there is nothing I could have done. But I can't help thinking there must have been some way I could have avoided it. If I had stayed at the dance for a few more minutes, the guy would have been home before I got there. Or if I had gone home the other way, it never would have happened. But because I wanted to get home, I left the dance early and took the shortcut. Because of that a man died. I just can't help but think it was all my fault. #1007

One may even blame oneself for acting contrary to another person's interests by preventing the person from hurting someone else.

> I was hanging out with a guy who wanted to date a very close friend of mine. I wasn't sure I trusted him, so I told her to be careful about him. The guy found out what I'd said to her, and when he and I were together one night, he asked me about it. This made me feel really guilty, even

though I felt I did the right thing. He and I don't speak to each other anymore. I guess I can't really blame him. #1008

Actions that people criticize themselves for and feel guilty about include the following:

1. Hurting or harming someone
2. Being unpleasant or too extreme in dealing with another person
3. Causing another to lose resources
4. Failing to help someone
5. Not doing one's share
6. Not living up to other people's expectations

1. Hurting or harming someone

People often feel guilty when they believe they have hurt or harmed someone.

Sometimes my cats get upset when I'm annoying them. But I keep doing it just to see their reaction. I'll pet them when they don't want to be petted, or I'll hold on to them or put them under a blanket when they want to get away. It's clear they don't like it. I feel guilty, and that I'm a really bad person. Why would I do stuff like that? #1009

I think a marriage breakup is hardest on the family pets. Kids understand, but pets don't. I left my husband, and our cat is really upset. She keeps pining, mewing, and crying all the time. Our dog travels back and forth between the two households and has been missing for the past week. The pets don't know where they belong. I feel guilty about the pets, because I'm the one who left. #1010

In high school no one keeps secrets. For example, my younger sister is interested in a boy. I told a friend, she repeated what I said, and my sister got quite upset. Another time I got a call from a girl I know. She wanted to know why I told someone the name of the guy she's interested in. The fact she called me up meant she didn't want me to tell. It made me think maybe I've got a problem here. I felt bad, not because I told, but because I never knew how much telling secrets could affect someone. I don't want to cause people distress. Now that I know that telling secrets does this, I won't do it anymore. #1011

Mike is a really nice guy, but he just doesn't turn me on. I feel so guilty because I hurt his feelings and his ego just because of his looks. He is not all that bad looking, but sort of wimpy, so I don't want to go out with him. It just wouldn't be good for my image if I was seen with a wimp. I know that is being a bitch, but I can't help it. I just can't bring myself to go out with a guy like that, but I do feel guilty about it. I mean, I know you are not supposed to judge a book by its cover. #1012

Pregnant women worry about the consequences of smoking and drinking. One woman I know smoked a lot while pregnant. She feels very guilty because her baby has asthma now and she thinks her smoking was the cause. Another friend got drunk before she knew she was pregnant. Her girl was born with a minor birth defect and she blames herself. She says, "I'm sure it was the drunk that caused it. I drank a lot that night. If I hadn't been so stupid, she'd have been born perfect." #1013

I loaned a book to my twelfth-grade history teacher, and a year later I went to see him to get the book back. He was very pleased to see me, because he thought I had come just to see him. I'm sure he was disappointed when I asked him about the book. I've always felt guilty that I wasn't there just to see him. The book doesn't matter anymore, but feeling guilty about disappointing him sure does. #1014

Dean was at a party one night with all his friends. He was only planning to drink a little because he was driving. But as the night progressed he said, "To hell with it!" and began to drink heavily. Soon there wasn't a sober person there. Dean had about twenty beer, and it was after two o'clock when he decided to go home. He lived only fifteen minutes away and got into his car singing and laughing. He thought, "What the hell can happen? I'll just drive slow." But he didn't react fast enough and his car swerved up on the sidewalk and struck a young male. When Dean got out of the car he found he had hit Tom, a friend of his, who had been walking home from the party. Dean was in shock and didn't know what to do. He drove back to the party and called the hospital and told them he had found his friend run down on the sidewalk. Tom recovered from his injuries, which included a sprained wrist and a concussion. No one ever found out he was hit by Dean. Dean lives with this guilt and can't let it go. #1015

2. Being unpleasant or too extreme in dealing with another person

Many people feel bad when they are unpleasant or too extreme in dealing with another person.

Sometimes I pass by someone I know before I recognize them, and it's too late to speak. I feel bad because they may think I don't want to speak. So I tell myself to be doubly sure to speak to them the next time I see them. #1016

When I went home after work a couple of weeks ago, I was tired and just didn't feel like talking. The taxi driver started asking me questions, and I was rather curt. Later I realized the driver probably wanted someone to talk to, and I shouldn't have been so inconsiderate. So I decided to try to be more responsive with drivers in the future. #1017

If someone ticks me off and I make a big deal about it, I feel guilty afterwards. The other day I was supposed to meet my best friend in front of our school lockers so we could go to lunch together. I was late when I got there, didn't see her, and went to lunch by myself. I was mad because I thought she'd left without me. When I ran into her later, I was angry when I asked her what happened. She told me she'd been late too, and I walked away without speaking. Eventually I got over it, and felt bad I'd reacted this way. A few hours later I saw her again and started talking to her. #1018

When my children were small I used to hit them a lot. My husband and I were separated and I was under lots of stress and was quite strict. This happened for a number of years. There are lots of things I wish I didn't do, and there are things I wish I had done instead. I don't like to think about it, because I feel guilty. I don't think I'm a good mother. #1019

I always try to be nice to other people. I know if I'm rude or petty with someone, I'll fret about what I've done for ages. I just won't be able to get it out of my mind. It's no fun feeling guilty about what you've done to someone, and I don't want the bother. #1020

3. Causing another to lose resources

Many people also feel bad when they cause another to lose resources.

> I just hate to make other people wait for me. I know how impatient I get, because I've always got better things to do than stand around waiting for someone else. I can get quite hyper when I know I'm making someone wait. I feel I'm at fault, and hurry as quickly as I can. #1021

> Often I don't get around to returning my library books for the longest time. It's because I'm lazy. I know others could be reading the books, and I feel guilty. #1022

> I convinced a friend of mine that stocks were a good thing to get into, and recommended some stocks to invest in. My friend, however, picked his own stocks. The stocks I picked went up, but those selected by my friend went down. Now I feel really bad that I encouraged him to get involved in the stock market in the first place. #1023

> A friend of mine gave me a job transcribing taped interviews for him. The first time I went to transcribe a tape, I got so involved in what was being said I listened to an entire side. However, I had the erase button on by mistake and wiped out the first forty-five minutes of the interview. I felt so bad about it. I wouldn't let him pay me for the time I took trying to remember and write out what was on the tape. #1024

> I took an overnight bus trip and made out with the girl in the next seat. She really didn't want to, but I pursued it, and we made out anyway. Later, when the bus stopped to let the passengers get a meal, she told me she was engaged. She said the fact we made out was forcing her to question whether she should marry the other guy. For a long time afterwards, I felt very guilty that I had undermined her future. #1025

4. Failing to help someone

People can also feel guilty when they fail to help someone who needs it.

I could have helped this blind man cross the street, but didn't because all these people were watching. I know I should have taken the time to help him, and I feel guilty I didn't. #1026

I was supposed to order a piano for my daughter two weeks ago, but didn't get around to it. I feel irresponsible, because she really needs it for her voice lessons. I should do a better job looking after her needs. #1027

When my girlfriend went to graduate school, she asked to borrow some money from me. I agreed, but because I had to borrow it from the bank to loan it to her, I asked her to pay the interest I would have to pay the bank. She refused to take the loan and claimed I was just trying to exploit her by charging her interest. I felt guilty that I wasn't helping her, because I knew how much she needed the money. So I just gave her the money as a gift, and made clear she wouldn't have to pay it back. #1028

When I was driving across the country last summer I passed this dog on the side of the highway. He was lying on his stomach with his head resting on his paws. I had already passed a couple of dogs that had been killed by cars, and I don't know whether this dog was dead, simply stunned, or OK. But by the time I'd thought it over, I was miles away from the scene. I've always felt bad I didn't go back to check it out. If he'd been stunned I would have taken him to a vet. #1029

5. Not doing one's share

People also feel guilty when they do less than others, and do not do their share.

I have to go to the co-op committee meeting tonight. I missed the last one and feel guilty leaving all the work for others to do. #1030

I always feel so guilty when the Public Broadcasting System has its fund-raising drive on TV. I watch their programs, but never make a donation. #1031

When you have people you do things with, or someone who frequently does things for you, you have to have a good sense of fairness. If you don't find adequate ways to reciprocate, it starts to look like you are exploiting the relationship. I hate people who are takers, not givers, and as soon as I realize someone is a taker, I want nothing more to do with them. I sure don't want to be a taker myself. I'd much rather do too much for others, than run the risk of being a taker. When I realize someone is doing more for me than I'm doing for them, I feel bad and start looking for things I can do in return. #1032

6. Not living up to other people's expectations

Another reason people feel guilty is because they think they have let someone down or disappointed him, or just not lived up to the other person's expectations. For example, they may fail to perform as expected as a member of a family, sports team, military unit, business enterprise, church, or community.

Every time I don't come through, I feel guilty. I was raised to be a dependable person others could rely on. As I look back over my past I find many situations which have caused me to feel ashamed. For example, I would promise my father I would do my chores without having to be constantly reminded, and then not carry through. Or I would skip classes at school, even though my parents believed I was a very responsible young man. When they found out, they didn't have to say a word because I felt so guilty. #1033

My brother has just had his braces taken off and now has to wear retainers every night. He says he feels guilty when he forgets to wear them. When his orthodontist asks, he lies and says he is putting them on every night. #1034

My parents make me feel guilty when they catch me in a lie. One time I told them I was going to spend the night at a friend's house. I told them this so I could go out drinking with my friends, and I still don't know how they found out. They'll say, "Why do you always lie to us? Lying is the worst thing you can do. You always get in more trouble for lying than if you tell us the truth. It seems like such a small thing to ask." #1035

My husband invites half-a-dozen guys over twice a week to play board games, and they often stay for eight hours or more. At first I prepared food for them to eat every night they were here. But it got to be too much. They must realize I work and don't have the time and energy to keep doing it. Now I only provide some junk-food snacks. But while they are here, I feel really guilty when I prepare a full meal for myself. Several of the guys take a careful look at what I'm eating, and it makes me feel I'm not sharing my food with them. I always feel guilty about it. #1036

When you are a single mother, you don't have a choice as to whether to work or not. Even so, your kids don't understand when they are little. Still, they are old enough to see that not all mothers work. So they say things, like "Please don't go to work," or even worse, "You love your work more than me." #1037

There were seven children in my family, and it was really important to my parents that we learn not to steal. Today I would feel miserable if I took something that wasn't mine. All seven of us feel this way. A couple of times I've accidentally taken something out of a store without paying for it. When it happens I just feel like dying, even though no one saw me do it. I go back to the store immediately and pay for it. #1038

I always feel I'm a bad girl when I do the things that people in my church don't approve of. My family goes to the Baptist church, and we were taught it's wrong to smoke, drink, and go to lounges. I've been out to lounges a few times. I always try to pick a lounge where no one will know me, and am really glad when no one does. Still, I feel bad about going, because I know our church disapproves. Even though I have fun while I'm there, afterwards I feel even worse, because one isn't supposed to have fun at such places. I also felt a little guilty when I went with a Catholic boy for a while. My church makes a big thing about Catholics, and a girl who dates one certainly can't expect a blessing. No one from the church came up and said, "Oh, how wonderful. You guys make a lovely couple." I still went to church, but my boyfriend didn't come with me. I wasn't going to invite him to a church that didn't want him. #1039

Not living up to expectations includes not meeting one's social obligations. Examples include failing to call, write, or see someone; not inviting someone one should invite or has promised to invite; and not reciprocating the favors one receives.

Feelings associated with hurting others

When people feel they may have hurt another person, they criticize themselves. This is a punishing experience which people describe as blaming yourself, feeling guilty, having a guilty conscience, feeling remorse, feeling ashamed, knowing you did wrong, considering yourself a bad person, wanting to kick yourself, and feeling really stupid. These are unpleasant feelings and a weight on people's minds.

Lots of times my guilt is so intense I can't get it out of my mind. [1040]

When people criticize themselves, they give themselves a negative reaction and feel hurt. Self-criticism makes people feel bad about themselves and unhappy, and produces many of their most painful memories.

A few weeks ago I was supposed to work Saturday night at the ticket office of the local theater. This completely slipped my mind, until my boss called and asked where the hell I was. I rushed to work as fast as I could and apologized profusely to the woman who had taken my place until I got there. I felt extremely guilty, not only because I was late, but because the woman had much more important things to do. Although I was forgiven, even now when I think of it, I cringe at the thought of how stupid I was. [1041]

My friend told me something, but he didn't tell me I wasn't supposed to tell others. So later that evening I did so. The next day he was right mad at me, and I felt like such a shit. I won't blame him if he never tells me another thing. [1042]

One time I was taking a flight and had a window seat. A businessman was sitting next to me, and when I got up to go to the washroom, I bumped his tray and his drink spilled all over his suit. I felt really bad about it, especially when the stewardesses ran over to wipe it up. I was practically in tears, but he made me feel better by telling me he didn't mind and accidents do happen. He made me feel a bit better, but I still felt bad about it. [1043]

A friend and I had arranged to meet at a restaurant to have lunch together, and I forgot all about it. Later that afternoon he called to find out if we had gotten our wires crossed. I wasn't in my office at the time and got his message just as I was leaving work. I have to be home at four o'clock every day to relieve the baby sitter. I was just in a panic to get home so I could call him and apologize. I felt so bad to have done this to a friend; I just felt rotten. #1044

I finally separated from my husband this past weekend, and moved into an apartment with our two children. I just feel tortured thinking about my husband having to be all alone. #1045

The bad feelings one experiences from self-criticism differ in degree, and range from a mild twinge to considerable anguish, depending on how one feels about what one has done and how others react. Such feelings can even produce physical effects.

I have to go to work each morning, and when my daughter sees the baby sitter arrive, she chants, "Bye! Bye!" at her. Clever kid; she knows I'm leaving. By the time I reach for my coat, she's wailing. I figure these are separation problems, and perfectly normal. But the heavy weight in my throat spreads through my chest, and by the time I get the car started, I can barely breathe. #1046

People also have dreams in which they experience guilt.

I had a dream in which I was at a party and left with a guy to go make out. As we were walking to his car, I saw my boyfriend, felt very guilty, and woke up. I was sleeping next to my boyfriend at the time, and when he snuggled up to me, I felt even more guilty. #1047

I grew up in Vietnam and our family had several pigs. The pigs lived in a pen beside our house and we would feed them twice a day, early in the morning and around supper time. When the pigs saw us come out of the house they would stick their noses through the fence and cry and cry for food. I used to feed them when I was between the ages of ten and sixteen. Occasionally I would forget, and feel very guilty afterwards because they were so hungry. That was about twenty-five years ago and I have lived in Canada for the past sixteen years. Today I still have an occasional dream in which I forget to feed these pigs, and I see how hungry they are when I finally remember. I feel really guilty in my dream. My older sister lives in Belgium and left Vietnam before I did. She continues to have the same dream I do in which she feels guilty for not remembering to feed our pigs. #1048

Knowledge that one is responsible for hurting others is concrete evidence that one is a bad person. This is inconsistent with one's image of oneself as a good person who deserves positive reactions from oneself and others, and this inconsistency produces tension and hurt.

People are very interested in avoiding self-criticism. They have a strong interest in not hurting others so it will not be necessary for them to criticize themselves. They remember feeling bad, and being disappointed, upset, or angry with themselves in the past when they hurt others, and they do not want to feel this way again.

If I had to sacrifice some fun in order to meet an obligation, I'd rather meet the obligation than have to deal with the guilt afterwards. Guilt is much harder to deal with than missing fun. #1049

People often continue to think about what they did "wrong," and what they should have done instead. Often they wish they could relive the experience and correct what they did. People sometimes continue to blame themselves for certain things for years, and feel bad each time they think of them.

I really feel bad about things I did years before. One thing was the way I treated my parents. They really didn't want me to go out with this one guy. I did anyway, and I quit speaking to my parents at the time. I've told them since I'm really sorry for the way I acted, but I still feel guilty about it. #1050

When I look back at my life, the thing I feel guiltiest about is pissing on a freshly dug grave. I was real young at the time, just seven or eight. I've never told anybody about it before, and I don't know why I did it. The other thing I feel guilty about is how much I hurt my parents when I had to go to jail on a drug charge. #1051

When I remember something I've done that I feel guilty about, I think very poorly of myself. Sometimes I tell myself I'm a bad person. I think the thing that has continued to bother me the most is what I did in the seventh grade. We had a teacher I really didn't like, and I got the students in the class to bring her fruit and cookies on the first of April. I had arranged to have someone call her out of the class and when she returned we would all be eating what we had brought her, and cry "April Fool!" Most of the students did bring something for her that day, and she was so moved she cried. She said it was the nicest thing anyone had ever done for her. Then she was called out of class as arranged. I can remember one of the girls asking me if we should go ahead with our trick, and I said, "Yes," and we did. I can still remember the teacher's expression when she realized what was happening. This occurred over thirty years ago, and I've felt guilty about it ever since. I think going ahead with the trick is one of the worst things I've ever done. I thought about it again the other day, and found myself saying, "Nasty person!" out loud to myself. #1052

When I was a child I spent one summer with my grandmother. I liked to crawl under the fence and go play in the yard next door. My grandmother didn't want me to bother the neighbors and told her maid to stop me if she saw me try to go next door. One day the maid tried to prevent me from going by wrapping her arms around me from behind. I raised my head suddenly and accidentally struck her in the mouth with my head and knocked out her front tooth. I am sure it was a real setback for her. I have felt bad about this for the past fifty years, and have no idea how she coped with the situation. I seriously doubt that she had enough money to get a false tooth. #1053

I'm not the only one who suffers from things they've done in the past. I heard a sermon on the radio this last Sunday about how to deal with a guilty conscience. It was really interesting. The minister said that the reason we have these awful feelings of remorse, regret, and shame is because we have broken the laws of God. And the way we should go about getting release from this guilt is to seek God's forgiveness. Then he went on to explain what we should do if we still feel guilty after we seek God's forgiveness. He said the feeling can remain because we haven't fully forgiven others, and we must do this in our mind. But according to him, even this may not do the job and the guilt may persist. So the next step is to ask the person we have done something to for forgiveness. Then if the guilt is still there, he suggested we go to a friend we can have confidence in, such as a minister or a Christian psychologist. They may see it from another perspective and be able to help us with it. It's like no matter what you do, sometimes you can't shake guilt. #1054

When I was eighteen my dad told me something that has been a helpful guide. He said, "It only takes a second to hurt someone, but knowing you hurt them lasts a lifetime." #1055

Often people do not want to talk about the things they blame themselves for, because when they do so they experience their unpleasant feelings again.

One irony is that people can harbor guilt for years for something they have done, while the person they did it to may have forgotten about it shortly after it happened, or may never have noticed it in the first place.

I was talking to a cousin of mine recently. She is in her forties, and told me she still feels sorry about the time I escorted her to her high school prom and she went off with her friends and ignored me. I had forgotten all about it, and was only able to produce the haziest memory of the event. Obviously it's bothered her all these years, or she would have forgotten about it too. #1056

I was very proud to make the girls' basketball team one year in high school. At the end of the year, my parents and I went to the sports banquet. Sports are not up my parents' alley, and I knew they felt out of place there. I was sitting across from them at one of the dining tables, and happened to look up while grace was being said. Everyone had a little glass of juice at their place, and my mother's was spilled all over the table. "Oh, no," I thought, "Mom has knocked hers over. I take them here, the first time they've been at my high school, and Mom spills her juice." However, it turned out someone else had knocked it over. My mother hadn't done it at all. But I felt so bad that my reaction was to feel embarrassed by my mother. It was terrible. That was five years ago, and I still feel really bad for thinking it at the time. After the banquet, all my friends were going to a party. I thought it would be kind of fun to go too. I told my parents I wanted to go along with another girl that they knew, and they said it was all right to go. But later I just felt terrible that I didn't go home with my parents. I told myself, "They made a special effort to come out to this banquet with you, and they really didn't want to. Then not only did you feel embarrassed when you thought your poor mother spilled the juice, but you didn't even go home with them. They'll think you really don't like them. You rotten kid." I felt so bad about not going home with them, that when I got home late that night I left a note on the cupboard thanking them for coming with me. And the crazy thing about it is that my mother certainly never knew I felt embarrassed by her, and my parents may even have been pleased that I went to the party with my friends. #1057

Feelings of guilt frequently change in intensity over time. They can become stronger or weaker each time one thinks about the situation which produces the feelings.

My parents are still living in England, and I often feel guilty that they don't get to enjoy my kids and that my kids can't really get to know them. It's an important part of life they can never have. So I've often considered moving back just so they can be together. My feelings of guilt over this get worse with time, because the older the kids get, the more childhood they've lost. Also, the longer I stay in Canada, the more obvious it is I'm not going back. I feel it's more and more likely that I'll move back to England. #1058

I have two very close friends and when I don't see them or speak to them for a while, I feel I really ought to get together with them for a coffee or at least call them. As time passes I feel I'm being negligent and become increasingly concerned about calling them. I worry that if I don't contact them they'll think I don't care. After I call, the feeling disappears until some time has passed and I start feeling it's time I got in touch again. #1059

Anita had been going out with Paul for several months when she had a date with another guy. She felt bad about doing it behind Paul's back, but she wasn't planning on doing it again, and was sure if she told Paul he would want to break up. So she kept it to herself. About five months later I asked Anita if she still felt guilty about the date. She replied it happened such a long time ago, she doesn't think about it at all, and it really doesn't bother her anymore. #1060

When one feels guilty about what one has done in regard to another person, the subsequent actions of that person influence the degree of guilt one feels.

I'd always gotten along well with one of our employees, but I felt I should call her into my office and tell her that what she was doing is not the way we do things in our department. I told her I was concerned that others would react negatively to all the benefits she was giving the customers. She got quite upset and argued she had good reason for her actions. I agreed she had good reason, but kept pointing out it just wouldn't be accepted here. Although I knew I was doing my job to talk to her about it, afterwards I felt bad about upsetting her. Then when I didn't see her for several weeks I figured she was avoiding me, so I still felt uncomfortable about it. But yesterday when I talked to her, she said she felt she could always talk to me because I was the only one who would be frank and tell her what was really going on. She also asked me to tell her anytime there was something else she should know about. Afterwards I felt much better, because things still seemed to be on a good basis between us. [#1061]

Last Sunday a guy I used to go out with called me up. Someone with my first name had left him a message and he figured it must be me. We talked for a few minutes and after we hung up I started feeling bad, because I thought my boyfriend is going to be mad about this. I was worried about telling him about the call, and I kept thinking, "He's not going to like this. I know he's not. And I shouldn't have talked to the guy. I should have told him, 'No, I didn't call you,' and just hung up. But stupid me, I sat there and chatted away." I figured I had to tell my boyfriend right off, because if I didn't and he ever did find out about the call, he'd be even madder. I had already planned to go over to his house that afternoon. When I got there I told him about the call, and he said, "I think he may still like you." I said to myself, "No, he doesn't! No, he doesn't! He really doesn't!" But I told my boy-friend, "No, I don't think he does." Then he asked, "Is that all he said?" I thought, "Oh, no, I said more. And I shouldn't have said more. I shouldn't have said anything else." And I told my boyfriend a little of what he said. But when my boyfriend didn't get mad or anything, I could see the call didn't bother him. So I started feeling OK, and didn't feel bad anymore. [#1062]

How people deal with self-criticism, or guilt

People differ in their responses to self-criticism in specific situations. Thus some people are more inclined to act to avoid or remove a particular source of guilt than are others.

It's interesting how friends can differ from each other. Often when I loan a book to a friend, they tend to keep the book forever. Over a month ago I asked a friend to return some books because someone else wants to see them. But my friend still hasn't returned them. She tells me she has them by the door and feels guilty every time she sees them. There's no way I could do that. If someone told me they needed something they'd loaned me, I'd bust my ass to get it to them that day or the next. Another thing is borrowing money. If I ever have to borrow a little from a friend, I live in fear I'll forget to repay it. I can't get it out of my mind. I keep reminding myself to repay it, and do so at the first opportunity. I'd walk from one end of town to the other to repay a nickel. But I've had friends repeatedly borrow money and forget all about it or just not get around to repaying it. A similar situation occurs in regard to lottery tickets. About a year ago two close friends and I decided we would buy lottery tickets together and take a trip somewhere if we won. The plan was for each of us to take turns buying all the tickets each month. But then one of the friends lost her job and didn't have the money to buy tickets on her month. Ever since then the other friend and I take turns buying for all three of us, and we've done so for half a year now. I can't understand how the friend without a job can let us buy her lottery tickets for her. It must bother her some, because she says occasionally that she wishes she could pay for them. There is no way I could let others pay my share month after month on something like this. I would just feel terrible, and my other friend says she would too. #1063

There are many things that people feel guilty about doing and not doing. Many of the things that people feel guilty about, they are quick to act on. Many other things that people feel guilty about they are slow to act on or never act on. The things they are quick to act on usually involve doing things for others who are dependent on them alone, or who provide a large proportion of their positive reactions. This includes helping their children, mate, pets, relatives, and friends. The things they are usually slow to act on, or never act on, involve doing things for themselves, or for others who are not dependent on them or who do not provide their positive reactions. Thus they are slow to take care of their own health, write distant friends and relatives they rarely see, help strangers, and make donations to charities.

People respond to self-criticism in a variety of ways, which include the following:

1. Not repeating the behavior
2. Not doing other things they would criticize themselves for
3. Doing the things they would criticize themselves for if they failed to do them
4. Not telling the truth
5. Apologizing
6. Making amends
7. Confessing what they did
8. Talking to a third party about what they did
9. Avoiding those they have "wronged" and the situations in which they did so
10. Rationalizing their behavior
11. Living with guilt
12. Combining responses

1. Not repeating the behavior

People try to avoid repeating what they criticize themselves for doing.

> My older brother used to shoplift all the time. So when I was in elementary school, I decided to steal a candy bar from the candy counter at Eaton's. The clerk asked if she could help me, I said, "No," and when she went away I grabbed the bar and ran. I ran all the way home and ate it as quickly as possible on the way. I couldn't have any evidence on me, because Mom would wonder where I got the money for it. I was really scared on the way home that someone would see me and catch me. At that time I was in junior choir in church. The following Sunday, they read the Ten Commandments before Holy Communion. One commandment, "Thou Shalt Not Steal," made me feel exceptionally bad and evil. So I never shoplifted again. It was the

one and only time. I felt I was a very bad person to have done it. Even today I know I was wrong, and I'm not proud of it. #1064

One summer when I was a teenager I decided to go spearfishing, and made a simple sling with some surgical tubing. But the spear traveled so slowly in the water, it was very hard to hit anything. Then one day I fired at a small school of good-sized mullet and pierced one through the side. It did a slow turn on the spear, got off, and continued swimming with its school as though nothing had happened. But I doubt if it survived. I felt so bad about what I'd done, I never went spearfishing again. #1065

I've learned to be scrupulously honest when I deal with a bank teller or someone working the cash register at a store. Every once in a while someone makes a mistake and gives me too much cash. If I take the extra money, my immediate response is to be pleased I got something for nothing. But then later I feel quite guilty and wonder whether the person had to make up the missing money from their own pocket. Once I took some German money to a bank, and when the clerk worked out what she owed me, she put her decimal in the wrong place and ended up paying me ten times what she should have. She told me she was new at the foreign exchange window and asked if the amount looked right to me. I said it did, even though I suspected she was making a mistake. Later, after I figured out the right amount, I was gleeful about getting fifty extra dollars, but that was eight years ago and I still feel bad when I remember it. So today when I'm given too much change, I return it immediately. Getting a few extra dollars is not worth having this weight on your conscience for years afterwards. #1066

When my girlfriend got pregnant I agreed with her decision to get an abortion. It's driving me fucking nuts. Every time I think about it, I know we made the wrong decision. If I had it to do again, I would do it all different. #1067

My cousin was always late for everything. She never rushed, even when she knew she'd be late. Once she was supposed to go to a hockey game with her friend Karen, who worked at the canteen in the rink. My cousin was late picking up Karen and Karen was half an hour late for work. She was supposed to open up the canteen that night and as a result lost her job. My cousin has never felt so guilty in her life, and now tries a lot harder to always be on time. #1068

My friend Jo and her sister Shelly always fought over the bathroom, phone, and clothes. One day Shelly wanted to wear a blouse of Jo's to a club in Charlottetown. Jo refused and this resulted in a major fight. That night Shelly was killed in a car accident on her way home from the club. Jo felt doubly bad because her last words with her sister were angry ones. Because of her guilt she resolved to act kinder toward her other brothers and sisters. [#1069]

When my son and I lived in Vietnam, before we came to Canada, I had to go to another province to work. I was only twenty at the time. My son was about four years old and I left him with my grandmother on my father's side. I was gone for a couple of weeks, and as soon as I got back I went to get him. It was afternoon when I entered my grandmother's house. My son was wearing a T-shirt and shorts, and when he saw me he didn't say a word. He just looked at me and lifted up his shirt. His stomach and chest were covered with infected chickenpox sores. No one had gotten him medication or looked after him. I can't talk about this without crying. I'll never forget this. I feel so terrible that I left him. I could not leave a child alone like that again. [#1070]

When I was in high school, my father's parents would come out to visit us frequently on Sunday afternoon. I would usually stay in my bedroom and study, and not go down and sit and chat with everyone else. This bothered me after my grandfather died. I would say, "Marcia, you stupid jerk, you've put studies ahead of family, and that's crazy." My father felt very bad for the longest time and still does, because he wasn't with my grandfather when he died. My grandfather had a stroke, and by the time they got in touch with my father and my father reached the hospital, my grandfather was dead. As a result, both my father and I have altered our behavior toward my grandmother. When I see my grandmother I am more sensitive to her needs. I ask her questions about herself and show more interest in her than I did when my grandfather was alive. I worry that I should spend more time with her, because I know if I don't, I will feel very bad when she dies. As for my father, whenever a thought crosses his mind about taking my grandmother some place, he does it right away. For example, he decided he wants to go on a trip across Canada, and he plans to take my grandmother with him. He keeps saying, "She won't be here much longer." I think it's so he won't feel guilty once she's gone about not having done things for her. [#1071]

I was pretty popular in high school and got around with the cool guys in school. We had no problem getting girls, and we usually had a favorite person to pick on during lunch and at any other opportunity we got. We picked on one guy who was shy and didn't dress like the rest of us. Then he committed suicide. For two weeks I could not get the guy out of my mind. I tried to make excuses, but I really felt I was partly to blame. Finally, I had to seek professional help. As long as I live, I will never make fun of anyone again, no matter what the situation. #1072

Guilt is guilt, no matter how you look at it. No matter how you try to avoid it, it will come looking for you, and eventually it's going to find you. So it's better to deal with it in the beginning. It just seems to get worse the longer you try to deny or ignore it. It's something that has to be faced head-on, and oftentimes it can be a good learning experience. I mean, when you do something and then feel guilty about it, you are not likely to go out and do the same thing again. #1073

People are much less likely to do the things they feel guilty about, than the things they do not feel guilty about.

2. Not doing other things they would criticize themselves for

People also avoid specific behaviors simply because they know they will feel guilty if they go ahead and do them. As a result, they avoid doing "the things they ought not to do."

I don't want to go to Mexico or other third-world countries on vacation. I'd feel guilty. There you are enjoying yourself and having a good time while they're suffering. #1074

I always go slow when I drive through residential areas, because I don't want to hit a cat or dog. I know how awful I would feel. #1075

My husband and I would love to go on a trip off by ourselves to a foreign country. Instead every year we spend our vacation time and money going to see his parents or mine. They would be so hurt if we didn't see them every Christmas and summer. As they get older they seem to be more dependent on these visits. I would just feel so guilty if we hurt them by going somewhere for ourselves. #1076

It can be really hard to break up with the person you've been involved with, because you know they are going to be very hurt and you're going to feel terribly guilty. A lot of times the fear of guilt keeps you from breaking up. #1077

I don't like to recommend stocks to others, because I would feel awful if they lost money on them. The other day I was telling an acquaintance about this exciting company I'd just found to invest in. He wanted to know more about the company so he could get some shares too. I discouraged him by telling him what had happened to the last company I was excited about. Its shares fell to one-sixth the price I bought them at. I sure don't want to feel responsible for someone else's losses. #1078

It would be fun to play around and have some sexual experiences when you're out of town and no one would know. But can you imagine how guilty you'd feel if you got AIDS and gave it to your family? I'd feel nothing but guilt for the rest of my life. #1079

3. Doing the things they would criticize themselves for if they failed to do them

A primary way people try to avoid self-criticism is by doing "the things they ought to do." People commonly do things because they know they would criticize themselves if they failed to do them.

There are times I'd like to quit my part-time job. But guilt keeps pushing me to go to work. I'm scheduled to leave the job in another month and a half, but without a little bit of guilt, I wouldn't go in. I'd say, "Screw you, guys!" and quit today because I need a break. But if I did quit now, I'd feel bad and think I shouldn't have done that. I'd say, "What have you done, you irresponsible thing? The only reason you quit is you were in a frivolous, silly mood. You're committed to them until the second week of May. You should stay and get that work done." #1080

When my wife wants us to take a walk or watch a movie, often I don't feel up to it. But I do so anyway. If I didn't, it wouldn't be fair to her, and I'd feel bad about it. #1081

My mother is quite sick in the hospital and I go visit her. When I don't spend time with her, I feel guilty. Because of this I'm well behind in my university courses. And when I do spend time with her, she feels guilty because she knows I'm behind. #1082

When I hear a dog barking outside, I know I have to make sure my cat, Loco, is inside. He's been declawed, and a dog would make short work of him. I glance in his hiding places as I head downstairs. If I don't see him, I open the back door to the porch. Often he's waiting at the door. If he's not there, I call him, and look outside to see if any dogs are in the backyard. If I see any dogs, I chase them out of the yard, and see if Loco needs help. I never feel like doing any of this, but I know how awful I would feel if something happened to him because I didn't act. It's the same reason I check for him under the car each time I drive out our driveway. #1083

There are some days when I have a bad cold and it would be in my interest to call the school and tell them I'm sick. But if I've scheduled a quiz and students have studied for it, or if students are prepared to give a presentation in class, there is no way I'll stay home. I'd feel really bad that I was letting them down. Even on days when I'm quite sick and none of the students have had to prepare for class, if I stay home I worry whether I'm just slacking off. #1084

I have only a few months to go as director of my department. I'm going to talk to the supervisor again about a guy we've had working for us on a part-time basis for so long it's immoral. Earlier this year I presented the case that we really should give him a full-time position. I have lots of other stuff to do, and it would be easy to let this slide. But the new budget is coming up and if I don't say anything more, the supervisor will conveniently forget about the matter. The fact is, money's so tight, there's about one chance in five they'll hire this guy on a regular basis. But if I don't go in and push, I'll feel I didn't do my job properly as director. I wouldn't want to remember I left my position without doing everything I could for him. #1085

At our family reunion we tried to show my brother-in-law how to use a computer someone had just given him. He's handicapped and his parents have no money to do things for him. He's still in high school and getting into computers would give him something to work at in the future so he won't be dependent on social services. But the computer he'd been given was such a clunker, and so out-of-date and difficult to operate, that if anything it would have turned him off computing. It really bothered me watching him try to learn to use this piece of junk. It was so obvious that he needed something current, that I went and bought a newspaper to check if anyone was selling a used model at a good price. To make a long story short, I ended up spending a couple of days finding and buying him a very competitive new model at a discount house. I really couldn't afford it, and my own kids need a computer too, but it just seemed to be the right thing to do in the situation. Nobody else was going to do it. And I would have felt bad if I hadn't. [#1086]

4. Not telling the truth

People are frequently dishonest with others in order to avoid hurting them. They lie to them and use false excuses, and they avoid telling them information which would upset them. By not telling others the truth, they do not make them feel bad, and therefore have little to feel guilty about. People tell numerous "little white lies" to avoid hurting others and to avoid feeling guilty. When they do attempt to say what they really think, they often try to be very diplomatic.

When someone has just bought some new clothing or had their hair done, they usually ask your opinion of it. There is no way you are going to say, "That looks awful," even if that's what you think. What they want are compliments from you, and you know how disappointed and discouraged they'll be if you are painfully honest. [#1087]

My friend got a new haircut which made her look ugly. When she asked if I liked it, what could I say? Because I'm her friend, I thought I should tell her it was not a flattering haircut, so she could change it before everyone saw it. I realized that if I tried to be nice and told her I liked it, she might get it cut the same way again in the future. So I just said that it was nice for a change, but the old way looked a little nicer on her. [#1088]

My sister is quite overweight, and she and I were in a store together looking for a nice dress for her. As she tried on dresses she would ask me if they made her look fat. Now what was I supposed to say? Of course you look fat? There's no way to hide all that weight? But of course, I didn't. I lied and said that some of the dresses were very slimming. After all, she is my sister. [#1089]

When people turn you down for a job, they usually try to do it in a way that doesn't hurt your feelings. Often they say that even though you are well qualified, the job has been filled, and they hope you will try again next time. #1090

Certain people call you up and want to get together, but you don't like doing things with them. When this happens to me, I don't tell them the truth. Instead, I lie and say I have a prior commitment or too much work to do. Then I make a point not to go where they say they're going. One time I told a girl I'd be home studying and then went somewhere with my friends and ran into her. So I had to tell another lie. I told her my friends had dropped over and practically dragged me out of the house. Then my friends had to lie too to back me up. #1091

I never told my best friend that her husband was playing around, and her other friends never told her either. It wouldn't have accomplished anything, and we didn't want to hurt her. #1092

A little white lie never hurt anybody. It spares feelings, and besides I'm not a cruel person who gets her kicks out of hurting people. I would much rather lie than make people insecure. #1093

I can't hurt other people's feelings. I lie a lot, because if I told the truth I would feel worse than the person I told the truth to. #1094

5. Apologizing

When people do things they feel guilty about, they frequently apologize.

The first time I went out with a girl, we went to a local pub. We talked about a hockey game and I used my hands to illustrate what I was talking about. Then I accidentally hit my glass and spilled beer all over her jeans. I felt like two cents, and all I could do was apologize. #1095

My stockbroker knows I'm concerned about the high cost of commissions, but I noticed I was mentioning this too much in conversations with her. I became worried when I heard myself making a gibe about it. This bothered me because she gives me superb service and we are friends too. So I didn't want this to become a sore point between us. Therefore, over lunch one day I told her I felt I owed her an apology.

I explained that even though I complain about the high cost of commissions, I really consider the service she gives me very much worth it. She was pleased and I felt relieved. #1096

When I hurt someone, I find the best way to deal with my feelings is to apologize. I am certain I will never be completely free of guilt. But if I try to deal with it immediately by apologizing, I can minimize the disturbing effects and save myself a lot of misery. #1097

Sometimes a person who has to deal with guilt, wishes he could apologize, but is unable to do so.

There are some things I've done in the past that I wish I could go back and apologize for. But it's too late now. Some of the people are dead, and you can't apologize to them. In other cases I would feel really stupid or foolish getting in touch with someone and saying, "You know that thing I did to you twenty-five years ago? Well I'm sorry." They might ask, "Who is this? What are you talking about?" But maybe this is just an excuse on my part, because it's so hard to talk about the really bad things you've done. I guess it's just as hard to apologize today for the things I did in the past as it would have been to apologize when I did them. #1098

6. Making amends

People also seek to make amends to the person they feel guilty about hurting.

I'm working as a teaching assistant, and occasionally I miss a class. Maybe I just goof off and don't get to work on time. The teacher never has to say anything, because I feel real bad. I tell myself I mustn't let this happen again. Sometimes I do something to make it up, like write up some instructions to help the kids do their research proposals, such as where to look when you're doing a literature review. I'll tell the teacher I've done this and give it to the students, and it helps me feel better. #1099

I invited a friend of mine to go hear Handel's Messiah with me during the Christmas season. She went to all this effort to get all dolled up and just looked great, but when we arrived that afternoon at the theater, it was closed. I had confused the date with the hour of the performance. I've never pulled a stunt like that before, and I just felt awful about it. My friend had to go somewhere that evening, so I couldn't take her out to dinner to make up for it, and she was going to be out of town on the date the performance was actually being held. I couldn't believe I had done this and I apologized lots of times. I bought her a two-record set of the Messiah for a Christmas present. It was the least I could do. I think getting her the records helped me feel better, and I don't feel guilty about it now. #1100

I was at a party in someone's home. I bumped into a table, and a leaf of the table fell and broke the chimney on an antique hurricane lamp. I felt terrible and said I would replace it. I spent many hours visiting all the antique shops and lighting-fixture stores in town, but couldn't find anything identical. Eventually I had someone from the family accompany me and help me make a decision as to which of several chimneys was most acceptable. I paid for it, they appreciated the trouble I went to, and I didn't feel as guilty about it anymore. #1101

People sometimes try to make amends in advance of hurting another person. They may be generous or nice in order to feel less guilty afterwards.

7. Confessing what they did

Another means people use to deal with guilt is to confess what they have done.

Karen and her boyfriend, Walter, had been going out together for three months when Karen went on a date with someone else. She felt so bad about it that she went home that night and cried for several hours. She knew Walter would be hurt and possibly break up with her if he found out. So she kept it a secret. But she felt so guilty during the next few months that she finally broke down and told Walter. He was hurt and they did break up for a short time. But when they got back together Karen felt much more deserving of Walter's affections. She still feels a little bit guilty, but says that since Walter has forgiven her, it doesn't matter that much anymore. #1102

8. Talking to a third party about what they did

People also attempt to deal with guilt by talking to friends about what they did. Not only are people likely to feel better after talking about what is bothering them, but a friend can provide support and suggestions as to how to rectify a situation.

A friend told me about the problems she is having with her work. She has been working on a project for two years, is unhappy doing the work, and really wants to leave. But the person she works for keeps telling her she would be a fool to leave. She is quite upset he is so insensitive to her need to leave the province and travel, or to do something else. The project has been underway for several years, and she feels obligated to see it through even though it may take another year or more. She knows she will feel very guilty if she leaves before all the work is finished. When she told me this I pointed out that she and no one else is responsible for her needs. Also, her boss may think that her plans to leave are just pipe dreams and figure if they are really all that important to her, she would just tell him that she's leaving and when she's going. I reassured her that she has been giving them full value for the money they are paying her and she doesn't owe them anything more. Also, that project was going on for some time before she came, and they will be able to find someone else to do it. I told her she should look after her own happiness, and encouraged her to go ahead and give them notice. Two days later she did so, and feels remarkably happy about her action. #1103

I was talking to a friend about pets, and she told me about the German shepherd she and her husband used to have. "We practically considered the dog to be our child. However, by the time he was eight years old he had rheumatism and was blind with glaucoma. Then we had to sell our house. But people with apartments for rent didn't want pets in them. Our parents suggested we have the dog put to sleep, but my husband was firmly against it. When my husband was out of town I took the dog to the vet to have him put down. I felt so bad, I couldn't take him in myself and had to have my mother do it. My husband has never forgiven me for this, and I still feel bad about it. Afterwards I had bad dreams about the dog. In one dream I entered this shed and there was a garbage bag. I could see through the bag and inside was our dog, moving her paws, and crying, 'Help! Help!' But we would have

403

had a very difficult time getting an apartment if we had kept her. I have always had to make the hard decisions in our marriage and then suffer the guilt afterwards." As my friend was telling me this, I agreed with the husband's position. But then I realized I wasn't being supportive. My friend looked like she was about to cry. So I put my arm around her and said it's no fun making hard decisions. I told her it was all right to go ahead and cry. #1104

Often people will only discuss what they feel guilty about with people who will not blame them for what they have done, and will not repeat what they say to others. People do not want what they have done to become public knowledge among people who might think poorly of them, who might use this information against them, or who might bring it up when talking to them.

9. Avoiding those they have "wronged" and the situations in which they did so

People also avoid others that they feel guilty about hurting or not helping, and they avoid the situations in which they hurt or fail to help others.

Two women were collecting money for the Salvation Army outside the shopping mall. Jennifer and I walked by without giving them any money, and Jennifer said to me, "I feel so guilty. They'll think we're real bitches for not giving anything. I mean everyone has at least a quarter to give, but we don't even have that. When we leave, let's go out another door so we don't pass them again." #1105

I always feel guilty when I don't go to church on Sunday. I'm Catholic and was taught it's a sin not to go. I also feel I'm disappointing my parents. If it weren't for them, I don't think it would bother me as much. I don't like to talk to my mother on the phone on Sundays, because she always asks, "Did you go to church?" And when I say no, I feel guilty. #1106

I copied another student's test during an exam and felt really guilty doing it. It made me feel so paranoid that it was weird. Because I felt so guilty, I thought for sure the professor was staring right at me and must know. But he probably didn't realize, or else he would have said something. I got a good mark on the exam, but I don't think it was worth it. Next time I think I'll study; it sure seems easier than dealing with the guilt. I don't think I'll ever be able to look that professor or the student I copied from in the eye again. #1107

Charles was driving his truck home from work and saw a car on the bridge. The roads were icy and he couldn't get his truck stopped in time and hit the car. A girl in the car was hurt and had to be taken to the hospital. Her injury was not serious, but Charles felt so guilty about hurting her that he wouldn't drive for a long time afterwards. #1108

I made love to a married man and felt so guilty afterwards that I wouldn't have anything more to do with him. The next time a married man wanted to make love, I warned him that we could stay friends if we didn't make love, but if we did make love I couldn't see him again. #1109

10. Rationalizing their behavior

People also rationalize their behavior. They use a variety of excuses to try to rationalize what they do. For example, "Well, the test was too hard anyway. There was no way you could pass it without cheating," "We're not really that serious, so it doesn't really matter if I see other people. She's probably doing the same thing anyway," and "I was just a kid at the time, and really didn't know any better. I wouldn't do it now."

I went with this guy, and the whole relationship from start to finish was a real horror show. He was a real jerk and went out with other girls any opportunity he had, regardless of how things were between us. So an opportunity arose for me to date someone else, and naturally I took it. I knew the guy I'd been seeing would get mad at me when I saw someone else, but I just kept doing it. I thought, "He's done this a lot before, so I should be able to do it too." But still, it bothered me, and the fact I did it still does bother me. I really shouldn't have. I should have talked it over with him and made sure everything was clear between us before I saw someone else. I felt really bad at the time, and thought I don't deserve to go out with anyone. #1110

My mother is dying this weekend in Edmonton and I feel guilty about not going out to see her. I haven't been to see her in five years. But I'm a "now" person who lives each day as it comes, and going to see my mother would involve paying bills in advance and getting someone else to look after things here at home. All this advance preparation. Also, my mother raised me and my brothers and sisters to be independent and to go off and lead our own lives. And I don't have the money to go. I'm headed back to my place now so I'll be there if my sister calls from the hospital. My brothers and sisters live in Edmonton and will be there for her. If they weren't, I'd think much more seriously about going there. #1111

11. Living with guilt

People also live with their guilt, and allow their guilt to continue to nag at them. Instead of doing something to remove the guilt, they try to ignore it and deal with other things.

I know I should write my relatives. But I've just been too busy to get to it. #1112

Also, people often continue to engage in certain behaviors they feel guilty about. They simply accept the guilt that goes with the behavior.

Every time I pick up a beer or a cigarette, I can see my mother and hear her voice saying, "Jan, you know that is bad for you. Why do you do it? It hurts your father and me to see you hurting yourself like that." I know it's crazy, but this is what happens. Still, I drink and smoke anyway. After all, I can live with guilt, but I would hate to have to live without beer and cigarettes. #1113

Frequently people feel they have no choice but to live with their guilt.

Guilt is a fact of life. There's no way you can undo what you've done. I still shudder when I think of things I did forty years ago. It's likely I'll carry my guilt with me to the grave. #1114

In addition, a great deal of guilt disappears on its own accord without doing anything about it. It is simply forgotten. Guilt is much more likely to disappear when the person one has wronged shows no signs of being hurt and acts as though everything is all right.

12. Combining responses

One often uses more than one of the above methods in dealing with guilt. In the following account the person does what he thinks he ought to do, avoids what he thinks he should not do, engages in the activity and lives with his guilt, and rationalizes what he is doing.

> I've always felt one should respect life because that's all any of us have. When I find a bug in my office or apartment I go to considerable trouble to put it safely outside. I always try to avoid stepping on ants, worms, and caterpillars. In fact, I wouldn't take biology labs because they "sacrificed" animals. Although I hunted and fished as a boy, I don't now because I realize animals feel pain as much as we do. I stopped riding horses when I learned that one controls a horse by using a torture device on its tongue, and I won't go to rodeos because they put a girdle around the animals which is so painful they are forced to buck. In addition, I rarely go to zoos and pet shops because I get quite unhappy seeing the animals in cages. I'm also very much opposed to animal research, because it is so unethical. It's a straight case of "might makes right." We do this research for our own interests. But if it is so important for us to do, let humans do it on themselves and be the volunteers. There are too many people as it is. Why torture and kill innocent animals? But I'm not consistent. I always swat mosquitoes that bite me. I figure they attack me and endanger me with disease, so I can attack them back. Also, I eat meat. I wish I didn't, but I don't go to the trouble to change. I would have to learn to prepare meals that are properly nutritious. Also, I eat out all the time, and local eateries serve very few vegetables and practically no vegetarian meals. There's another thing I do. I often buy products, such as drugs, toilet articles, and foods, which are made by companies which test them on animals. It's too much trouble to find other things to use. [#1115]

Functions of not hurting others

People experience hurt when others cause them pain, injure them, reject them, criticize them, cause them to lose money or possessions, neglect them, embarrass them, are rude to them, cause them inconvenience, let them down, fail to meet promises to them, fail to help them, disappoint them, and do things they disapprove of. Most hurt occurs in connection with real or potential physical damage or resource loss. When person A physically or materially hurts person B, person B is damaged and is less able to provide person A with resources. Also, when B feels hurt by A, he associates the memory of the hurt with A, and is more likely to avoid A in the future. Because he is more likely to avoid A, he is less likely to provide A with resources. Person B may even seek to retaliate by hurting A. Therefore when people avoid doing things which hurt others, they are less likely to damage or alienate others, and more likely to maintain their access to resources from them. When they attempt to make amends to others after doing things which damage or alienate them, they help to restore relations with others and to maintain or reestablish access to their resources. Therefore feeling bad as a result of self-criticism helps people maintain their access to resources from other people. The more successful a person is in feeling bad as a result of self-criticism, the less likely he is to hurt others, the more likely he is to make amends when he does hurt others, and the less likely he is to lose resources. People frequently realize that their actions which hurt others may cause them to lose resources from them. In the following examples, one person is concerned about losing her job, and another her boyfriend.

> Susan, a friend of mine, works at a bookstore. One day she discovered she had forgotten to bring money to pay for her lunch and she took four dollars from the cash register. She intended to go to the bank after lunch and then return the money. She didn't have time to get to the bank and decided not to bother paying the money back at all. Then Susan began to feel very guilty, as well as paranoid that her boss had somehow found out. After about a week, Susan put the money back with an excuse as to why she had taken it out in the first place. [#1116]

My friend's boyfriend, Tom, is attending university in another province. When he is gone my friend gets lonely. So one night she accepted a date with another guy. She told me, "I felt so guilty. Tom would be so hurt if he ever found out. I'll never be able to do it again. I didn't even have a good time, because all I could think about was Tom and that he would kill me if he ever found out." #1117

When people express their hurt, they protect themselves and their resources. When person A does something to person B and person B shows signs of being hurt, person A is made aware that he has hurt person B. Person B shows signs of being hurt by crying out, crying, using facial expressions which indicate hurt, acting hurt, avoiding A, and telling A he has hurt him. The more successful B is in showing signs of being hurt, the better he can activate self-criticism in A and get A to stop hurting him, and the less likely it is that B will experience additional injury or loss of resources. When a person sees that he has hurt another and feels bad as a result, he associates a memory of feeling bad with the specific action which caused the hurt. Therefore he is less likely to engage in that action in the future. As a result, he is less likely to hurt others in the future, and less likely to lose the resources he would receive from them.

People feel hurt as soon as others cause them real or potential physical damage or resource loss. This hurt provides them with an immediate indication that they or their resources are threatened. As a result they have a maximum amount of time to try to rectify the situation and minimize damage. In the following example, the male is threatened with losing an important relationship, immediately feels hurt, and acts to protect his relationship and the resources he receives from it.

I told my boyfriend that he had treated me badly so long, I didn't want to see him anymore. He started crying and told me he is not a good person, but has been bad so long he doesn't know how to be good. He told me he really loves me and cares for me and will try to be good in the future. I started crying too, and decided to give him another chance. #1118

The faster people show signs of being hurt, the sooner they are likely to stop the other person from hurting them.

At the same time, people frequently engage in self-criticism and feel bad as soon as they receive signs that they are hurting another person. The sooner they stop hurting the other person, the sooner they protect the resources they are likely to receive from the other person. In the previous example, when the female receives signs she is hurting the male, she feels bad and stops hurting him, thereby protecting the resources she receives through her relationship with the male. Sometimes there is a delay between the time people hurt a person and the time they feel guilty for what they have done. One reason is that the person gives no sign of being hurt, and it is some time later that people realize they have probably hurt him.

Members of a species can easily hurt each other. The same biological tools and weapons that are used to obtain food can also kill, injure, and maim another member of one's own species. This is also true of material tools and weapons which are used by some species, such as humans. In addition, if one is not circumspect one can hit, poke, trip, or step on an individual; knock him into an object; drop something on him; or cause him to fall. It is easy to cause permanent damage to another individual's sensory organs and to produce bodily wounds that become infected. The young are especially vulnerable because they are smaller, weaker, and less experienced than adults. Guilt, or self-criticism, causes members of a species to take particular care not to injure and kill each other.

People have most of their contacts with a few other people. These are the people they receive most of their resources from, and these are the people they are most likely to hurt. It is very much in their interest to maintain good relations with them. It is an expensive process to locate and establish relations with new people in order to obtain the same resources one is already getting. It is not in a person's interest to reduce the ability or willingness of those he already deals with to provide him with resources. Therefore, the less that people hurt those who provide them with resources or who may do so in the future, the better people help themselves. Guilt encourages people to take good care of their human resources so they do not lose them.

Maintaining one's human resources

As a result of self-criticism, people maintain their human resources. They do so in the following ways:

1. Not causing other people pain, injury, or loss of resources
2. Sharing resources with others
3. Maintaining good relations with others
4. Meeting obligations and commitments to others
5. Conforming to other people's expectations
6. Restoring good relations when they are threatened

1. Not causing other people pain, injury, or loss of resources

People do not want to cause others pain and injury, because of the guilt they would feel afterwards. People are very careful that they do not step on others, trip them, knock them down, hit them, poke them, or otherwise harm them. In most cases, people are also careful not to damage another person's resources, take his resources, or cause him to lose his resources.

> The other night when my daughter came home from karate practice we were standing in the hall and she pretended to try out some kicks on me. I grabbed hold of her leg and she started hitting me lightly. I knocked her other leg out from under her and we both fell to the floor. As we fell her head hit the doorjamb. Fortunately, all she got was a headache. But I can't believe I did that. I always tell the kids not to play in the house because it's so easy to get injured. I just acted without thinking, and maybe the thick rug under us made me ignore the door. I can't believe I was so stupid. She could have been permanently injured, and I would have hated myself for the rest of my life. #1119

> One day last week I went in the bathroom, and at the last second I noticed my cat was following me. I was just closing the door on his neck, and could have easily broken it. It was so close. I know how awful I would feel if I had. I've got to be more careful. #1120

2. Sharing resources with others

Guilt encourages people to share their resources with others. As a result they provide others with food, goods, money, time, help, protection, positive reactions, and sex. Most of this sharing is directed toward those one is in closest contact with, such as one's mate, children, relatives, and friends. This is because one is most familiar with their needs and their

411

lack of alternative means to get resources. Because of close contact, one is frequently reminded of their needs. Therefore one feels responsible for helping them and is more likely to feel guilty if one does not.

Because I am an adult with a family, deciding to go to university is a major decision in my life. There is the question whether my family can make it financially, and what we have to give up. I feel guilty in regard to the extra burden I'm putting on my wife, because she has to carry this financial load for the next five years. Also, I wonder whether I am taking away too many of the comforts my family deserve. Then there is the problem of time. There is the time I need with my wife, the time I should spend with my children, and the time I need to make decent marks in my courses. Not a day goes by that I don't wonder whether I've allotted enough time to each of these areas of my life. I promised myself I would not put university ahead of my family. I believe this decision is very important to my marriage, but there are times I'm caught up in an emotional turmoil because of the conflicting demands. #1121

When I don't have sex with my boyfriend, I worry he'll think I don't love him. I feel so guilty when I say no. I do love him, it's just that sometimes I don't feel like having sex. But I don't think he understands this. He takes it personally and I feel like such a bitch for hurting him. #1122

My girlfriend tells me she loves me so much she wouldn't want to go on living without me. She is quite sincere and says it all the time. It's like psychological blackmail. It doesn't matter if I were to find someone I am more compatible with, or if I decide I would be happier single, because there is no way I can leave her. If I did so, I think she might well be devastated for the rest of her life. It would easily be the worst thing I've ever done, and I sure wouldn't want it on my conscience. #1123

I feel guilty that I can't provide very well for my children. One of my girls really wanted a toy roadster for her Barbie dolls. She pestered me to get it for her for Christmas. It cost thirty-five dollars and I really thought it was a waste of money. Besides, I was already getting her a lot of other things. I never did get the roadster for her, and I felt really guilty about it, because it was what she really wanted. I think she got over it before I did.

Then last year another of my girls wanted a robot. I thought this is a really dumb present. I could just see her play with it for a day and then forget about it. I kept trying to explain this to her, but she kept saying she really wanted the robot. My mother sent me some money to buy Christmas presents for them, and it was about the only money I had for gifts. When I told my mother that she wanted a robot, Mom said, "Well get her one." But I just couldn't do it. I have so little money, I can't bear to waste it. And I felt awful I didn't get it for her. I worried about it and felt terrible all year. In fact, this Christmas I went out and bought her a robot. Of course, what happened was she played with it about two hours, and I haven't seen her touch it since.

I feel so guilty when I always have to say, "You can't have that because I can't afford it." It just reminds me of when I was a child. My mother said the same thing to me and I always hated it. I just gave up asking for anything, because I learned it was hopeless. I knew if I asked my mother for anything, it would make her feel really bad, because she'd have to say no. And it made me feel really guilty about wanting anything. I always resolved that if my children asked for something, I'd try to give it to them if I could possibly afford it. But because I have so little money, I can't afford to get them things they want, and I feel guilty about that. I don't think it's fair to them.

Then there are other things. I can't afford to get them dancing lessons. My parents couldn't afford to get me dancing lessons either, and I always wanted them. It seemed like all my friends took them, and now it seems like all of my children's friends have them. My kids are very bright and really talented. They are at the top of their class in school, and they are very original. But I just can't give them anything like that. I'd also really like to get them a piano and get them piano lessons. And there gets to be a point where it's too late for them to learn. If they are going to be really good, it's better they start early. The fact I can't do these things niggles at me, and I feel bad about it.

I also feel guilty if I think I'm not giving them enough attention. Because they are so bright, I never bother about their schoolwork. I regularly ask them, "Have you done your homework?" and they always say they have. But when I went to the parent-teacher interviews, I learned one of my girls is really behind in her math. She'd become bored with it and quit doing her work. I felt really guilty, because I should have known this was happening. I should have been checking more and I felt I was neglecting her. With a little bit of encouragement, she could have easily kept up with it. Instead of blaming my children, I blame myself. I had a serious talk with her and stressed how important her math is. I told her to tell me if she falls behind, and I'd help her if she needs it.

It's clear I put the kids' needs first all the time. If I get the family allowance check or any other extra money, I always ask the kids what's worn-out or what they've grown out of. They always need sneakers, jackets, boots, things like that. Or else there's something they just really want that's in fashion and all their friends are wearing. These days it's these big tops and stirrup pants. I also get an awful lot of hand-me-downs from other people. But by the time we get them, they're out of fashion. No matter how much I explain to the kids, "We're really poor. You really ought to wear these, because these are very nice clothes," they won't look at them. When it comes to me, I never even think of buying anything. If I bought some clothes or went to the hairdresser, I'd feel really selfish and guilty. I'm an adult, I know I'm poor, and I can do without these things. But I'd like to spare the kids from poverty as much as I possibly can, which isn't very much.

It's a funny thing, but I think I give my kids more because we are so poor. If we were both working and had a decent income, I wouldn't feel so bad about telling them, "Look, I'm not going to buy you this. I don't think you need it." But when you're poor you feel guilty about it, and you really feel you have to give them more somehow. I'd feel terrible if I couldn't support them at all. It's unthinkable. I don't care what I'd have to do. I'd go stand on a corner in Charlottetown and sell my body first. When you have kids, you do what you have to to take care of them. #1124

I find being a parent an ongoing saga of guilt. When my daughter was two years old, I realized for the first time I didn't want to stay home anymore with her twenty-four hours a day. I was devastated by this realization. I had always assumed I would be like my mother, who I considered the perfect parent. She was extraordinarily patient, and she didn't start work until her youngest child was well along in school. Because I didn't feel the same way as my mother, my guilt was over-powering.

Then when I went to work, life became a juggling act. There is the nagging sense of guilt that you ought to be with your children more, and at the same time you feel guilty for not giving more attention to your work. Later when my daughter got older she was exposed to new people and new ideas, some of which were not acceptable to me. I found myself being very firm about what I believed was right. We had battles over television, violence, acceptable clothing, and proper food. I would feel guilty because I was yelling instead of discussing the issue calmly and rationally. I would worry I was being too intense, and that our quarreling would shape her development.

There is also the conflict between what we think we ought to feel and what we really feel. Parents develop many angry, hateful, and violent feelings toward their children, but because we believe parents ought to feel nothing but love for them, we think something is wrong with us for feeling this way. But we get angry with our children, wonder whether we love them, and go through periods when we can't stand them and wish they would disappear. This makes us not only feel guilty, but wonder whether we might be a little crazy for feeling this way. It doesn't help that others never volunteer their feelings about their own children, and we feel too guilty about these emotions to dare to ask anyone else if they feel the same way. Often the harshest voices of all are those we hear inside our heads. #1125

When you know someone that you care for needs a lot of help, you help them, even at considerable cost to yourself. Because you are around them all the time, you are very aware of all the help they need and what you could do for them. When my wife set up a new business in a very competitive industry, I put in more time at her business than I did on my own job. It was like having two jobs. I was constantly trying to think of ways to improve her business and putting my thoughts into action. When I wasn't there, I felt I was neglecting her needs, because I knew how much she had to do and saw how much pressure she was under. I felt guilty because I wasn't doing more. I neglected my own job and this made me feel quite frustrated at times, but helping her was more important to me. #1126

When I separated from my wife I gave her our house. I didn't have to, but I wanted to be more than fair because I didn't want to have anything on my conscience later. #1127

My grandmother, who lives on the West Coast, has only a couple of close relatives who are still living, and I'm one of them. She doesn't have anyone else, so I call her fairly often, send her Christmas presents, and go see her every few years. She has been really helpful to me in the past; she helped pay for my education. I know when she dies I would feel really guilty if I hadn't been paying any attention to her. #1128

3. Maintaining good relations with others

Guilt encourages people to maintain good relations with others.

> A friend and I were sitting in a restaurant complaining about how bad the food was. In the midst of our complaining the waiter came up and asked if everything was all right. Both of us said the meal was just fine. Neither of us wanted to be unfriendly to the waiter and then fret afterwards about what we'd said to him. [#1129]

> My boyfriend and I usually talk to each other on the phone every evening. Last night I was at a dinner party with some friends and it was getting late. Because my boyfriend goes to bed fairly early during the week, I became anxious I would get home too late to call him. I didn't want my friends to overhear our conversation, so I couldn't call him from their home. When I wanted to leave, my friends weren't ready to give me a drive. Then when I finally reached home, I rushed up the stairs and called him first thing. I was pleased he hadn't gone to bed yet. I know if I hadn't called, I would have felt bad because he might think I don't care enough about him. [#1130]

4. Meeting obligations and commitments to others

Guilt encourages people to meet their obligations and commitments to others. As a result, people try to be on time, do and bring what they say they will, and fulfill their duties and promises.

> My daughter sings in a choir, and her choir won the top award at the music festival. I'm glad I went to hear her sing. If I hadn't gone, I'd have felt I was a bad mother. [#1131]

> I promised to be home at a certain time, but didn't get away. When I finally did get home, the hurt look from my wife sent me on a guilt trip. I tried to justify myself, but I knew I was in the wrong. It is certainly easier to be responsible for those who depend on you, than it is to be irresponsible and deal with the guilt. [#1132]

> I've been hired to work on a research project for a professor at the university. There is so much work that needs to be done on the project, I can't get it out of my mind. I'm paid by the hour and when I'm not

as productive as I'd like, I don't report all the hours I've worked. I keep thinking if someone else were doing this project, they'd probably have had it done long ago. I can't enjoy any free time, because I keep thinking I should get this project done. I live for the weekends because I can leave town and go home and it's impossible for me to work on the project. When I am out with other people, they take my mind off the project a little bit. But if I stay in town, I start thinking I should be at the university working. Last weekend my parents came into town from the country for a dance. I visited them at their hotel room, but then after half an hour I got to feeling so guilty about not working on the project, I had to return to the university. Then when I got to the university, I couldn't get any work done. All I could do was sit there and feel guilty that I hadn't spent more time with my parents. I just belittled myself and thought of all they do for me. The ideal daughter would have said, "Frig the work!" and stayed with them. But I couldn't say, "Frig the work!" because I have all this stuff to do. I felt so guilty, I was immobilized. I just couldn't win. No matter what I did, I felt guilty. I told myself, "I'm driving myself crazy. Mentally and physically, I can not take this much guilt." #1133

On the weekends I leave Charlottetown and stay at my parents' home in the country. However, while I'm there, I spend most of my time at my boyfriend's house. And I feel guilty, because I think I should be spending more time at home with my parents. I worry they'll think I don't like them or that I like my boyfriend more than them. A girlfriend of mine is planning on getting married, and she feels her parents will think she is deserting them. She says you just have to get used to this. The same thing happened to my younger sister. She lived with my parents until she got married at nineteen. Now she lives just a quarter of a mile away from them. She says one of the biggest problems of being married is trying not to feel bad about leaving Mom and Dad. She worries that they'll think she doesn't want or need them anymore. I don't think my parents have tried to make us feel guilty about this. But it is clear they like to have us there. When I talk to them on the phone, they frequently ask, "You're going to be up next weekend?" and "You're coming to supper with us, aren't you?" I spend more time with them as a result. #1134

I listened to a sermon on the radio. The minister said that guilt motivates us to behave responsibly. Because of guilt, we aren't unfaithful to our spouse, and we don't take the money the family needs to survive and use it to buy a pleasure boat for ourselves. #1135

5. Conforming to other people's expectations

Guilt can also encourage people to alter their behavior to conform to the expectations of others.

Parents are good at making you feel guilty when they want you to go somewhere with them, and you don't want to. There are times when my parents want me to visit my grandparents but I've already made plans for the weekend. They'll say, "You know your grandparents would like to see you. They haven't seen you in a long time. Anyway, you can wait and do what you want to do next weekend. But you can't see your grandparents whenever you want." So often I go along with them. #1136

I've been working as a research assistant and doing several assignments for this scientist. One of my assignments is a survey of the research literature, but I'd been so busy working on other things for him, I didn't get much done on it. Last week he came in and asked if I'd completed a particular section of the survey, and I had to say no. He said, "We'll have to get moving on that," and left. I just felt terrible. I felt so guilty I was almost panic-stricken. I felt so bad that I knew I wouldn't be able to get anything else done that day until I dealt with the survey. So I dropped what I was doing and ran over to the computer center. I talked to a technician about getting the information from the computer. After I did this I felt much better and came back and returned to work. #1137

When we were teenagers a bunch of us started a rock band together, but we didn't include one of the guys we got around with. He used to go out with girls who were a number of years younger than him, and we felt this was really childish. When he learned about our band, he told us every chance he got what pricks we were for not including him. He also reminded us of all the times he'd driven us places we wanted to go. Eventually we felt so guilty we let him work the lights for us. But this didn't satisfy him. After a few months he quit and started hanging around with a different bunch of guys. #1138

Friends can really make you feel guilty about what you do and don't do. My best friend would say that if I didn't stop two-timing my girlfriend and start treating her better, he was going to kick my ass all over town. Another of my closest friends got on my case too. He said it was the worst thing I could do to my girlfriend and he couldn't believe I would stoop so low. Because of what he said I broke up with my girlfriend and continued going out with the other girl. But every time I broke up with a girl, her friends would make me feel guilty. They would say I was a bastard for hurting her and that I had destroyed her life. I find my friends can put me on a worse guilt trip than my parents can. Your parents won't leave you, but your friends might. #1139

6. Restoring good relations when they are threatened

Another function of guilt is that it encourages people to smooth over disagreements, mend hurt feelings, and act to restore good relations with other people.

> When I fuss at my wife, or tell her what she does that upsets me, I feel relieved to finally get it off my chest. But then I start thinking I've been heavy-handed and overdone it. I feel awful for attacking her and hurting her. Then I try to make things right by being very affectionate and solicitous. It's the same thing a friend of mine does with her children. She says after she puts her foot down, she feels so guilty she goes to them and grovels. #1140

> Two friends of mine, Len and Tracy, were out together on Len's motorbike. Tracy had to be back at the university to take a class quiz at three o'clock. However, when it was time to return, the motorbike wouldn't start, so Tracy missed her test. Len felt so bad he bought Tracy the book she needed to read for her next quiz. #1141

Actions such as apologizing, making amends, and confessing often help to remove a feeling of unease from one's mind. They enable a person to release the mental tension he is feeling in the form of guilt. Such actions also enable a person to determine if he has damaged his relationship with the other person. Apparently people do not like to live with the ambiguity of not knowing whether their relationship with the other person has suffered. By broaching the subject through apologizing, making amends, or confessing, a person can quickly determine what the other person's feelings are in the matter. When person A indicates he knows he was in the wrong, person B is more willing to forgive and forget. If B reassures A that everything is all right between them, it is easier for A to stop feeling guilty. One reason why people continue to feel guilty for years afterwards is because for some reason or another they have been unable or unwilling to apologize, make amends, or confess what they have done to the person they have wronged, and therefore can not obtain reassurance from the other person.

Using guilt to deal with others

People know others feel guilty and take this into consideration in their dealings with them. Guilt provides people with a tool to try to obtain resources from others.

> I don't want to be vice-president of the association this year, but they are trying to get me to take the job. The president got me to take it last year, and keeps saying, "What will we do without you?" I feel really guilty about it, but I just don't have the time. #1142

> I am a Big Sister for a thirteen-year-old girl, and when she wants to go somewhere she starts begging, "Please, please, please, please," until you feel so guilty you give in. She does this with her father and always gets what she wants. Once she called me three times on the phone to get me to take her to the circus. I refused because I didn't have the money, and I had already told her I don't like her begging and it's not going to get her anywhere. Then I got a phone call from her father saying that he would pay for both of us if I would take her, but I refused to give in. Obviously she'd gone to work on him too. #1143

> My mother gets me to do things around the house by making me feel guilty when I don't do them. She'll say, "Why can't you do something without being asked first? You can see it needs to be done." One night she came home from work and asked why I hadn't cleaned the house that day, which she'd asked me to do. I told her I'd forgotten, and she said, "Boy, it would be different if I was to forget to clean up, or if I forgot from now on that you need new clothes." Another time I forgot to put the roast in the oven, and when she came home and saw it on the counter she said, "All I asked you to do was one simple thing and you forgot. Just one small, stupid thing. I'll bet all day all you thought

about was yourself, and what I asked just slipped your mind." If I don't start supper, or complain about having to do it, she says, "Jeez, when I was your age I had to keep the wood stove going, cook supper, set the table, and do the housework for the whole family." She talks about how lucky kids are these days, because they don't have to do anything. And if my parents are working in the yard, Mom will make me feel guilty by saying, "You know our health isn't all that great. Why can't you come out and help?" She always mentions all the things she does for me that I don't even recognize or show appreciation for. The problem is she tries to make me feel guilty too often, and it loses its effectiveness. #1144

When I was in high school my family lived in the United States and I had a job delivering telegrams for Western Union. I found that most people were so concerned about opening their telegram and finding out what it said that they rarely gave me a tip. So I learned to say, "You're welcome!" as though I was quite put out. This worked much better. I had people run after me in the rain, and drive two miles into town to the Western Union office, just to make sure they gave me a tip. #1145

Jeannie asked Mary if she could copy her answers during the exam because she hadn't had time to study. Mary said she wouldn't feel right about it. Then Jeannie got quite upset and told Mary she thought they were best friends and she couldn't understand why Mary wanted her to fail. Jeannie also said if Mary had asked for her help, she'd have given it. Mary felt very guilty, and let Jeannie see her answers, but told her it was the last time she'd do so. #1146

My grandmother is quite old and lives by herself in her own home over a thousand miles away. Every time I call her she tells me how lame and blind she is, and that she can't wait to die. She says she knows she's going to die soon, but she's said this for the last twenty years. Then she talks about how very good her neighbors are, how they do all her errands, and how she wouldn't be able to make it without them. What she's really saying is that her relatives should be doing these things for her, not her neighbors, and her relatives don't really care. She's just trying to make me feel guilty about not being there to help her all the time, and she's trying to get me to visit. I do visit her more often as a result. However, every time I visit I discover she's doing just fine. #1147

My husband wanted us to live apart for a while, and I agreed. Later I moved in with another man, but as soon as my husband found out, he did everything he could to get me back. He wrote all these letters and wouldn't leave me alone. He said if I didn't return he would have to drop out of medical school and be admitted to a mental institution. I knew he would make a very good doctor, and I didn't want to see him leave medical school. Also, I knew his parents would blame me for causing him to drop out. He made me feel so guilty, I moved back with him. #1148

In contrast, people sometimes try to prevent others from feeling guilty.

A month ago, a friend of mine went on an all-out program to give up smoking and was making good progress. But when I had lunch with her yesterday, she lit up a cigarette. I was going to ask how her efforts to give it up were going, but then didn't because I didn't want to make her feel guilty. #1149

One of my colleagues has continued to mention that he was wrong to ax my research proposal twenty years ago. At that time he was head of the research committee which considered it. He told me he didn't think the project could be done, and I've since proved him wrong. Because he kept bringing this up when he talked with me, I realized it continued to bother him. So I made a point of telling him that I took the money that he had allotted me for a different project and used it to work on the one he turned down. Although I was pissed off at him at the time, we get along well today, and I didn't see any sense in having him continue to feel guilty about this. #1150

Excess behavior

Excess behavior is behavior in response to feelings which results in one acting contrary to the purposes the feelings are designed for. As a consequence, one loses resources rather than gains or protects them. For example, the feeling of guilt encourages people to avoid hurting others, and by not hurting others people maintain their access to resources from others. However, there are situations in which people seek to avoid hurting others, but actually lose resources.

People try to avoid hurting individuals who are very unlikely to provide them with resources, and they feel guilty when they do hurt them or fail to help them. This is wasted energy, because people gain no resources for their efforts.

When I was traveling in Asia, I decided I would cut my stay in Calcutta short. So I went to a travel agency and told them I wanted to take a plane that evening to Rangoon. It was too late to change a traveler's check, because the banks were closed. So an employee of the travel agency went with me to change a traveler's check on the black market. The employee was Eurasian, and en route he told me his dream was to one day get the money together to buy working passage on a ship to England. I asked how much it would take, and he said two hundred dollars. After we got back to the travel agency, the employee left and went home. As they were fixing my plane ticket, I thought about his situation, and decided to give him the two hundred dollars. They didn't know his home address, so the only choice I had was to leave the money at the agency for him. I asked for an envelope and told the owner of the agency what I was doing in front of the other employees, because I didn't want the owner to take the money for himself. The owner was concerned the employee had asked me for the money, and I assured him he hadn't. Ever since, I've felt I did the wrong thing and guilty about what I did, because I may have cost the employee his job, he may never have received the money, and his dream may have only been a dream which he had no intention of acting on. [#1151]

I use a hollow concrete block to keep the wind from blowing over a sign I set up in front of my store every day. Last night when I closed the store, I lifted up the concrete block to carry it inside, and noticed a large spider inside the block. I didn't want to hurt the spider, but I didn't want it inside my store, so I hit the block lightly against the sidewalk to knock the spider out. Unfortunately the spider was injured when it fell. Two of its legs were damaged and it crawled off as best it could. I'm really sorry I injured it. It was so neat and precise. I would much rather have had the spider inside my store than to have injured it. [#1152]

When people hurt someone who does not provide them with resources, people often try to make amends, which provides them with additional costs and no benefits.

People also continue to feel guilty when they are no longer in contact with the person they hurt. Because they can no longer receive resources from the other person, feeling guilty about hurting him is wasted time and energy. In the extreme form, one feels guilty about something one did to a person who has since died, and therefore one has no hope of ever receiving resources from the person. In such cases guilt fails to satisfy its function, which is to ensure that the people one deals with remain able and willing to provide one with resources. Nevertheless, when one feels guilty about something one did to a person one does not receive resources from, one is less likely to do the same thing to the people one currently receives resources from.

People sometimes feel guilty when they are not actually responsible for a) hurting others, or b) preventing them from being hurt.

> This girl I'd seen around town committed suicide. Ever since, I've wished I had done something that might have prevented her from doing so. I'd seen her several times with some people I know, but I was never introduced to her. She always seemed like a friendly person, and I considered speaking to her. I think if I had taken the initiative to speak and gotten to know her, it might have made a difference. #1153

In addition, people frequently express hurt, perhaps by crying or looking hurt, when they are not in the presence of the person who is hurting them. Such expressions of hurt are usually wasted, because the person who hurts them is not present to see their expression, feel guilty, and stop hurting them.

In order to avoid self-criticism, or guilt, people lose opportunities to obtain more resources. They remain in less productive relationships, occupations, and activities, because if they left them they would hurt others and feel guilty. They may remain in such situations for years. As a result they obtain less resources than they might in alternative relationships, occupations, and activities, and they lose additional resources feeling trapped and frustrated.

> I go spend the evening with my mother twice a week. It's an ordeal and very unpleasant. She's always on my case, and does everything she can to make me feel guilty about going out with a guy she does not approve of. But if I didn't go see her I'd feel terribly guilty. #1154

Society and not hurting others

Society and organizations within it seek to prevent people from hurting others, being hurt, and experiencing guilt. In addition, guilt is used to obtain aid for those who need help. Families, schools, and churches instruct children and adults not to hurt others and inform them which actions are likely to do so. Laws and regulations are instituted and enforced in the society concerning murder, rape, maiming, torture, brutality, abortion, infanticide, physical abuse, corporal punishment, fighting, psychological and sexual abuse, the exposure of children to violence in the mass media, and the use of drugs, tobacco, and alcohol. Measures are also taken to protect people from loss of resources as a result of theft, vandalism, arson, fraud, desertion, misrepresentation, and gambling. Efforts are made to minimize pain and suffering, through the use of painkillers, anesthetics, and painless methods of euthanasia and execution. People receive psychological counseling to deal with experiencing hurt, hurting others, and guilt in connection with family, relationships, work, and war. In addition, individuals, organizations, and the mass media obtain financial and other aid from people by making them personally aware of strangers who experience hurt.

> After I watched the news reports about millions of African refugees facing starvation and cholera, I was quite moved and awed by the hopelessness of their situation. Others must have felt the same way, because they organized a street dance to raise money for the refugees. When I learned there was a place to leave a donation, I went out of my way to give twenty dollars, and would have felt quite bad if I hadn't. #1155

4. APPROACHES

Contents

The study of behavior

Science is the search for better models. Better models let us describe reality with greater economy. Until better models are identified, scientists spend their time and energy working with existing models. Existing models are fully exploited in the attempt to explain phenomena. When phenomena remain unexplained, it means that existing models are inadequate or inappropriate and will have to be replaced by better models.

In working with models, scientists label certain research methods proper, and other research methods improper. These alternatives are outlined in Model 4. Normally those methods which produced the existing

Model 4: Models and methods

	Existing models	Better models
Proper methods		
Improper methods		

models are labeled proper, and are worshiped. However, no method is inherently proper or improper. Whether a method is proper or improper depends on whether it provides us with better models. If it does provide us with better models, then it is a proper method. If it fails to provide us with better models, then it is an improper method. If, for example, so-called hard methods fail to identify better models, while so-called soft methods succeed in identifying better models, then soft methods are proper methods. At another time, soft methods may fail to provide better models, and they will be improper methods. In order to identify better models which will replace existing models, one often has to use different methods than those that produced the existing models. What is proper and improper methodology is always in a state of change.

If the behavior of humans and other species is best explained in terms of feelings, then we want to study behavior by studying feelings. Feelings are not easily controlled by rigorous methods, but that is no excuse to ignore them. Similarly, if humans and other species share a common set of feelings, then we want to apply our knowledge of human feelings to other species. In this case, "anthropomorphism" is a proper research method. If we continue to treat anthropomorphism as an inherently improper method, we will continue to impede science.

One of our difficulties is knowing where we want to end up. It is an enormous temptation to try to explain social behavior in terms of microscopic biology without identifying what lies between. What if we tried to explain the diversity of species in terms of differences between cells and genes before we recognized the significance of natural selection and evolution? How many levels of explanation lie between social behavior and genes, or between social behavior and neurons? As in the case of evolution, certain of these intermediate levels may explain a great deal in a very meaningful way.

If people engage in certain of their behaviors because it is advantageous for the brain to operate that way, then it is necessary to understand the brain if we wish to understand behavior. What is advantageous for the brain can be costly in terms of behavior. Therefore, if one limits oneself to explaining behavior in terms of what is advantageous, or less costly, for behavior, one will misunderstand what is taking place.

It is no easier to understand the brain than it is to understand other phenomena. But it may not be any harder. What one does is observe the brain in operation, construct models, see how well the models work, and improve the models. The operation of the brain is revealed through our behavior, and there is ample behavior to observe. Our attempts to glorify ourselves by presenting the human brain as the most complex phenomenon in the known universe and therefore the pinnacle of evolution may be good for our egos, but it is not good for the development of our understanding of ourselves and other species. This attitude does not promote the search for simple, neat, succinct ways to describe and understand the mind and brain. Instead it presents the brain as impossibly complex, and something that may lie beyond human understanding. Another attitude that hinders us is the belief that it will take hundreds of years before we will be able to explain how the brain works. Therefore, it follows that we should be satisfied with trivial investigations and messy, complicated conclusions. A much more constructive approach is to assume that clear and straightforward means of understanding the brain (as well as other phenomena) are present today, lying just beneath the surface, waiting for someone to take the trouble to dig them up.

Humans and nonhumans

The similarities between humans and nonhumans are far more significant than the differences. If we can not recognize the role that feelings play in ourselves, even though we experience them, is it surprising we do not recognize their role in other species? What else do we have in common that we have not recognized? Humans have an embarrassing track record of refusing to recognize humanity in groups other than their own. This track record is so bad that whenever humans claim a group lacks humanity, we can expect that history will prove them wrong.

Then there is the matter of vested interests. Would you trust slave traders and plantation owners to make an objective decision regarding the humanity of slaves? If any one species has a vested interest in denying human traits to other species, it is man. Man eats other species; enslaves them; farms them; imprisons them; places them in solitary confinement; uses them for medical, scientific, and industrial experiments and products; forces them to entertain him; abuses them; tortures them; mutilates them; kills them for pleasure; exterminates them; and destroys their habitats. Should we be surprised that man insists that other species are simple biological machines which lack awareness, feelings, consciousness, intelligence, and minds?

The human mind operates on the principle of consistency, and human beliefs are designed to be consistent with human behavior. Inconsistency creates tension. This tension is very uncomfortable, and people seek consistency in order to release it. Consider the tension that is produced by either of the following two sets of beliefs.

1. Animals have feelings, consciousness, and minds.
2. I hurt animals.
3. I am a good person and deserve positive reactions.

1. Animals have feelings, consciousness, and minds.
2. Humans hurt animals.
3. Humans are a good species and deserve positive reactions.

Because each of the above set of beliefs is inconsistent, it produces tension and is difficult for a person to hold. On the other hand, the following two sets of beliefs are more consistent.

1. Animals have feelings, consciousness, and minds.
2. I hurt animals.
3. I am a bad person and deserve negative reactions.

1. Animals have feelings, consciousness, and minds.
2. Humans hurt animals.
3. Humans are a bad species and deserve negative reactions.

However, these last two sets of beliefs are unacceptable to people, because people want very much to think that they and the groups they are associated with are good and deserve positive reactions. Therefore people develop belief systems which are consistent with the position that they are good and deserve good things. The easiest way to do this is to say, "animals do not have feelings, consciousness, and minds" or "animals are simple biological mechanisms which do not matter." As a result people adopt the following sets of beliefs.

1. Animals do *not* have feelings, consciousness, and minds.
2. (Therefore it does not matter that) I hurt animals.
3. I am a good person and deserve positive reactions.

1. Animals do *not* have feelings, consciousness, and minds.
2. (Therefore it does not matter that) humans hurt animals.
3. Humans are a good species and deserve positive reactions.

The belief that "animals do not have feelings, consciousness, and minds" enables individuals both to continue hurting animals and to continue believing that they themselves are good and deserve positive reactions. Humans do not want to admit that "animals have feelings, consciousness, and minds," because humans want to continue hurting animals and do not want to accept that humans are bad and deserve negative reactions.

Humans take the position: "until we have conclusive proof that animals have the same thoughts and feelings as humans, it is all right for humans to do anything they want to animals." This is no different than taking the positions: "until we have conclusive proof that Africans have the same thoughts and feelings as Europeans, it is all right for Europeans to do anything they want to Africans," and "until we have conclusive proof that women have the same thoughts and feelings as men, it is all right for men to do anything they want to women." However, whether or not we find that the thoughts and feelings of animals, Africans, or women are the same or different from those of other groups does not justify their abuse. The ethical position is that we should not abuse animals, Africans, or women unless we have conclusive proof that they have *no* thoughts and feelings. As long as there is any possibility or hint that they might have thoughts and feelings, it is wrong to mistreat them.

What is ironic is that the traits we want to label human have been present in other species for hundreds of millions of years, but we insist on exclusive right to them in order to pretend we are distinct. What we do is divide species into two groups, humans and nonhumans, and identify two sets of traits, A and B. Then we claim that set A is present in humans and set B is present in nonhumans. But in reality, both sets may be present in both groups. We simply ignore the presence of set B in humans and the presence of set A in nonhumans. As the evidence mounts that nonhumans have traits which we once considered the exclusive property of humans, we do not acknowledge our similarity and change our treatment of other species. Instead, we redefine the traits in set A and set B so we can continue to brag how unique and wonderful we are. A typology which does not distinguish humans from the other species is very likely to be considered incorrect and unacceptable by humans.

Much of the difficulty people have in recognizing thoughts, feelings, minds, and consciousness in other species, stems from the view people have of themselves. Individuals want to believe that they themselves and the groups they identify with are unique, special, and of greater value than other individuals and groups, and therefore are more deserving of positive reactions and various resources. Because people believe their own species is special, different, and better than other species, they seek to identify properties in their species which "prove" this. The way they "prove" this is to identify properties of their own species, and then claim other species lack these same properties and therefore must be inferior. As an example, consider the following set of assumptions:

1. Humans have reason.
2. Humans are different from animals.
3. Therefore animals do not have reason.
4. Because animals lack reason, they must have something else to direct their behavior, and we will call this instinct.

This is similar to making the following set of assumptions:

1. Humans have digestive systems.
2. Humans are different from animals.
3. Therefore animals do not have digestive systems.
4. Because animals lack digestive systems, they must have something else for obtaining nutrients, and we will call this factor X.

Humans recognize that they think and feel and have minds and consciousness. Because humans want to believe humans are unique, they assume and argue that other species must not think and feel or have minds and consciousness. If people were to recognize these same properties in other species, their assumption that humans are unique, different, and better than other species would be threatened. Also, people do not want to see their sacred cows secularized. Their sacred cows include feelings, love, the arts, personality, individuality, language, culture, learning, thinking, imagination, creativity, intelligence, consciousness, the mind, and the brain. People do not appreciate having these treated as common, ordinary, widespread, natural phenomena. Our belief that we are unique, special, and better than other species prevents us from understanding human nature and the nature of other species, just as this same belief interfered with and delayed our understanding of our location in space and our origin through evolution. Science teaches us that phenomena are not unique. Anytime we think something is unique, we are looking at it in the wrong way, i.e., in an inefficient way.

Humans assume that human properties are advanced and superior, and that the properties of other species are primitive and inferior. Humans think that their own properties are absent in other species, because other species are too primitive or simple to have them. And humans think that the properties of other species are missing in humans, because humans are too advanced to have them. Consider the following set of assumptions:

1. Humans are advanced.
2. Humans have thoughts, feelings, minds, and consciousness.
3. Therefore thoughts, feelings, minds, and consciousness are advanced.
4. Other species are primitive.
5. Because thoughts, feelings, minds, and consciousness are advanced, other species are too primitive to have them.
6. Other species must have something else that is primitive to replace thoughts, feelings, minds, and consciousness, and we will call this instincts.
7. Humans do not have instincts because humans are too advanced to have them.
8. Also, humans do not need instincts because they have thoughts, feelings, minds, and consciousness.

Now consider how much simpler and more straightforward it is to assume the following:

1. Humans are another animal species.
2. Animal species have thoughts, feelings, minds, and consciousness.

When we finally develop an understanding of the mechanisms underlying thoughts, feelings, minds, and consciousness, we may find that they involve simple phenomena that lie well within the capacities of simple organisms. If we are slow in understanding a phenomenon, the difficulty may occur because we are slow, not because the phenomenon is complicated.

With different assumptions, humans would see other species very differently. This would be the case if we believed that humans are just one variant in a common theme. Then the emphasis would be on identifying what that common theme is and what various species have in common, and the assumption would be that the properties we can recognize in humans are likely to be present in other species also. Accordingly, we would assume that because humans think and feel and have minds and consciousness, other species are likely to think and feel and have minds and consciousness too. Only if we were unable to find these properties in other species, would our assumption that humans are just one variant in a common theme be challenged.

Even if we insist on seeing ourselves as different from other species, we should ask how different we are and how significant the differences are. The first few fish species that crawled up on the land differed little from the other fish, and the first few reptile species that flew differed little from the other reptiles. It is very likely that the first few mammalian species to use our kind of language and technology differ little from the other mammals. For this reason alone we should assume that other mammalian species have an emotional and mental life that is very similar to our own. However, humans characterize animals as acting on instinct, and being small brained, simple, dumb, programmed, amoral, dirty, and lacking souls. In contrast, humans characterize themselves as having reason, learning, culture, and art, and being big brained, complex, intelligent, creative, inventive, moral, and having souls. But does it really seem likely that using sounds which are more specific would transform us from beasts into gods? We humans do excel at one thing; we are pretentious.

The argument that humans are superior to other species is no different than the argument that one's own race, culture, society, or country is superior to others. This idea implies that other groups are less deserving than one's own and that one has a natural right to take everything they have for oneself. Again and again this argument is used to justify a total disregard of the rights of weaker groups, and to support their material exploitation and physical annihilation. The argument, "because humans are stronger than other species, the human species must be superior to other species," is the same as the argument, "because Nazis are stronger than Jews, the Aryan race must be superior to the Jewish race." Just as the Nazis were far more interested in recognizing the superiority of the Aryan race than in recognizing the equality of races, humans have been far more interested in recognizing the superiority of the human species than in recognizing the equality of species. Rather than identify with our fellow species on earth, who share many of our feelings, thoughts, and experiences, we renounce them and identify instead with "intelligent" species which dominate alien worlds.

The refusal of the scientific community to recognize the role of feelings and consciousness in animal behavior is the equivalent of the scientific commmunity's refusal in the past to recognize evolution or the rotation of the planets around the sun. This refusal is a major impediment to our progress in understanding behavior.

If we decide to keep our present assumptions and continue to view ourselves as the gods of the universe, we should at least ask ourselves what kinds of gods we want to be. Do we want to be brutal, cruel, and destructive, and use our power to cause the members of other species great pain and suffering? Or do we want to be kind, understanding, and loving, and use our power to cooperate with other species? We have very much more in common with other species than we have been willing to admit, and it is quite possible to design approaches which enable us to cooperate with them.* If we do choose to continue to act as evil gods, there is one consolation. When we encounter a stronger species, there is nothing they will do to us that we do not deserve.

Humans constitute an animal species that is able to use its animal abilities to obtain a wealth of resources that were previously unavailable to animals. However, instead of sharing this wealth with the other animals, humans use these resources to obliterate them. We are the animal that has run amok. This is our moment in time and space. Is this the contribution we want to make?

---

* Wills, Richard H., "A Desirable Environmental Model," *Journal of Environmental Systems*, Vol. 5(3), 1975, pp. 153-162.

ACKNOWLEDGMENTS

I most sincerely thank the residents of Prince Edward Island for their patience, openness, and cooperation with this research. Hundreds of people have contributed their time and labor. They have provided information about their families, friends, and neighbors, as well as themselves, for the sole purpose of helping to identify types of behavior. Because of the private nature of much of the information, most of those participating have asked that their names not be mentioned. As a result, I am hesitant to mention the few who indicated they do not care whether I use their names. I certainly would not want these few criticized for information which they did not provide. Therefore, my policy is to identify as few names as possible. If, however, someone wishes to have their name mentioned in connection with specific pieces of information which they provided, I will be happy to do so if this book is reprinted, as long as this does not place others in an embarrassing position.

I wish to single out Sharon Myers, who has been an invaluable assistant in collecting case studies for this research. She gathered excellent information, painstakingly placed this within a proper context, helped me understand the significance of behavior, answered my numerous questions, and patiently corrected me when I was off base. She has made a significant contribution to our understanding of rural life. I can not thank her enough. Many others have worked for me as research assistants during various stages of this study, and their contribution has been enormous. Regrettably, most have requested that I not mention them by name. I very much thank all of these individuals for the care, attention, and interest they have given this project.

I also greatly thank Hoa Huynh and Llewellyn Watson for their patience and cooperation in serving as sounding boards as I have written up my information and developed my ideas. Often they put aside their own work to listen to me. Their thoughtful comments have helped me deal with certain weaknesses in the study, their examples have clarified the subject matter, and their encouragement has boosted my morale.

Acknowledgments

I very much want to thank Bill Charlesworth for his interest in and intellectual support for this project. I also very much appreciate the encouagement I have received from Laurence Butler, Benet Davetian, Matthew MacKay, and Michael McGuire. I sincerely thank Elizabeth Hall and John DeGrace for all of their support.

Many other individuals have been extremely helpful in answering specific questions which have arisen during the course of the study. These include Danny Bowles, Doreley Coll, Satadal Dasgupta, Kay Diviney, Anne Marie Eberhardt, Frank Falvo, Susan Gallant, Egbert Huynh, Joseph Kopachevsky, Frank Ledwell, Simon Lloyd, Brent MacLaine, William Mason, Shannon Murray, Annie Myer, Wayne Peters, Asia Saint, Harold Saint, John Joe Sark, Barbara Seeber, Charlotte Stewart, Elizabeth Thai, Tien Thai, Linda Trenton, Tom Trenton, Judi Wagner, and David Weale. Thank you very much.

A number of individuals have freely loaned me slides and photographs and have given me a great deal of help understanding their content. Some have also gone to considerable trouble to take photographs for me. These include Laurence Butler, Barbara Currie, Marshall Dempster, Graham Diamond, Ron Eckroth, Mamdouh Elgharib, Margot Elgharib, Charles Holmes, Hoa Huynh, Thuy Huynh, Vicki Huynh, Udo Krautwurst, Amanda MacIntyre, Fred Martens, Maria Martens, Jean Mitchell, Nhuong Nguyen, Harold Saint, Charlotte Stewart, Elizabeth Thai, Ut Thai, Llewellyn Watson, Gertrude Wills, Derek Wolf, and Marty Zelenietz. Laurence Butler, Yogi Fell, Helen Huynh, David Magda, Harold Saint, and Alina Toma have gone to considerable effort to help me obtain useful photos. I very much appreciate their help, and am certain this research would be much poorer without it.

I have also received an enormous amount of technical help. Marc Beland, Dave Cairns, Bruce Ferguson, Nancy Kemp, Scott MacDonald, Walter Pirch, Evelyn Read, Bonnie Suen, Chris Vessey, Kent Villard, and Larry Yeo have provided excellent advice and support with computers and word processing. Donya Beaton, Katie Compton, Shelley Ebbett, Richard Haines, Angela Hughes, and Tom MacDonald have gone far beyond the call of duty and have carefully prepared countless outstanding photographs. Glenda Clements-Smith, John Cox, Janos Fedak, Sibyl Frei, Matthew MacKay, Walter Pirch, Floyd Trainor, Mary Ada Upstone, and Kent Villard have given me excellent advice and a great deal of help with illustrations, layout, and printing. Mary Ada Upstone and Matthew MacKay have created the very useful maps. Judi Wagner has been very helpful in preparing manuscripts.

I particularly want to thank my wife, Hoa Huynh, who has given me an enormous amount of help and support. It is not possible to express how much this means to me. She understands how important it is to me to spend so much time on this project.

Although numerous individuals have given freely of their time and help, limitations in the conduct, analysis, organization, and interpretation of this research must be recognized as my own.

SOURCES OF PHOTOGRAPHS

R. E.   Ron Eckroth

H. H.   Hoa Huynh

V. H.   Vicki Huynh

A. M.   Amanda MacIntyre

N. N.   Nhuong Nguyen

H. S.   Harold Saint

E. T.   Elizabeth Thai

U. T.   Ut Thai

M. Z.   Marty Zelenietz

The remaining photographs are provided by the author.

INDEX OF NUMBERED EXAMPLES

The numbers below refer to the consecutive numbers which follow the indented quotations in the text.

445

"If I hadn't gone, I'd have felt I was a bad mother," #1131

making sure one's cat is safe when a dog enters the yard, #1083

moving back to live with husband so their separation won't destroy his career, #1148

not breaking up, #1077

not hurting feelings (*see* lies)

not killing insects, riding horses, or going to rodeos, #1115

not leaving girlfriend who says she wouldn't want to go on living without him, #1123

not making fun of others, #1072

not quitting one's part-time job, #1080

not quitting work on an unfinished research project, #1103

not recommending stocks, #1078

not vacationing in third world countries, #1074

paying attention to grandmother before she dies, #1128

putting children's needs ahead of one's own, #1124

remaining faithful and not infecting family with AIDS, #1079

taking a walk or watching a movie when one's wife wants to do so, #1081

treating grandmother well before she dies, #1071

trying to get full-time employment for part-time employee, #1085

visiting parents on vacation instead of traveling where one wants to go, #1076

avoiding rejection, #876-#979. *See also* rejected

> because of tremendous fear of rejection, #978
>
> by
>
> > avoiding people, #978
> >
> > not applying for jobs, #976
> >
> > not asking a girl out, #973
> >
> > not asking girls to dance, #940, #974
> >
> > not looking for a relationship, #975
> >
> > not speaking first to a girl one doesn't know, #972
> >
> > not submitting the short stories one has written, #977
> >
> > staying in one's room, #978

avoiding situations in which one feels guilty. *See also* guilt

> avoids married man that she made love to, #1109
>
> avoids Salvation Army collection, #1105
>
> doesn't like to phone mother on Sunday because mother asks if she went to church, #1106
>
> stops driving after has traffic accident, #1108

avoiding those who mistreat him

> weird kid, #643
>
> young guy, #472

avoiding woman from mental ward, #899

awards night. *See* hockey

baby. *See also* brother; children; crying; guilty; mother; pregnant

> falls off table on concrete floor, #993

baby (*continued*)

"I have a child walking around somewhere who is going to think I didn't want him," #999

mother wonders if she was wrong to put her baby up for adoption, #999

single mother wonders if it would have been better to give her baby up for adoption, #998

baby pictures, older sister burns, #654

baby sitter, when children become older no longer excited to see popular, #882

baby-sitting

argument between children over possession of book, #730

efforts of children to get positive reactions

by following closely, #142

by standing right in front of you, #124

in two different families, #50

of young girl, #120, #142

for grandchildren so she doesn't have to be alone, #408

back scratch from wife. *See* married couple

back, talked about behind one's, #783

backward town, embarrassed that sister dating guy from, #585

bad

feel I'm a bad girl when I do what my church disapproves of, #1039

feel I'm a bad person for playing April fool trick on teacher, #1052

bad breath, friend says one should deal with one's, #620

bad mood, person receives attention from friends because of, #290

bad reputation

attacks referee and gets a, #600

child is shunned because family has a, #864

if you do one or two things people disapprove of, #809

as a result of people talking about you, #783

bald, twenty year old believes he is laughed at because going, #458

Bali, lonely in, #370

ball. *See also* sports

last one chosen to play, #936

nags older brother to play ball with him, #953

ballet

corrections in class, #791

improved arms because of criticism in ballet school, #935

says quitting ballet when fails ballet examination, #979

ballet examination. *See* ballet

ballgame. *See also* zipper

spilling food and drinks on a fan at a, #453

balloons. *See* rubber

band. *See* rock band

bank

boyfriend has to borrow from bank to loan money to girlfriend, #1028

mistakes "psychology professor" while in the, #683

Index of numbered examples

joke, jokes (*continued*)
    telling jokes, #202, #203
    told that one's joke is not funny, #621
juice. *See also* orange juice
    embarrassed at banquet when thinks mother spilled her, #1057

karate, nearly injures daughter at home fooling around with, #1119
key not working and getting help from security guard, #93
kid, kids. *See also* children
    weird (*see* weird)
kiss, kissing
    good-night kiss interrupted by father, #705
    kiss and hug (*see* affection)
    kissing scene (*see* movie)
    smoked cigarette and not kissable, #650
knapsack and spilled underwear, #667

lack of interest. *See also* lack of response
    in other person's computer, #36
    on part of poor listener, #40
    in relationship revealed by not seeing the play the other person is directing, #26
    in what other says because trying to think of something funny to say, #38
lack of response. *See also* lack of interest
    to boxes of toys, #43
    of boy in school to girl who is interested in him, #41
    to what other says, #40
ladder. *See* pants
language class. *See* singing
large front teeth. *See* teeth
late, causes friend to lose job at canteen because arrives, #1068
laugh, laughing. *See also* joke
    at class clown, #316
    colleagues, #104
    girl with ridiculous, #307
    making funny cracks to get others to, #105, #201
    in response to invented accident, #205
    and singles, #103, #105
    telling jokes and, #202, #203
    trying to elicit laughs through witty remarks and expressions, #198, #199
    wanting to join, #102
    when embarrassed, #667, #689, #690, #714
    when others are insulted, #201
    when talking, #106
laundry. *See* wash on Sunday
law school, listening to woman talk about her problems in, #433

mail, homesick university students and the importance of, #412

mainline relationship, #398

maintaining relationships. *See also* relationships

    by attending friend's dinner parties, #155

makes out with engaged girl on bus trip, #1025

making amends

    buying a course book for girl after causing her to miss her test, #1141

    buys recording of Handel's Messiah for date after taking her to concert on wrong day, #1100

    groveling before family members after fussing at or correcting them, #1140

    letting friend work the lights for their rock band, #1138

    replacing chimney of the host's hurricane lamp that she broke, #1101

    replacing money that she took from the cash register, #1116

    reporting less hours than she actually works, #1133

    teaching assistant makes up for missing class by preparing helpful material for students, #1099

making a move on a girl. *See* club

making fun of

    boyfriend running out of gas, #507

    each other within a group of friends, #201

    others, #204

    upset girl in lounge wanting to get back at Alice for what she said at age six, #450

    a young guy's looks and clothes, #472

making noise

    doing homework, #118

    lifting heavy weights, #119

making the other person feel guilty. *See* guilt

manure, steps in horse, during parade, #703

map. *See* taxi driver

marriage. *See also* marriage breakup; married couple; relationships

    husband says he is bored with their, #790

    marries girl he isn't in love with after those he does love reject him, #963

    "You know your marriage is secure," #420

marriage breakup

    girl checks to see if another male is still available after her, #880

    gives wife house so won't feel guilty later, #1127

    "I just feel tortured thinking about my husband having to be all alone," #1045

    is hardest on the family pets, #1010

    after separation husband makes wife feel so guilty she moves back with him, #1148

married couple. *See also* affairs; marriage

    affection of married couple at party, #420

    husband getting back scratch from wife, #210

married man, making love to a, #1109

martial arts competition, son goes to a, #737

Index of numbered examples

Mistral. *See* windsurfing board
money
    avoids guilt by not taking advantage of mistakes with money made by others,
        #1066
    drops change on floor during church collection, #513
    father calls him a bum when he asks for, #695
    found on sidewalk and shared, #191
    friend who never pays her own way, #434
    getting a few extra dollars is not worth this weight on your conscience for years
        afterwards, #1066
    replaces money she took from cash register, #1116
    used by two bullies (brothers) to ridicule other kids at day camp, #319
Montreal, going on shopping and clubbing trip with friend to, #371
mood, bad. *See* bad mood
mother. *See also* avoiding guilt; baby; child; daughter; family; guilt; pregnant; son
    children correct their mother on unimportant details, #614
    complains to butcher about roast, #582
    corrects child's grammar and punctuation, #613
    covers daughter's nude boyfriend with blanket, #680
    critical of son's skinny physique, #841
    daughter feels guilty if she doesn't visit her mother even though each visit is an
        ordeal, #1154
    daughter feels guilty that not going to Edmonton to see her dying mother, #1111
    drives slowly and parks in small places, #603
    fires cleaning woman, #838
    "I don't think I'm a good mother," #1019
    I was too strict when my children were small, #1019
    thinks prices are too high, #604
    told by daughter she smells and needs a deodorant, #822
    uses guilt to try to make daughter stop seeing a specific guy, #992, #1154
    "You only say what Dad tells you to say," her child tells her, #847
motorbike won't start and girl misses her quiz, #1141
motorcycles. *See* Harley Club
mouth, feeling down in the, #330
a move on, a girl you are making. *See* club
"Move over, the cow is coming through," #736
movie
    actor does something foolish in film and viewer feels embarrassed, #588
    boys sitting behind girls at the, #317
    can't get movie projector to work, #542
    child embarrassed by kissing scene in, #588
    embarrassed when has to help drunk friend return to seat in, #579
    hides crying during film in movie theater, #537
    not wanting to appear alone and throwing popcorn at the, #344
    Terry annoying others at drive-in, #321
movie projector. *See* movie

standing a foot in front of your face to get attention, #124
statistics course, have to take, #930
staying close
    to family members, #144
    to a person, #142, #143
steak bone. *See* eat
steal, stealing. *See also* shoplifting
    and deliberately getting caught, #313
    library books on embarrassing topics, #723
    parents emphasize to all seven of their children that they should not steal, #1038
steering wheel, getting finger caught in, #499
stew, pours salt in. *See* food
stockbroker. *See also* stocks
    apologizes to stockbroker for complaining about commissions, #1096
    moves to another firm and is upset when loses some accounts, #909
stocks. *See also* stockbroker
    avoids guilt by not recommending stocks, #1078
    feels guilty after convinces friend to buy stocks and their prices fall, #1023
    mutual interest in, #165
    stockbroker calling to ask about mining, #257
stomach growls, #663
stood up on a date, #405, #911
    wants to talk about it to a friend afterwards, #405, #911
"Stop picking on me!" #798
store
    buys items in store which are incorrectly priced, but doesn't shoplift, #1003
    dances and sings in store, #593
    employee cooperation and store success, #869
    returns immediately to store if forgets to pay for an item, #1038
stories
    makes up stories about the guy who rejected her, #956
    mother repeats the same, #610
    tells stories at a party, #272
straightens house. *See* house
strange outfits. *See* clothes
strict with her children, mother is too, #1019
strip shows, won't mention interest in, #825
student evaluations, #845
students
    avoid doing oral presentations, #873
    top student decides to pursue acting rather than a more stable career, in order to
        get attention, #437
    trying to make clever remarks about other students, #735
study
    can study by self if going to see girlfriend later, #395
    while friends go to a club he tries to, #347

SUBJECT INDEX

See also a) the tables of contents and tables of detailed contents for the individual chapters, and b) the index of numbered examples.